Relating

CONNECTIONS 2

Relating

EDITED BY

Richard Davies and Glen Kirkland

gage PUBLISHING LIMITED
TORONTO ONTARIO CANADA

ISBN 0-7715-1160-4

DESIGN
Frank Newfeld

ILLUSTRATIONS
Dianne Richardson
Frank Newfeld

COVER
Frank Newfeld

1 2 3 4 5 6 7 8 9 BP 85 84 83 82 81

Printed and bound in Canada

Contents

People as Characters

The Yellow Sweater 2 *Hugh Garner* (STORY)

Like a Rolling Stone 9 *Bob Dylan* (SONG)

Girl's-Eye View of Relatives 11 *Phyllis McGinley* (POEMS)

Lies My Father Told Me 12 *Ted Allan* (STORY)

Sophie 17 *Emily Carr* (ESSAY)

A Most Peculiar Man 23 *Paul Simon* (SONG)

My Beginnings 24 *Gilles Villeneuve*
with Wayne Grigsby (ESSAY)

The Gold Medal 27 *Nancy Greene* (ESSAY)

The Agony and the Ecstasy of Terry Fox 31 *Warren Gerard* (ESSAY)

Herman 34 *Jim Unger* (CARTOON)

Fame 35 *Arthur Miller* (DRAMA)

Wayne and Shuster: 43 *Robert Collins* (ESSAY)
Canada's Stay-at-Home Clowns

The World Is Mean to Millionnaires 48 *J. Paul Getty* (ESSAY)

The Blue-Eyed Mistress of the Keys 52 *Peter McLaren* (ESSAY)

Ex-Basketball Player 56 *John Updike* (POEM)

Remembering "The Chief" 57 *Janice Tyrwhitt* (ESSAY)

Crimes, Criminals, and Detectives

Great Detectives: Ageless Fictions 64 *Anonymous* (ESSAY)

The Man with the Twisted Lip 66 *Sir Arthur Conan Doyle* (STORY)

Wasps' Nest 82 *Agatha Christie* (STORY)

John Dobbin, from Beyond the Quicksands 88 *John Wilson Murray* (STORY)

One's a Heifer 94 *Sinclair Ross and Rudi Dorn* (DRAMA)

Paid-up Member 102 *Will R. Bird* (STORY)

Porphyria's Lover 104 *Robert Browning* (POEM)

Hangman Patiently Waits 106 *Eddie Collister* (ESSAY)
for Return of the Noose

Herman 109 *Jim Unger* (CARTOON)

The Parsley Garden 110 *William Saroyan* (STORY)

The Dinner Party 115 *James Michael Ullman* (STORY)

Hijack 119 *Robert L. Fish* (STORY)

The Ransom of Red Chief 126 *O. Henry* (STORY)

Are You a Highway Killer? 134 *Tom Hirsh* (ESSAY)

Everything Put Together Falls Apart 137 *Paul Simon* (SONG)

The Drunk Tank 138 *Al Purdy* (POEM)

Understanding Differences

As I Grew Older 140 *Langston Hughes* (POEM)

My Very Good Dear Friends... 141 *Chief Dan George* (ESSAY)

Back Door 145 *William Paluk* (DRAMA)

What Do I Remember of the Evacuation? 154 *Joy Kogawa* (POEM)

Select Samaritan 155 *Robert Finch* (POEM)

O-Oh Say, What They See! 156 *Walter Stewart* (ESSAY)

Jamie 161 *Elizabeth Brewster* (POEM)

Light for the Blind 162 *Russell Freedman* (ESSAY)

My Well-Balanced Life on a Wooden Leg 170 *Al Capp* (ESSAY)

Of Men and Women 176 *Anonymous* (ESSAY)

A Call in December 177 *Alden Nowlan* (STORY)

"Look, Granddad, a Have-not." 180 *James Mulligan* (CARTOON)

Home from the Forest 181 *Gordon Lightfoot* (SONG)

Aging in the Land of the Young 182 *Sharon Curtin* (ESSAY)

No Man Is an Island 184 *John Donne* (POEM)

Youth: The Awakening Years

Where Are You Now, Batman? 186 *Brian Patten* (POEM)

Boys and Girls 188 *Alice Munro* (STORY)

The Mate 198 *James Stokely* (POEM)

The Wise and the Weak 199 *Philip Aponte* (STORY)

The Taste of Melon 203 *Borden Deal* (STORY)

Help, I've Just Been Run Over by a Bus 212 *Gwen Hauser* (POEM)

At Seventeen 213 *Janis Ian* (SONG)

For Monnie 214 *Marc Plourde* (POEM)

Frame-up on the Highway 215 *John and Ward Hawkins* (STORY)

How to Survive Your Adolescent 232 *Joan Rattner Heilman*
with Martin Symonds (ESSAY)

What's Wrong with Grown-ups? 235 *Anonymous* (ESSAY)

"Look on the Bright Side...." 236 *Ben Wicks* (CARTOON)

Leaving Home 237 *David French* (DRAMA)

The Threshold 241 *Charlene Keel* (STORY)

Departure 248 *Glen Kirkland* (POEM)

People
as
Characters

Hugh Garner

The Yellow Sweater

As he turned a bend in the road
he saw the girl
about a quarter of a mile ahead.

He stepped on the gas when he reached the edge of town. The big car took hold of the pavement and began to eat up the miles on the straight, almost level, highway. With his elbow stuck through the open window he stared ahead at the shimmering greyness of the road. He felt heavy and pleasantly satiated after his good small-town breakfast, and he shifted his bulk in the seat, at the same time brushing some cigar ash from the front of his salient vest. In another four hours he would be home – a day ahead of himself this trip, but with plenty to show the office for last week's work. He unconsciously patted the wallet resting in the inside pocket of his jacket as he thought of the orders he had taken.

Four thousand units to Slanders...his second-best line too...four thousand at twelve percent...four hundred and eighty dollars! He rolled the sum over in his mind as if tasting it, enjoying its tartness like a kid with a gumdrop.

He drove steadily for nearly an hour, ignorant of the smell of spring in the air, pushing the car ahead with his mind as well as with his foot against the pedal. The success of his trip and the feeling of power it gave him carried him along toward the triumph of his homecoming.

Outside a small village he was forced to slow down for a road repair crew. He punched twice on the horn as he passed them, basking in the stares of the yokels who looked up from their shovels, and smiling at the envy showing on their faces.

A rather down-at-heel young man carrying an army kit-bag stepped out from the office of a filling station and gave him the thumb. He pretended not to see the gesture, and pressed down slightly on the gas so that the car began to purr along the free and open road.

It was easy to see that the warm weather was approaching, he thought. The roads were becoming cluttered up once more with hitchhikers. Why the government didn't clamp down on them was more than he could understand. Why should people pay taxes so that other lazy bums could fritter away their time roaming the country, getting free rides, going God knows where? They were dangerous too. It was only the week before that two of them had beaten up and robbed a man on this very same road. They stood a fat chance of *him* picking them up.

And yet they always thumbed him, or almost always. When they didn't he felt cheated, as a person does when he makes up his mind not to answer another's greeting, only to have them pass by without noticing him.

He glanced at his face in the rearview mirror. It was a typical middle-aged businessman's face, plump and well-barbered, the shiny skin stretched taut across the cheeks. It was a face that was familiar to him not only from his possession of it, but because it was also the face of most of his friends. What was it the speaker at the service club luncheon had called it? "The physiognomy of success."

As he turned a bend in the road he saw the girl about a quarter of a mile ahead. She was not on the pavement, but was walking slowly along the shoulder of the highway, bent over with the weight of the bag she was carrying. He slowed down, expecting her to turn and thumb him, but she plodded on as though impervious to his approach. He sized her up as he drew near. She was young by the look of her back...stocking seams straight...heels muddy but not rundown. As he passed he stared at her face. She was a good-looking kid, probably eighteen or nineteen.

It was the first time in years that he had slowed down for a hiker. His reasons evaded him, and whether it was the feel of the morning, the fact of his going home, or the girl's apparent independence, he could not tell. Perhaps it was a combination of all three, plus the boredom of a long drive. It might be fun to pick her up, to cross-examine her while she was trapped in the seat beside him.

Easing the big car to a stop about fifty yards in front of her he looked back through the mirror. She kept glancing at the car, but her pace had not changed, and she came on as though she had expected him to stop. For a moment he was tempted to drive on again, angered by her indifference. She was not a regular hitchhiker or she would have waited at the edge of town instead of setting out to

4 walk while carrying such a heavy bag. But there was something about her that compelled him to wait – something which aroused in him an almost forgotten sense of adventure, an eagerness not experienced for years.

She opened the right rear door, saying at the same time, "Thank you very much, sir," in a frightened little voice.

"Put your bag in the back. That's it, on the floor," he ordered, turning towards her with his hand along the back of the seat. "Come and sit up here."

She did as he commanded, sitting very stiff and straight against the door. She was small, almost fragile, with long dark hair that waved where it touched upon the collar of her light-colored topcoat. Despite the warmth of the morning the coat was buttoned, and she held it to her in a way that suggested modesty or fear.

"Are you going very far?" he asked, looking straight ahead through the windshield, trying not to let the question sound too friendly.

"To the city," she answered, with the politeness and eagerness of the recipient of a favor.

"For a job?"

"Well, not exactly – " she began. Then she said, "Yes, for a job."

As they passed the next group of farm buildings she stared hard at them, her head turning with her eyes until they were too far back to be seen.

Something about her reminded him of his eldest daughter, but he shrugged off the comparison. It was silly of him to compare the two, one a hitchhiking farm skivvy and the other one soon to come home from finishing school. In his mind's eye he could see the photograph of his daughter Shirley that hung on the wall of the living room. It had been taken with a color camera during the Easter vacation, and in it Shirley was wearing a bright yellow sweater.

"Do you live around here?" he asked, switching his thoughts back to the present.

"I was living about a mile down the road from where you picked me up."

"Sick of the farm?" he asked.

"No." She shook her head slowly, seriously.

"Have you anywhere to go in the city?"

"I'll get a job somewhere."

He turned then and got his first good look at her face. She was pretty, he saw, with the country girl's good complexion, her features small and even. "You're young to be leaving home like this," he said.

"That wasn't my home," she murmured. "I was living with my Aunt Bernice and her husband."

He noticed that she did not call the man her uncle.

"You sound as though you don't like the man your aunt is married to?"

"I hate him!" she whispered vehemently.

To change the subject he said, "You've chosen a nice day to leave, anyhow."

"Yes."

He felt a slight tingling along his spine. It was the same feeling he had experienced once when sitting in the darkened interior of a movie house beside a strange yet, somehow, intimate young woman. The feeling that if he wished he had only to let his hand fall along her leg . . .

"You're not very talkative," he said, more friendly now.

She turned quickly and faced him. "I'm sorry. I was thinking about – about a lot of things."

"It's too nice a morning to think of much," he said. "Tell me more about your reasons for leaving home."

"I wanted to get away, that's all."

He stared at her again, letting his eyes

follow the contours of her body. "Don't tell me you're in trouble?" he asked.

She lowered her eyes to her hands. They were engaged in twisting the clasp on a cheap black handbag. "I'm not in trouble like that," she said slowly, although the tone of her voice belied her words.

He waited for her to continue. There was a sense of power in being able to question her like this without fear of having to answer any questions himself. He said, "There can't be much else wrong. Was it boy trouble?"

"Yes, that's it," she answered hastily.

"Where's the boy? Is he back there or in the city?"

"Back there," she answered.

He was aware of her nearness, of her young body beside him on the seat. "You're too pretty to worry about one boy," he said, trying to bridge the gap between them with unfamiliar flattery.

She did not answer him, but smiled nervously in homage to his remark.

They drove on through the morning, and by skillful questioning he got her to tell him more about her life. She had been born near the spot where he had picked her up, she said. She was an orphan, eighteen years old, who for the past three years had been living on her aunt's farm. On his part he told her a little about his job, but not too much. He spoke in generalities, yet let her see how important he was in his field.

They stopped for lunch at a drive-in restaurant outside a small town. While they were eating he noticed that some of the other customers were staring at them. It angered him until he realized that they probably thought she was his mistress. This flattered him and he tried to imagine that it was true. During the meal he became animated, and he laughed loudly at his risqué little jokes.

She ate sparingly, politely, not knowing what to do with her hands between courses.

She smiled at the things he said, even at the remarks that were obviously beyond her.

After they had finished their lunch he said to her jovially, "Here we've been, travelling together for two hours and we don't even know each other's names yet."

"Mine's Marie. Marie Edwards."

"You can call me Tom," he said expansively.

When he drew out his wallet to pay the checks he was careful to cover the initials G.G.M. with the palm of his hand.

As they headed down the highway once again, Marie seemed to have lost some of her timidity and she talked and laughed with him as though he were an old friend. Once he stole a glance at her through the corner of his eye. She was staring ahead as if trying to unveil the future that was being overtaken by the onrushing car.

"A penny for your thoughts, Marie," he said.

"I was just thinking how nice it would be to keep going like this forever."

"Why?" he asked, her words revealing an unsuspected facet to her personality.

"I dunno," she answered, rubbing the palm of her hand along the upholstery of the seat in a gesture that was wholly feminine. "It seems so – safe here, somehow." She smiled as though apologizing for thinking such things. "It seems as if nothing bad could ever catch up to me again."

He gave her a quick glance before staring ahead at the road once more.

The afternoon was beautiful, the warm dampness of the fields bearing aloft the smell of uncovered earth and budding plants. The sun-warmed pavement sang like muted violins beneath the spinning tires of the car. The clear air echoed the sound of life and growth and the urgency of spring.

As the miles clicked off, and they were brought closer to their inevitable parting, an

6 | idea took shape in his mind and grew with every passing minute. Why bother hurrying home, he asked himself. After all he hadn't notified his wife to expect him, and he wasn't due back until tomorrow.

He wondered how the girl would react if he should suggest postponing the rest of the trip overnight. He would make it worth her while. There was a tourist camp on the shore of a small lake about twenty miles north of the highway. No one would be the wiser, he told himself. They were both fancy-free.

The idea excited him, yet he found himself too timid to suggest it. He tried to imagine how he must appear to the girl. The picture he conjured up was a mature figure, inclined to stoutness, much older than she was in years but not in spirit. Many men his age had formed liaisons with young women. In fact it was the accepted thing among some of the other salesmen he knew.

But there remained the voicing of the questions. She appeared so guileless, so – innocent of his intentions. And yet it was hard to tell; she wasn't as innocent as she let on.

She interrupted his train of thought. "On an afternoon like this I'd like to paddle my feet in a stream," she said.

"I'm afraid the water would be pretty cold."

"Yes, it would be cold, but it'd be nice too. When we were kids we used to go paddling in the creek behind the schoolhouse. The water was strong with the spring freshet, and it would tug at our ankles and send a warm ticklish feeling up to our knees. The smooth pebbles on the bottom would make us twist our feet, and we'd try to grab them with our toes....I guess I must sound crazy," she finished.

No longer hesitant he said, "I'm going to turn the car into one of these side roads, Marie. On a long trip I usually like to park for a while under some trees. It makes a little break in the journey."

She nodded her head happily. "That would be nice," she said.

He turned the car off the highway and they travelled north along the road that curved gently between wide stretches of steaming fields. The speed of the car was seemingly increased by the drumming of gravel against the inside of the fenders.

It was time to bring the conversation back to a more personal footing, so he asked. "What happened between you and your boyfriend, Marie?" He had to raise his voice above the noise of the hurtling stones.

"Nothing much," she answered, hesitating as if making up the answer. "We had a fight, that's all."

"Serious?"

"I guess so."

"What happened? Did he try to get a little fresh maybe?"

She had dropped her head, and he could see the color rising along her neck and into the hair behind her ears.

"Does that embarrass you?" he asked, taking his hand from the wheel and placing it along the collar of her coat.

She tensed herself at his touch and tried to draw away, but he grasped her shoulder and pulled her against him. He could feel the fragility of her beneath his hand and the trembling of her skin beneath the cloth of her coat. The odor of her hair and of some cheap scent filled his nostrils.

She cried, "Don't, please!" and broke away from the grip of his hand. She inched herself into the far corner of the seat again.

"You're a little touchy, aren't you?" he asked, trying to cover up his embarrassment at being repulsed so quickly.

"Why did you have to spoil it?"

His frustration kindled a feeling of anger against her. He knew her type all right. Pretending that butter wouldn't melt in her mouth, while all the time she was secretly laughing at him for being the sucker who picked her up, bought her a lunch, and drove her into town. She couldn't fool him; he'd met her type before.

He swung the car down a narrow lane, and they flowed along over the rutted wheel tracks beneath a flimsy ceiling of budding trees.

"Where are we going?" she asked, her voice apprehensive now.

"Along here a piece," he answered, trying to keep his anger from showing.

"Where does this road lead?"

"I don't know. Maybe there's a stream you can paddle in."

There was a note of relief in her voice as she said, "Oh! I didn't mean for us – for you to find a stream."

"You don't seem to know *what* you mean, do you?"

She became silent then and seemed to shrink farther into the corner.

The trees got thicker, and soon they found themselves in the middle of a small wood. The branches of the hardwoods were mottled green, their buds flicking like fingers in the breeze. He brought the car to a stop against the side of the road.

The girl watched him, the corners of her mouth trembling with fear. She slid her hand up the door and grabbed the handle. He tried to make his voice matter-of-fact as he said, "Well, here we are."

Her eyes ate into his face like those of a mesmerized rabbit watching a snake.

He opened a glove compartment and pulled out a package of cigarettes. He offered the package to her, but she shook her head.

"Let's get going," she pleaded.

"What, already? Maybe we should make a day of it."

She did not speak, but the question stood in her eyes. He leaned back against the seat, puffing on his cigarette. "There's a tourist camp on a lake a few miles north of here. We could stay there and go on to the city tomorrow."

She stifled a gasp. "I can't. I didn't think – I had no idea when we – "

He pressed his advantage. "Why can't you stay? Nobody'll know. I may be in a position to help you afterwards. You'll need help, you know."

"No. No, I couldn't," she answered. Her eyes filled with tears.

He had not expected her to cry. Perhaps he had been wrong in his estimation of her. He felt suddenly bored with the whole business, and ashamed of the feelings she had ignited in him.

"Please take me back to the highway," she said, pulling a carefully folded handkerchief from her handbag.

"Sure. In a few minutes." He wanted time to think things out; to find some way of saving face.

"You're just like he was," she blurted out, her words distorted by her handkerchief. "You're all the same."

Her outburst frightened him. "Marie," he said, reaching over to her. He wanted to quiet her, to show her that his actions had been the result of an old man's foolish impulse.

As soon as his hand touched her shoulder she gave a short cry and twisted the door handle. "No. No, please!" she cried.

"Marie, come here!" he shouted, trying to stop her. He grabbed her by the shoulder, but she tore herself from his grasp and fell through the door.

She jumped up from the road and staggered back through the grass into the belt of trees. Her stockings and the bottom of her coat were brown with mud.

"Don't follow me!" she yelled.

"I'm not going to follow you. Come back here and I'll drive you back to the city."

"No you don't! You're the same as he was!" she cried. "I know your tricks!"

He looked about him at the deserted stretch of trees, wondering if anybody could be listening. It would place him in a terrible position to be found with her like this. Pleading with her he said, "Come on, Marie. I've got to go."

She began to laugh hysterically, her voice reverberating through the trees.

"Marie, come on," he coaxed. "I won't hurt you."

"No! Leave me alone. Please leave me alone!"

His pleas only seemed to make things worse. "I'm going," he said hurriedly, pulling the car door shut.

"Just leave me alone!" she cried. Then she began sobbing, "Bernice! Bernice!"

What dark fears had been released by his actions of the afternoon he did not know, but they frightened and horrified him. He turned the car around in the narrow lane and let it idle for a moment as he waited, hoping she would change her mind. She pressed herself deeper into the trees, wailing at the top of her voice.

From behind him came a racking noise from down the road, and he looked back and saw a tractor coming around a bend. A man was driving it and there was another one riding behind. He put the car in gear and stepped on the gas.

Before the car reached the first turn beneath the trees he looked back. The girl was standing in the middle of the road beside the tractor and she was pointing his way and talking to the men. He wondered if they had his licence number, and what sort of a story she was telling them.

He had almost reached the highway again before he remembered her suitcase standing on the floor behind the front seat. His possession of it seemed to tie him to the girl; to make him partner to her terror. He pulled the car to a quick stop, leaned over the back of the seat and picked the suitcase up from the floor. Opening the door he tossed it lightly to the side of the road with a feeling a relief. The frail clasp on the cheap bag opened as it hit the ground and its contents spilled into the ditch. There was a framed photograph, some letters and papers held together with an elastic band, a comb and brush, and some clothing, including a girl's yellow sweater.

"I'm no thief," he said, pushing the car into motion again, trying to escape from the sight of the opened bag. He wasn't to blame for the things that had happened to her. It wasn't his fault that her stupid little life was spilled there in the ditch.

"I've done nothing wrong," he said, as if pleading his case with himself. But there was a feeling of obscene guilt beating his brain like a reiteration. Something of hers seemed to attach itself to his memory. Then suddenly he knew what it was – the sweater, the damned yellow sweater. His hands trembled around the wheel as he sent the car hurtling towards the safe anonymity of the city.

He tried to recapture his feelings of the morning, but when he looked at himself in the mirror all he saw was the staring face of a fat, frightened old man.

Bob Dylan

Like a Rolling Stone

Once upon a time you dressed so fine,
You threw the bums a dime in your prime, didn't you?
People call say, "Beware doll, you're bound to fall."
You thought they were all kiddin' you.
You used to laugh about
Everybody that was hangin' out.
Now you don't talk so loud,
Now you don't seem so proud,
About having to be scrounging your next meal.

How does it feel,
How does it feel,
To be without a home,
Like a complete unknown,
Like a rolling stone?

You've gone to the finest school all right, Miss Lonely,
But you know you only used to get juiced in it.
Nobody's ever taught you how to live out on the street,
And now you're gonna have to get used to it.
You say you never compromise
With the mystery tramp, but now you realize
He's not selling any alibis,
As you stare into the vacuum of his eyes,
And say, "Do you want to make a deal?"

How does it feel,
How does it feel,
To be on your own,
With no direction home,
A complete unknown,
Like a rolling stone?

You never turned around to see the frowns on the jugglers and the clowns
When they all did tricks for you.
You've never understood that it ain't no good,
You shouldn't let other people get your kicks for you.

10

You used to ride on a chrome horse with your diplomat
Who carried on his shoulder a Siamese cat.
Ain't it hard when you've discovered that
He really wasn't where it's at,
After he took from you everything he could steal?

How does it feel,
How does it feel,
To be on your own,
No direction home,
Like a complete unknown,
Like a rolling stone?

Princess on the steeple and all the pretty people,
They're all drinkin', thinkin' that they've got it made.
Exchanging all precious gifts,
You'd better take your diamond ring, you'd better pawn it, babe.
You used to be so amused
At Napoleon in rags and the language that he used.
Go to him now, he calls you, you can't refuse
When you ain't got nothing, you got nothing to lose.
You're invisible now, you've got no secrets to conceal.

How does it feel,
How does it feel,
To be on your own,
With no direction home,
Like a complete unknown,
Like a rolling stone?

Phyllis McGinley

Girl's-Eye View of Relatives

FIRST LESSON

The thing to remember about fathers is they're men.
A girl has to keep it in mind.
They are dragon-seekers, bent on improbable rescues.
Scratch any father, you find
Someone chock-full of qualms and romantic terrors,
Believing change is a threat —
Like your first shoes with heels on, like your first bicycle
It took such months to get.

Walk in strange woods, they warn you about the snakes there.
Climb, and they fear you'll fall.
Books, angular boys, or swimming in deep water —
Fathers mistrust them all.
Men are the worriers. It is difficult for them
To learn what they must learn:
How you have a journey to take and very likely,
For a while, will not return.

TRIOLET AGAINST SISTERS

Sisters are always drying their hair.
    Locked into rooms, alone,
They pose at the mirror, shoulders bare,
Trying this way and that their hair.
Or fly importunate down the stair
    To answer a telephone.
Sisters are always drying their hair,
    Locked into rooms, alone.

THE ADVERSARY

A mother's hardest to forgive.
Life is the fruit she longs to hand you,
Ripe on a plate. And while you live,
Relentlessly she understands you.

Ted Allan

Lies My Father Told Me

In between prayers
he rode around on a wagon
which...rolled on
despite all the laws of
physics and mechanics.

My grandfather stood six feet three in his worn-out bedroom slippers. He had a long grey beard with streaks of white running through it. When he prayed, his voice boomed like a choir as he turned the pages of his prayer book with one hand and stroked his beard with the other. His hands were bony and looked like tree roots; they were powerful. My grandpa had been a farmer in the old country. In Montreal he conducted what he called "a second-hand business."

In his youth, I was told, Grandpa had been something of a wild man, drinking and playing with the village wenches until my grandmother took him in hand. In his old age, when I knew him, he had become a very religious man. He prayed three times a day on weekdays and all day on Saturday. In between prayers he rode around on a wagon which, as I look back, rolled on despite all the laws of physics and mechanics. Its four wheels always seemed to be going in every direction but forward. The horse that pulled the wagon was called Ferdeleh. He was my pet and it was only much later, when I had seen many other horses, that I realized that Ferdeleh was not everything a horse could have been. His belly hung very low, almost touching the street when he walked. His head went back and forth in jerky motions in complete disharmony with the rest of him. He moved slowly, almost painfully, apparently realizing that he was capable of only one speed and determined to go no faster or slower than the rate he had established some time back. Next to Grandpa I loved Ferdeleh best, with the possible exception of God, or my mother when she gave me candy.

On Sundays, when it didn't rain, Grandpa, Ferdeleh, and myself would go riding through the back lanes of Montreal. The lanes then were not paved as they are now, and after a rainy Saturday, the mud would be inches deep and the wagon heaved and shook like a barge in a stormy sea. Ferdeleh's pace remained as always, the same. He liked the mud. It was easy on his feet.

When the sun shone through my windows on Sunday morning I would jump out of bed, wash, dress, run into the kitchen where Grandpa and I said our morning prayers, and then we'd both go to harness and feed Ferdeleh. On Sundays Ferdeleh would whinny like a happy child. He knew it was an extra special day for all of us. By the time he had finished his oats and hay Grandpa and I would be finished with our breakfast which Grandma and Mother had prepared for us.

Then we'd go through what Grandpa called "the women's Sunday song." It went like this: "Don't let him hold the reins crossing streets. Be sure to come back if it starts to rain. Be sure not to let him hold the reins crossing streets. Be sure to come back if it starts to rain." They would repeat this about three hundred times until Grandpa and I were weary from nodding our heads and saying, "Yes." We could hear it until we turned the corner and went up the lane of the next street.

Then began the most wonderful of days as we drove through the dirt lanes of Montreal, skirting the garbage cans, jolting and bouncing through the mud and dust, calling every cat by name – and every cat meowing its hello, and Grandpa and I holding our hands to our ears and shouting out at the top of our lungs, "Regs, cloze, botels! Regs, cloze, botels!"

What a wonderful game that was! I would run up the back stairs and return with all kinds of fascinating things, old dresses, suits, pants, rags, newspapers, all shapes of bottles, all shapes of trash, everything you can think of, until the wagon was filled.

Sometimes a woman would ask me to send Grandpa up to give her a price on what she had, and Grandpa would shout up from downstairs, "My feet ache. The boy will give you a price." I knew what he offered for an old suit, for an old dress, and I would shout down describing the items in question and the state of deterioration. For clothes that were nothing better than rags we offered a standard price, "Fifteen cents, take it or leave it." Clothes that might be repaired I would hold out for Grandpa to see and he'd appraise them. And so we'd go through the lanes of the city.

Sometimes the women would not be satisfied with the money Grandpa had given me for them. Grandpa would always say, "Eleshka, women always want more than they get. Remember that. Give them a finger and they want the whole hand."

My Sunday rides were the happiest times I spent. Sometimes Grandpa would let me wear his derby hat which came down over my ears, and people would look at me and laugh and I'd feel even happier feeling how happy everyone was on Sunday.

Sometimes strange, wonderful smells would come over the city, muffling the smell of the garbage cans. When this happened we would stop Ferdeleh and breathe deeply. It smelled of sea and of oak trees and flowers. Then we knew we were near the mountain in the centre of the city and that the wind from the river was bringing the perfumes of the mountain and spraying it over the city. Often we would ride out of the back lanes and up the mountain road. We couldn't go too far up because it was a strain on Ferdeleh. As far as we went, surrounded on each side by tall poplars and evergreens, Grandpa would tell me about the old country, about the rivers and the farms, and sometimes he'd get off the wagon and pick up some black earth in his hands. He'd squat, letting the earth fall between his fingers, and I'd squat beside him doing the same thing.

When we came to the mountain Grandpa's mood would change and he would talk to me of the great land that Canada was, and of the great things the young people growing up were going to do in this great land. Ferdeleh would walk to the edge of the road and eat the thick grass on the sides. Grandpa was at home among the trees and black earth and thick grass and on our way down the mountain road he would sing songs that weren't prayers, but happy songs in Russian. Sometimes he'd clap his hands to the song as I held the reins and Ferdeleh would look back at him and shake his head with pleasure.

One Sunday on our ride home through the mountain a group of young boys and girls threw stones at us and shouted in French "Juif...Juif...!" Grandpa held his strong arm around me and cursed back muttering "anti-Semites" under his breath. When I asked him what he said he answered, "It is something I hope you never learn." The boys and girls laughed and got tired of throwing stones. That was the last Sunday we went to the mountain.

If it rained on Sunday my mother wouldn't let me go out so every Saturday evening I prayed for the sun to shine on Sunday. Once I almost lost faith in God and in the power of prayer but Grandpa fixed it. For three Sundays in succession it rained. In my desperation I took it out on God. What was the use of praying to Him if He didn't listen to you? I complained to Grandpa.

"Perhaps you don't pray right," he suggested.

"But I do. I say, Our God in heaven, hallowed be Thy name, Thy will on earth as it is in heaven. Please don't let it rain tomorrow."

"Ah! In English you pray?" my grandfather exclaimed triumphantly.

"Yes," I answered.

"But God only answers prayers in Hebrew. I will teach you how to say that prayer in Hebrew. And, if God doesn't answer it's your own fault. He's angry because you didn't use the Holy Language." But God wasn't angry because next Sunday the sun shone its brightest and the three of us went for our Sunday ride.

On weekdays, Grandpa and I rose early, a little after daybreak, and said our morning prayers. I would mimic his sing-song lamentations, sounding as if my heart were breaking and wondering why we both had to sound so sad. I must have put everything I had into it because Grandpa assured me that one day I would become a great cantor and a leader of the Hebrews. "You will sing so that the ocean will open up a path before you and you will lead our people to a new paradise."

I was six then and he was the only man I ever understood even when I didn't understand his words. I learned a lot from him. If he didn't learn a lot from me, he made me feel he did.

I remember once saying, "You know, sometimes I think I'm the son of God. Is it possible?"

"It is possible," he answered, "but don't rely on it. Many of us are sons of God. The important thing is not to rely too much upon it. The harder we work, the harder we study, the more we accomplish, the surer we are that we are sons of God."

At the synagogue on Saturday his old, white-bearded friends would surround me and ask me questions. Grandpa would stand by and burst with pride. I strutted like a peacock.

"Who is David?" the old men would ask me.

"He's the man with the beard, the man with the bearded words." And they laughed.

"And who is God?" they would ask me.

"King and Creator of the Universe, the All-Powerful One, the Almighty One, more powerful even than Grandpa." They laughed again and I thought I was pretty smart. So did Grandpa. So did my grandmother and my mother.

So did everyone, except my father. I didn't like my father. He said things to me like, "For God's sake, you're smart, but not as smart as you think. Nobody is that smart." He was jealous of me and he told me lies. He told me lies about Ferdeleh.

"Ferdeleh is one part horse, one part camel, and one part chicken," he told me. Grandpa told me that was a lie; Ferdeleh was all horse. "If he is part anything, he is part human," said Grandpa. I agreed with him. Ferdeleh understood everything we said to him. No matter what part of the city he was in, he could find his way home, even in the dark.

"Ferdeleh is going to collapse one day in one heap," my father said. "Ferdeleh is carrying twins." "Ferdeleh is going to keel over one day and die." "He should be shot now or he'll collapse under you one of these days," my father would say. Neither I nor Grandpa had much use for the opinions of my father.

On top of everything, my father had no beard, didn't pray, didn't go to the synagogue on the Sabbath, read English books and never read the prayer books, played piano on the Sabbath and sometimes would draw my mother into his villainies by making her sing while he played. On the Sabbath this was an abomination to both Grandpa and me.

One day I told my father, "Papa, you have forsaken your forefathers." He burst our laughing and kissed me and then my mother kissed me, which infuriated me all the more.

I could forgive my father these indignities, his not treating me as an equal, but I couldn't forgive his telling lies about Ferdeleh. Once he said that Ferdeleh "smelled up" the whole house, and demanded that Grandpa move the stable. It was true that the kitchen, being next to the stable, which was in the back shed, did sometimes smell of hay and manure but, as Grandpa said, "What is wrong with such a smell? It is a good healthy smell."

It was a house divided, with my grandmother, mother, and father on one side, and Grandpa, Ferdeleh, and me on the other. One day a man came to the house and said he was from the Board of Health and that the neighbors had complained about the stable. Grandpa and I knew we were beaten then. You could get around the Board of Health, Grandpa informed me, if you could grease the palms of the officials. I suggested the obvious but Grandpa explained that this type of "grease" was made of gold. The stable would have to be moved. But where?

As it turned out, Grandpa didn't have to worry about it. The whole matter was taken out of his hands a few weeks later.

Next Sunday the sun shone brightly and I ran to the kitchen to say my prayers with Grandpa. But Grandpa wasn't there. I found my grandmother there instead – weeping.

Grandpa was in his room ill. He had a sickness they called diabetes and at that time the only thing you could do about diabetes was weep. I fed Ferdeleh and soothed him because I knew how disappointed he was.

That week I was taken to an aunt of mine. There was no explanation given. My parents thought I was too young to need any explanations. On Saturday next I was brought home, too late to see Grandpa that evening, but I felt good knowing that I would spend the next day with him and Ferdeleh again.

When I came to the kitchen Sunday morning Grandpa was not there. Ferdeleh was not in the stable. I thought they were playing a joke on me so I rushed to the front of the house expecting to see Grandpa sitting atop the wagon waiting for me.

But there wasn't any wagon. My father came up behind me and put his hand on my head. I looked up questioningly and he said, "Grandpa and Ferdeleh have gone to heaven...."

When he told me they were *never* coming back, I moved away from him and went to my room. I lay down on my bed and cried, not for Grandpa and Ferdeleh, because I knew they would never do such a thing to me, but about my father, because he had told me such a horrible lie.

Emily Carr

Sophie

"Baskets. I got baskets."
They were beautiful,
made by her own people,
West Coast Indian baskets.

18

Sophie knocked gently on my Vancouver studio door.

"Baskets. I got baskets."

They were beautiful, made by her own people, West Coast Indian baskets. She had big ones in a cloth tied at the four corners and little ones in a flour sack.

She had a baby slung on her back in a shawl, a girl child clinging to her skirts, and a heavy-faced boy plodding behind her.

"I have no money for baskets."

"Money no matter," said Sophie. "Old clo', waum skirt – good fo' basket."

I wanted the big round one. Its price was eight dollars.

"Next month I am going to Victoria. I will bring back some clothes and get your basket."

I asked her in to rest a while and gave the youngsters bread and jam. When she tied up her baskets she left the one I coveted on the floor.

"Take it away," I said. "It will be a month before I can go to Victoria. Then I will bring clothes back with me and come to get the basket."

"You keep now. Bymby pay," said Sophie.

"Where do you live?"

"North Vancouver Mission."

"What is your name?"

"Me Sophie Frank. Everybody know me."

Sophie's house was bare but clean. It had three rooms. Later when it got cold Sophie's Frank would cut out all the partition walls. Sophie said, "Thlee loom, thlee stobe. One loom, one stobe." The floor of the house was clean scrubbed. It was chair, table, and bed for the family. There was one chair; the coal-oil lamp sat on that. Sophie pushed the babies into corners, spread my old clothes on the floor to appraise them, and was satisfied. So, having tested each other's trade-straightness, we began a long, long friendship – forty years. I have seen Sophie glad, sad, sick, and drunk. I have asked her why she did this or that thing – Indian ways that I did not understand – her answer was invariably "Nice ladies always do." That was Sophie's ideal – being nice.

Every year Sophie had a new baby. Almost every year she buried one. Her little graves were dotted all over the cemetery. I never knew more than three of her twenty-one children to be alive at one time. By the time she was in her early fifties every child was dead and Sophie had cried her eyes dry. Then she took to drink.

"I got a new baby. I got a new baby."

Sophie, seated on the floor of her house, saw me coming through the open door and waved the papoose cradle. Two little girls rolled round on the floor; the new baby was near her in a basket-cradle. Sophie took off the cloth tented over the basket and exhibited the baby, a lean poor thing.

Sophie herself was small and spare. Her black hair sprang thick and strong on each side of the clean, straight parting and hung in twin braids across her shoulders. Her eyes were sad and heavy-lidded. Between prominent, rounded cheekbones her nose lay rather flat, broadening and snubby at the tip. Her wide upper lip pouted. It was sharp-edged, puckering over a row of poor teeth – the soothing pucker of lips trying to ease an aching tooth or to hush a crying child. She had a soft little body, a back straight as honesty itself, and the small hands and feet of an Indian.

Sophie's English was good enough, but when Frank, her husband, was there she became dumb as a plate.

"Why won't you talk before Frank, Sophie?"

"Frank he learn school English. Me, no. Frank laugh my English words."

When we were alone she chattered to me like a sparrow.

In May, when the village was white with cherry blossom and the blue water of Burrard Inlet crept almost to Sophie's door – just a streak of grey sand and a plank walk between – and when Vancouver city was more beautiful to look at across the water than to be in – it was then I loved to take the ferry to the North Shore and go to Sophie's.

Behind the village stood mountains topped by the grand old "Lions," twin peaks, very white and blue. The nearer mountains were every shade of young foliage, tender grey-green, getting greener and greener till, when they were close, you saw that the village grass outgreened them all. Hens strutted their broods, papooses and pups and kittens rolled everywhere – it was good indeed to spend a day on the Reserve in spring.

Sophie and I went to see her babies' graves first. Sophie took her best plaid skirt, the one that had three rows of velvet ribbon round the hem, from a nail on the wall, and bound a yellow silk handkerchief round her head. No matter what the weather, she always wore her great shawl, clamping it down with her arms, the fringe trickling over her fingers. Sophie wore her shoes when she walked with me, if she remembered.

Across the water we could see the city. The Indian Reserve was a different world – no hurry, no business.

We walked over the twisty, up-and-down road to the cemetery. Casamin, Tommy, George, Rosie, Maria, Mary, Emily, and all the rest were there under a tangle of vines. We rambled, seeking out Sophie's graves.

Some had little wooden crosses, some had stones. Two babies lay outside the cemetery fence: they had not faced life long enough for baptism.

"See! Me got stone for Rosie now."

"It looks very nice. It must have cost lots of money, Sophie."

"Grave man make cheap for me. He say, 'You got lots, lots stone from me, Sophie. Maybe bymby you get some more died baby, then you want more stone. So I make cheap for you.'"

Sophie's kitchen was crammed with excited women. They had come to see Sophie's brand-new twins. Sophie was on a mattress beside the cook stove. The twin girls were in small basket papoose cradles, woven by Sophie herself. The babies were wrapped in cotton wool which made their dark little faces look darker; they were laced into their baskets and stuck up at the edge of Sophie's mattress beside the kitchen stove. Their brown, wrinkled faces were like potatoes baked in their jackets, their hands no bigger than brown spiders.

They were thrilling, those very, very tiny babies. Everybody was excited over them. I sat down on the floor close to Sophie.

"Sophie, if the baby was a girl it was to have my name. There are two babies and I have only one name. What are we going to do about it?"

"The biggest and the best is yours," said Sophie.

My Em'ly lived three months. Sophie's Maria lived three weeks. I bought Em'ly's tombstone. Sophie bought Maria's.

Sophie's "mad" rampaged inside her like a lion roaring in the breast of a dove.

"Look see," she said, holding a red and yellow handkerchief, caught together at the corners and chinking with broken glass and

20

bits of plaster of Paris. "Bad boy bloke my grave flower! Cost five dollar one, and now boy all bloke fo' me. Bad, bad boy! You come talk me fo' p'liceman?"

At the City Hall she spread the handkerchief on the table and held half a plaster of Paris lily and a dove's tail up to the eyes of the law, while I talked.

"My mad fo' boy bloke my plitty glave flower," she said, forgetting, in her fury, to be shy of the "English words."

The big man of the law was kind. He said, "It's too bad, Sophie. What do you want me to do about it?"

"You make boy buy more this plitty kind for my glave."

"The boy has no money but I can make his old grandmother pay a little every week."

Sophie looked long at the broken pieces and shook her head.

"That ole, ole woman got no money." Sophie's anger was dying, soothed by sympathy like a child, the woman in her tender toward old Granny. "My bloke no matter for ole woman," said Sophie, gathering up the pieces. "You scold boy big, Policeman? No make glanny pay."

"I sure will, Sophie."

There was a black skirt spread over the top of the packing case in the centre of Sophie's room. On it stood the small white coffin. A lighted candle was at the head, another at the foot. The little dead girl in the coffin held a doll in her arms. It had hardly been out of them since I had taken it to her a week before. The glassy eyes of the doll stared out of the coffin, up past the closed eyelids of the child.

Though Sophie had been through this nineteen times before, the twentieth time was no easier. Her two friends, Susan and Sara, were there by the coffin, crying for her.

The outer door opened and half a dozen women came in, their shawls drawn low across their foreheads, their faces grim. They stepped over to the coffin and looked in. Then they sat around it on the floor and began to cry, first with baby whimpers, softly, then louder, louder still – with violence and strong howling: torrents of tears burst from their eyes and rolled down their cheeks. Sophie and Sara and Susan did it too. It sounded horrible – like tortured dogs.

Suddenly they stopped. Sophie went to the bucket and got water in a tin basin. She took a towel in her hand and went to each of the guests in turn holding the basin while they washed their faces and dried them on the towel. Then the women all went out except Sophie, Sara and Susan. This crying had gone on at intervals for three days – ever since the child had died. Sophie was worn out. There had been, too, all the long weeks of Rosie's tubercular dying to go through.

"Sophie, couldn't you lie down and rest?"

She shook her head. "Nobody sleep in Injun house till dead people go to cemet'ry."

The beds had all been taken away.

"When is the funeral?"

"I dunno. Pliest go Vancouver. He not come two more day."

She laid her hand on the corner of the little coffin.

"See! Coffin-man think box fo' Injun baby no matter."

The seams of the cheap little coffin had burst.

As Sophie and I were coming down the village street we met an Indian woman whom I did not know. She nodded to Sophie, looked at me and half paused. Sophie's mouth was set, her bare feet pattered quick, hurrying me past the woman.

"Go church house now?" she asked me.

The Catholic church had twin towers. Wide steps led up to the front door which was always open. Inside it was bright, in a misty way, and still except for the wind and sea-echoes. The windows were gay colored glass; when you knelt the wooden footstools and pews creaked. Hush lurked in every corner. Always a few candles burned. Everything but those flickers of flame was stone-still.

When we came out of the church we sat on the steps for a little. I said, "Who was that woman we met, Sophie?"

"Mrs. Chief Joe Capilano."

"Oh! I would like to know Mrs. Chief Joe Capilano. Why did you hurry by so quick? She wanted to stop."

"I don' want you know Mrs. Chief Joe."

"Why?"

"You fliend for me, not fliend for her."

"My heart has room for more than one friend, Sophie."

"You fliend for me, I not want Mrs. Chief Joe get you."

"You are always my first and best friend, Sophie." She hung her head, her mouth obstinate. We went to Sara's house.

Sara was Sophie's aunt, a wizened bit of a woman whose eyes, nose, mouth, and wrinkles were all twisted to the perpetual expressing of pain. Once she had had a merry heart, but pain had trampled out the merriness. She lay on a bed draped with hangings of clean, white rags dangling from poles. The wall behind her bed, too, was padded heavily with newspaper to keep drafts off her "Lumatiz."

"Hello, Sara. How are you?"

"Em'ly! Sophie's Em'ly!"

The pain wrinkles scuttled off to make way for Sara's smile, but hurried back to twist for her pain.

"I dunno what for I got Lumatiz, Em'ly. I dunno. I dunno."

Everything perplexed poor Sara. Her merry heart and tortured body were always at odds. She drew a humped wrist across her nose and said, "I dunno, I dunno," after each remark.

"Goodbye, Sophie's Em'ly; come some more soon. I like that you come. I dunno why I got pain, lots pain. I dunno — I dunno."

I said to Sophie, "You see! The others know I am your big friend. They call me 'Sophie's Em'ly.'"

She was happy.

Susan lived on one side of Sophie's house and Mrs. Johnson, the Indian widow of a white man, on the other. The widow's house was beyond words clean. The cookstove was a mirror, the floor white as a sheet from scrubbing. Mrs. Johnson's hands were clever and busy. The row of hard kitchen chairs had each its own antimacassar and cushion. The crocheted bedspread and embroidered pillowslips, all the work of Mrs. Johnson's hands, were smoothed taut. Mrs. Johnson's husband had been a sea captain. She had loved him deeply and remained a widow though she had had many offers of marriage after he died. Once the Indian agent came, and said:

"Mrs. Johnson, there is a good man who has a farm and money in the bank. He is shy, so he sent me to ask if you will marry him."

"Tell that good man, 'Thank you,' Mr. Agent, but tell him, too, that Mrs. Johnson only got love for her dead Johnson."

Sophie's other neighbor, Susan, produced and buried babies almost as fast as Sophie herself. The two women laughed for each other and cried for each other. With babies on their backs and baskets on their arms they crossed over on the ferry to Vancouver and sold their baskets from door to door. When they came to my studio they rested and drank tea with me. My parrot, sheep dog, the white rats, and the totem pole pictures all interested them. "An' you got Injun flower, too," said Susan.

22

"Indian flowers?"

She pointed to ferns and wild things I had brought in from the woods.

Sophie's house was shut up. There was a chain and padlock on the gate. I went to Susan.

"Where is Sophie?"

"Sophie in sick house. Got sick eye."

I went to the hospital. The little Indian ward had four beds. I took ice cream and the nurse divided it into four portions.

A homesick little Indian girl cried in the bed in one corner, an old woman grumbled in another. In a third there was a young mother with a baby, and in the fourth bed was Sophie.

There were flowers. The room was bright. It seemed to me that the four brown faces on the four white pillows should be happier and far more comfortable here than lying on mattresses on the hard floors in the village, with all the family muddle going on about them.

"How nice it is here, Sophie."

"Not much good of hospital, Em'ly."

"Oh! What is the matter with it?"

"Bad bed."

"What is wrong with the beds?"

"Move, move, all time shake. 'Spose me move, bed move too."

She rolled herself to show how the springs worked. "Me ole-fashion, Em'ly. Me like kitchen floor fo' sick."

Susan and Sophie were in my kitchen, rocking their sorrows back and forth and alternately wagging their heads and giggling with shut eyes at some small joke.

"You go live Victoria now, Em'ly," wailed Sophie, "and we never see those babies, never!"

Neither woman had a baby on her back these days. But each had a little new grave in the cemetery. I had told them about a friend's twin babies. I went to the telephone.

"Mrs. Dingle, you said I might bring Sophie to see the twins?"

"Surely, any time," came the ready reply.

"Come, Sophie and Susan, we can go and see the babies now."

The mothers of all those little cemetery mounds stood looking and looking at the thriving white babies, kicking and sprawling on their bed. The women said, "Oh my! – Oh my!" over and over.

Susan's hand crept from beneath her shawl to touch a baby's leg. Sophie's hand shot out and slapped Susan's.

The mother of the babies said, "It's all right, Susan; you may touch my baby."

Sophie's eyes burned Susan for daring to do what she so longed to do herself. She folded her hands resolutely under her shawl and whispered to me.

"Nice ladies don't touch, Em'ly."

Paul Simon

A Most Peculiar Man

"He was a most peculiar man."
That's what Mrs. Riordan says, and she should know.
She lived upstairs from him.
She said, "He was a most peculiar man."

He was a most peculiar man.
He lived all alone within a house,
Within a room, within himself,
A most peculiar man.

He had no friends, he seldom spoke.
And no one in turn ever spoke to him,
'Cause he wasn't friendly, and he didn't care,
    and he wasn't like them.
Oh no, he was a most peculiar man.

He died last Saturday.
He turned on the gas and he went to sleep
With the windows closed so he'd never wake up
To his silent world and his tiny room.

And Mrs. Riordan says he has a brother somewhere,
Who should be notified soon.
And all the people said, "What a shame that he's dead,
But wasn't he a most peculiar man?"

Gilles Villeneuve

My Beginnings

The sheer excitement,
the sheer challenge of getting through,
of going where they said you couldn't go,
was a real thrill.

I can't remember whether I was eight or nine when I first drove a car all by myself. My father had just started up a small clothing manufacturing business, and he'd traded the family car for a Volkswagen bus, the brand-new thing in '59 or '60. We were driving down one of those long, straight country roads near Berthierville, Quebec, my home town. No one around but us, a clear, hot summer's day, so my father let me drive. What a thrill! It's the clearest image I have of my childhood.

Like a lot of country kids, I'd been allowed to drive trucks and tractors in the fields. And ever since I can remember, my father had let me sit on his lap when he drove. I guess I liked speed even then, because I can remember yelling, "Faster, Daddy, faster!" or, "Pass him, pass him!" I loved it when the tires squealed. But I don't think I was all that much different from any other kid that age.

I liked mechanical things. My mother's family had a construction firm, and I loved the bulldozers, the trucks, and the idea of building things. When we moved to Berthier from Richelieu, Quebec, my father bought an old farmhouse and completely rebuilt the interior. I got to bang away at the wood, hammer in the odd nail. I loved it. I was a great one for playing with trucks and bulldozers in the sandbox. I was forever building roads and bridges and the like. But the toy bulldozers and trucks had to be realistic or I wouldn't play with them. They had to have the right number of wheels and axles or they just wouldn't do.

My great obsession was the trumpet. I wanted to be a musician in the worst way. I practised five, sometimes six hours a day and played in the school band at the Séminaire de Joliette. I really took it seriously, playing scales by the hour. Not because I wanted to play any particular style of music. I was just determined to master the technique. But, I don't know, the shape of my mouth changed as I got older, or something, and it got to the point where I couldn't play without my lip hurting. So I had to give it up.

I took school pretty seriously in the early years. At five or six years old, if I didn't come first in the class I cried. Not that there was any pressure from my parents. I just had to be the best. But as I got older, I got more realistic. I figured out that it took so much effort to come first, and if I only put in enough effort to come sixth or seventh, then I was satisfied to come sixth or seventh. And I also realized that some people were just better at certain things than I was. So, if I was running a foot race with someone who would normally beat me, I was satisfied if I finished a little closer than last time.

I hated the food at school. I mean, I *hated* it. I hated the fact that when the meal bell rang, everybody ran to get into line. I hated the idea of waiting in line, especially the idea of waiting in line to eat this awful, disgusting, inedible food. Since I was a boarder at the school, it was a real problem. When I went home on the weekends, I stocked up with cakes and smuggled in a bottle of peanut butter. I managed to survive on one meal a day at school – breakfast. Even that wasn't easy. It meant sneaking into the kitchen when the brothers weren't looking to butter some toast hot off the toaster instead of cold off the rack outside. I wasn't supposed to have the peanut butter, so I had to hide the bottle under the table while I spread it on my toast. Then on weekends I'd go home and fill up. But even then I was a picky eater. Meat, especially a hamburger, and chicken with potatoes were okay. But no fruits, vegetables

Reprinted by permission of Wayne Grigsby. First appeared in *Today* magazine.

26 or fish. I must've driven my mother crazy. Stranger still, I was never sick.

For all that I had a pretty average child-hood. My parents spent a lot of time with me and my brother, and while we didn't have a lot of extra money we didn't lack much either. In the summer we rode our bikes and played with friends in the hay. In the winter we skated on the river or went sliding on cardboard boxes. I loved winter storms. There was always someone to dig out, or snowbanks to crash through to get to my grandparents' home. The sheer excitement, the sheer challenge of getting through, of going where they said you couldn't go, was a real thrill. To this day I'll go out in snowstorms (in a 4x4 nowadays) and pull cars out of snowbanks, help stranded driv-ers. It's the challenge of it that I like.

Cars became the centre of my life when I became a teenager. I'd been interested, I'd always liked mechanics, but by the time I was fourteen, they were a night-and-day obsession. There wasn't a lot I could do about it, though. Legally, I couldn't drive till I was seventeen. Luckily, my father was still letting me drive from time to time, and there were a couple of occasions when I borrowed the truck or the family car for little runs. Nothing serious. Snowmobiles were a bit of an outlet. I was racing them at sixteen, and that same year, my father bought me a broken-down '58 MGA which I tried to fix up. I tore down the engine and rebuilt it, without the help of a manual. I just figured it out. A couple of friends helped, but basically I did it myself. I just wanted to make it work. I did − for a couple of weeks here and there. It was the beginning of a long, long string of cars.

The one I remember best was my second car, an ancient Skoda. I got it the year I got my licence, and I don't think I've ever enjoyed myself, felt as completely free, as I did that summer. We drove that thing every-where. We had to push it to get it started. I don't think it could do more than thirty-five miles an hour, but still we tried to make it corner on two wheels. We hit every dance, every party in the county.

One night, coming home from a dance at midnight, four of us decided to go up to Mont Tremblant, a good 150 miles away, to see the auto races. I was all for that! So at midnight we packed the tents, the sleeping bags, the cooler, the beer, the pots and pans, and then took off for Mont Tremblant. We crashed the fence to get in, we partied for what was left of the night, and the cops threw us out − twice.

By the next morning we'd settled down enough to watch the races, the first auto races I'd ever seen. I was really disappointed. The Trans-Am races were okay, but the regional races, the preliminaries, were a complete bust as far as I was concerned. They mixed classes, cars, tire sizes. It was a real hodgepodge, not a real race at all. And the drivers. Well, they braked too soon, they hit the curves all wrong. It was a real farce. I remember sitting on the edge of a hill look-ing down and saying, "I can do better."

Nancy Greene

The Gold Medal

I let my skis run for me,
the way a racer does
when he's travelling
with all the stops out....

The first time I saw the courses at Grenoble came the day I arrived there in early February to practise for the Games. I think I was lucky that they were new to me. Some of the other skiers on the team had skied in Grenoble earlier in the year, at a time when I'd been sick, and they came away moaning. Brother, they kept telling me, those runs are so hard, they're so steep, so icy, those kids had already created a tremendous obstacle in their own minds, but I was spared the advance fears. I guess I had it both ways – I had no basis for building up my hopes and at the same time I hadn't psyched myself out with needless worrying.

The team went through all the familiar arriving rituals when we reached Olympic Village. There was the usual unpacking, touring the area, greeting our fellow racers, and all the other first-day business. Maybe the whole thing was *too* familiar to me. It was my third Olympics and some things struck me as being a little corny. Opening the boxes of clothes was hardly the thrill it had been at my first Olympics in 1960. This time, the clothing seemed intended for schoolgirls, not for someone like me, in her mid-twenties. There was a suit made of white Orlon pile that made you look like a snowball when you put it on, and the Hudson's Bay blanket coats, which were by tradition a regular part of the Canadian uniform, didn't seem nearly as smart in 1968. But it was the after-ski boots that really took the cake – they were actually Ernie Richardson Official Curling Boots. Apart from looking terribly homely, they were totally impractical for wear around the ski area because they let in the snow. Dressed up in all our garb, I thought we Canadians looked kind of dowdy, just about on a par with the Russians.

Reprinted by permission of Nancy Greene Limited.

The opening ceremonies were as impressive as ever. I had the honor of carrying the Canadian flag, and along with the other flag bearers, I watched the ceremonies from a higher vantage point than the other competitors. Everything looked twice as thrilling. There were fireworks and music and marching and jet planes dipping overhead, a couple of speeches and a torch-lighting ceremony. Nothing was missing from the spectacle. There was even a tiny bit of humor when Leo Lacroix, a skier on the French team, took the Olympic Oath. That was pretty funny, or at least ironic, since Leo and his cousin happened to be in the ski-manufacturing business, making money out of skiing at the very moment that Leo was swearing under the Olympic Oath that he was an amateur.

We had about a week at Grenoble to train on the courses and to tune up our technique before the races began. I didn't feel much pressure during this period. I knew that everybody, the press, my fellow racers, a lot of people back in Canada, expected me to really shine in the '68 Games, and I suppose the knowledge of their anticipation should have heaped some pressure on me. It didn't. The simple fact was that no one expected anything more of me than I expected of myself.

I was especially anxious, *very* anxious, to win the downhill. It's funny, I've always liked the downhill the best of all the events, but people have never believed me, largely because I made my reputation in 1967 and after as a winner in the slalom and giant slalom. I wanted to prove that I was a winning downhill racer as well, and I was determined to prove it in the Olympics. And the downhill course at Grenoble encouraged me to think I *could* win on it. I liked the course. It just seemed to suit me in practice, and I didn't see why it shouldn't suit me on the day of the race.

But I blew it.

My troubles began with the wax, an old familiar story with me. Usually on the day of a race, after we'd waxed our skis, we would take one short trial run. That seemed to work the wax into the best texture for racing. It was the practice everyone followed. But on the morning of the Olympic downhill, for some reason, perhaps because of the excitement of the day, we didn't take that first short spin. Instead, without any preliminary testing, I moved up to the starting point, which at Grenoble happened to be surrounded on three sides, on all but the side that opened on to the course, by a crude little hut. The hut was designed to protect the starters and other officials from the cold and wind, and while it may have been a comfort to them, it constituted a special hazard to all the racers. And it was a positive booby trap for me.

The trouble was the dirt. Inside the hut, the snow was covered with mud, dust, and all sorts of dirty residue from the officials' boots. The snow was black with filth, and, as I later figured out, my skis picked up acres of the stuff. Well, it *seemed* like acres. My wax was, of course, still fresh, as fresh as the moment I'd put it on, without even the benefit of one short practice run. Worse, it was a soft wax, and it couldn't help soaking up all the dirt in the vicinity of that hut.

I knew the moment I pushed off and started down the course that I wasn't making time, and I learned from the official course timers after the race that I lost at least two seconds to the other racers in the top part of the course. My skis just wouldn't go. They weren't running. The course was fairly slow anyway, slow for everyone, but it was twice as bad for me. And everything else seemed to go wrong. I steered wide on turns when I should have cut the gates closely, and, generally, I skied the course the way I had always skied it in practice, instead of making allowances for the changed conditions.

At the bottom I felt washed out. I went numb. I knew I'd failed and so did everyone else. Skiers and officials rushed over asking me what had happened. Why was I so slow? I couldn't answer. I could hardly bear to wait around the course. But I stood there and watched the rest of the skiers run the hill. Olga Pall of Austria won the race, ahead of Isabelle Mir of France in second place and Christl Haas, making her comeback, in third. I finished tenth, and I went back to my room and just bawled my eyes out.

It was the worst disappointment of my career, the absolute rock bottom. Portillo may have been bad, but Grenoble was far worse. I felt disgusted, disturbed, sorry for myself, desperate. That afternoon, after the tears, I went out on the hills and skied slalom as recklessly as I could. I kept falling and crashing all over the place, but I didn't care whether I hurt myself or anything. I just didn't care.

The next race, the slalom, was only a couple of days away, and I approached it with a minimum of confidence. I hadn't been sharp in the slalom races in the early part of the 1968 season. I'd raced beautifully in slaloms in 1967, but in '68, out of two competitive slaloms prior to the Games, I'd finished third in one and I'd missed a gate, disqualifying myself, in the other. With that record, and with my downhill failure, I went into the Olympic slalom radiating pessimism.

Given the situation, given my mood, I positively stunned myself when I wound up close to the top at the end of the first run. I didn't ski a great race, but I was steady and in control, and I managed to take the course as it came. I stood fifth, with the American girl, Judy Nagle, in first place. She was the sixteen-year-old who had pushed Penny McCoy off the U.S. Olympic Team, and she skied an even more surprising slalom than I did to lead the field by two full seconds.

But Judy met her Waterloo in the second run and I could almost predicted her fate. After the first run, Judy and I climbed back up the hill together, heading for our second slalom runs, and all the way up, fans along the side of the course, especially American fans, kept calling out to her, stopping her to chat and offer a few words of encouragement. People like that turn up at all the meets, and unless you want to lose your concentration altogether, you have to learn to ignore them and blot their voices out of your consciousness. But Judy was very nervous and she didn't have the experience to cut off her friends. There was one fellow in particular who bugged her that day. I recognized him. He hung around all the ski meets, talking to the racers, usually bothering them, and as I passed him on the hill, I told him to leave Judy alone. But he couldn't resist and I could hear him babbling away at her. By the time Judy reached the starting gate her concentration had vanished and she was a nervous wreck. I felt so sorry for her — she wasn't used to the pressure. And she'd only skied through a couple of gates on her second run when she fell and couldn't finish the race.

I felt loose and free as I waited for my second run. I guess my showing in the first run had boosted my confidence and I made an even better run the second time down the hill. A lot of other girls, like Judy, fell or missed gates or skied poorly. Marielle Goitschel was the one exception and she finished first. My two good runs, combined with the other girls' poor runs, boosted me into second place, with Annie Famose third. I'd won a silver medal, my first in the Olympics, and I was extremely proud, but I still wanted a gold, and after the slalom, I was sure I'd get one in the giant slalom.

My whole attitude changed with the silver medal. From the depressed, desperate skier I'd been after the downhill, I turned into a matter-of-fact confident racer. I studied the giant slalom course very coolly and I found it ideal for my technique – long and smooth, the kind of course where you had to really work. I knew I could win on it, and approaching the race I expected nothing less, nothing more, than a first-place finish.

The night before the race I had waxed my two pairs of giant slalom skis. Very deliberately I prepared them in exactly the same way, and next morning I put on one pair while I inspected the course. I skied down the side of the run once and then once more, until I was certain I had memorized every bump, every gate, every turn, practically every snow flake on the thing. I had that course down cold. I was certain of it.

The second pair of skis were, of course, for the race, the skis I expected to wear while I *won* the race. I took them up to the top of the course and sat down with John Platt, the National Team head coach, and Verne Anderson, my coach, and we talked for a while. We talked deeply and seriously and even philosophically. We talked about a lot of things, about everything *except* the day's giant slalom. I guess their idea was to keep my mind from brooding on the race, and they were so successful that we were almost late for the start. I'd become too engrossed to notice that it was time for my run.

I stood up, put on my skis, and pushed down to the starting gate. I saw that Annie Famose was leading the field up to that point. I knew that Annie had a cold, and I thought to myself, as I waited, that if she could lead in her sick condition, then surely I could win.

I came out of the starting gate very quickly and took off from there. I'd really have to say, with unblushing immodesty, that I skied just about a perfect run. A couple of months later, I saw films of that race on television and, watching my run, I realized that there wasn't a move I made that I would change if I had to ski the giant slalom again. I skated furiously on the flat part of the course where I had to work to gain acceleration, and I shot down the bottom part of the course, which was steep and icy, with absolute freedom. I let my skis run for me, the way a racer does when he's travelling with all the stops out, and when I whipped across the finish line, I knew I had what I wanted.

I was, I must say, surprised that I won by such a wide margin. I finished almost three seconds ahead of Annie Famose who was in second place, and that's remarkable for an Olympic competition. Marielle Goitschel came down the hill after me, but I knew she wouldn't beat my time and she didn't. She finished far back. She'd won her gold medal. Now it was my turn.

An Olympic Gold Medal! All mine!

I honestly could hardly believe it once it had finally happened. But it was true, all true.

Warren Gerard

The Agony and the Ecstasy

# of Terry Fox

It was as if
he were inspired,
and nothing, no one,
would change his heart.

He wasn't suddenly smitten, but early last week Terry Fox knew something was terribly wrong. The hopping, running twenty-two-year-old amputee was well over the halfway mark in his coast-to-coast odyssey to show Canada he could *do* it – and to raise funds for cancer research. From April 12 [1980], when he dipped his artificial limb into the Atlantic Ocean at St. John's and began his run, until last week and 5,342 km later, Terry Fox had become a national symbol of courage, and some close to him said even stubbornness. But it wasn't to end as Terry Fox thought, and as every Canadian hoped, reminded daily as they were by the catchy jingle on radio and television, *Run Terry, Run.* Rather, it ended on the Thunder Bay bypass headed for the Red River Road in Northern Ontario. For two days, maybe three, he hadn't felt right – but he wasn't about to quit. Then, at the 29-km point on Tuesday's run, he recalled, "There was hardness of breath. I was coughing, I started to choke. I didn't know what was going on." In severe pain, he still wouldn't quit. People were lining the road ahead and he wanted to run out of people before he quit. "There was no way I was going to stop running, not with all those people there." So he ran another mile and then there were no more people. And for Terry, no more road.

He was taken to Port Arthur General Hospital. Canadian Cancer Society officials had been talking about a sore ankle and then about taking X rays of his lungs. The first set showed that his left lung had partly collapsed. "They said it could have been caused by an infection, but I could tell right away. I asked them if it could be cancer – these guys have seen this before – and they said it could be a tumor."

His parents, Rolly and Betty Fox, flew from their home in Port Coquitlam, B.C., to be with Terry. The cancer that had caused him to have his leg amputated had returned, this time to his lungs. That afternoon, his silent father on one side of a stretcher bed, his mother, unable to hold back the emotion, on the other, Terry held a press conference: "Do you want to ask questions or should I just say what I want?" He went ahead. "I didn't think this would happen; it was an unbelievable shock. I mean, I've been doing great, doing those twenty-six miles every day, up those hills, I had less than two thousand to go. I thought I was lucky as I could get. Well, you know I had primary cancer in my knee three and a half years ago, and now the cancer is in my lungs, and I really have to go home and have some more X rays, and maybe an operation that will involve opening up my chest, or more drugs. I'll do everything I can. I'm gonna do my very best, I'll fight, I promise I won't give up."

Later, Rolly Fox was heard to say: "I think it's unfair. Very unfair." He said it for the nation. In homes, offices and factories, in the newspapers, on radio and television, there was an outpouring of emotion across the country: it just wasn't fair. "I don't feel that this is unfair," Terry said. "That's the thing about cancer. I'm not the only one, it happens all the time, to other people. I'm not special. This just intensifies what I did, it gives it more meaning, it'll inspire more people."

Terry and his parents flew to Vancouver on a small chartered jet. It landed and taxied to an isolated terminal where a stretcher and an ambulance were waiting. He had ordered a change in the arrival location to avoid reporters and Cancer Society officials. Later he relented and, at a press conference at the Royal Columbian Hospital in New Westminster, he spoke once more, fighting a persistent and obviously painful cough. Wearing his MARATHON OF HOPE T-shirt, he said: "I did my very best." And in his determined way he said he wanted to return to complete his journey.

During the run, Cancer Society officials found out just how stubborn and determined Terry was. Even though they made repeated requests that he have regular medical checkups, he refused: "There's no doctor in the world who has had an amputee who's doing anything on an artificial leg like I am. If I went to see a doctor, he'd have a pessimistic approach to me."

It was as if he were inspired, and nothing, no one, would change his heart. When he first thought of the idea three years ago even his mother, Betty, despite knowing intimately her son's stubborn gutsiness, told him he was "crazy." He went to see Blair MacKenzie, executive-director of the B.C. and Yukon division of the Cancer Society, who said that when he first saw the young, curly-headed youth limp into his office on a metal-and-plastic leg he was sceptical. "We get a lot of requests that are a little off-centre, so I said, fine, organize it yourself, and he did. I was really taken with him."

Terry organized a dance and approached Vancouver businessmen for support. "I'm not a dreamer," he said in his appeals for aid, "and I'm not saying that this will initiate any kind of definitive answer or cure to cancer, but I believe in miracles. I have to." At the same time, Terry, a B-average student at Simon Fraser University, had been training. At first he hobbled through the streets of Port Coquitlam, for almost a kilometre, then he increased the distance by the same amount each week – up to 42 km a day. He won over some sceptics, but the group that saw him off to St. John's last April was small – his family, an airline representative, Blair MacKenzie and his two children, and two other Cancer Society officials. "No one could possibly have seen the magnitude of this," MacKenzie says now. "This is the most significant thing in the forty-two-year history of the Cancer Society."

As Terry, in his odd hop-and-run style, moved westward, the country became more aware of what he was doing. On May 18, he was in Sherbrooke, N.S., saying the trip so far was a "piece of cake." On June 4, he was in Fredericton, N.B., losing weight and having problems with his artificial leg. But now the money was coming in – $100,000, and the $1-million mark looked good. On June 21 he was in Quebec: "At a press conference nobody knew what we were talking about."

On a couple of occasions he was nearly run off the road by transport trucks, and police barred him from the Trans-Canada Highway as a traffic hazard. He was pelted by hailstones as big as golfballs and the leg continued to fall off, and to hurt. On his way he met Governor General Ed Schreyer and Prime Minister Pierre Trudeau, who said he didn't have time to run with Terry. He met his hockey heroes, Darryl Sittler and Bobby Orr. Sittler later said he would carry on the run if that's what Terry wanted. In Toronto, the crowds were overwhelming – ten thousand at city hall – and cops were seen to cry.

There were reports of his bad temper along the route, that he felt exploited by the Cancer Society – and others who wanted to make a buck for Terry and themselves – but he refused for himself, and he defended the Cancer Society. At the point where he stopped in Northern Ontario, out of sight of the crowds, proud, still determined, Terry Fox had done something that no individual had ever done before – he had raised almost $2 million for cancer research.

At week's end he was still in hospital, in good spirits. Meanwhile, the country is in a flurry of fund-raising for cancer research. Contributions are coming from everywhere. Governments, cities, small communities are making pledges. The CTV network said it would open up four hours of prime-time Sunday-night television for a tribute to Terry Fox. Pledges will be taken. One radio station, CKFM, in Toronto has raised more than $236 000. The country is in a frenzy of giving – not so much, perhaps, for cancer research, but for Terry Fox.

Meanwhile, he is undergoing chemotherapy. The prognosis varies. Dr. Raymond Bush, director of the Ontario Cancer Foundation, says that during the last few years the success rate for treatment of Terry's type of cancer has improved from 20 per cent to anywhere between 60 and 70 per cent. Yet other medical experts from Vancouver say that Terry's cancer is one of the most dangerous, spreading frequently to other parts of the body, especially the lungs. One cancer expert said bone cancer hits young people between ages ten and thirty especially hard, and that there is only a ten-per-cent survival rate over a five-year period.

Terry bravely promises to return, to finish the run he started, next year, the year after – maybe. But he accomplished what he set out to do. It was summed up by Sheila Fox (no kin to Terry) of Kitchener, Ont., a Cancer Society representative, who said: "You know, they say the United States is built on a history of heroes while Canada has none to look up to. But when I looked down the street today and saw Terry, I said, 'There's a hero.'"

Jim Unger

Herman

"You're not Robert Redford."

Arthur Miller

Fame

Characters
MEYER SHINE
CAR SALESMAN
SALLY
RHODA
BESS
VINNY
PEPE
PROFESSOR JENNINGS
BILLY DORFMAN
MRS. DORFMAN
MAÎTRE D'
CABBY

It is nearly six o'clock on a sunny afternoon in late spring. The crowd along 57th St. in New York City is fairly light, many couples at this hour on their eager way to a drink before dinner, late shoppers in a hurry to get home, local residents strolling with dogs, and all pretty well-dressed. Everyone, in short, seems on his way somewhere. Now we notice a man who isn't. He is about forty. He hasn't shaved today. His tweed jacket is held together by the top button, the other two having vanished. · The elbows of the jacket are frayed. His pants droop over his shoetops, unpressed. Unlike the others, he is obviously not oriented toward a destination, and is moving along in a world of his own, blind to his surroundings. Yet there is some intensity on his face as he peers ahead or lowers his eyes to the sidewalk, like a man looking for change people might have dropped. But he isn't looking for change. Vagrantly turning his head, he happens to notice Tiffany's a few yards ahead and saunters over to stand looking at a majestic rope of pearls in the window. His previous haziness flows away at the sight, and he is either frowning at the pearls or perhaps even calculating – so much so, in fact, that a cop moves into view and stands there looking towards him. MEYER notices him and, sensing inhospitality, turns and shuffles away.

When we next glimpse MEYER he is once again in his dream-world, oblivious to the passing people whose speed of movement contrasts with his wayward shuffle. Crossing the street, MEYER is somehow awakened by the wide expanse of the windows of a Rolls-Royce showroom. He looks through the glass at the gorgeous automobile and its Greek-temple grille. Again he comes awake, his expression a mixture of calculation and brow-knitted confusion. But this time something close to decision seems to rise in him and he walks over to the door and goes inside.

He faces a bewildering collection of

36

gleaming machines in the vault-like silence, and moves over to the one closest to him, letting his eyes caress its flanks. Off in the distance two salesmen are standing observing him, a public nuisance. Each of them offers the other the opportunity of making the approach – in silent mime, of course – and finally one, a silver-grey-haired gentleman with the comportment of a duke's equerry, walks over to MEYER. MEYER *has now brought himself to open the front door of a car and is about to lay his fingers on the leather seat when the salesman materializes behind him.*

SALESMAN: May I help you, sir?

MEYER: How're these on gas?

SALESMAN: (*archly*) That would depend on your speed.

MEYER: Oh, right. (*He stands there nodding as he looks again at the car.*) What would this cost?

SALESMAN: This machine is priced at 47 850.

MEYER: Forty-seven. Some reason I thought they were more.

SALESMAN: This one has been used.

MEYER: Oh, right. (*He glances at another car.*) What about that one there?

SALESMAN: That's new. $94 680.

MEYER: (*nodding*) Right. (*Now he looks out over all the cars. Taking them all in.*) How much would all of them cost?

SALESMAN: (*jaundice in his eye, he fixes* MEYER *in his gaze*) I suppose in the neighborhood of...oh, a quarter of a million dollars.

MEYER: Right. (*He takes in this information, nodding, and absorbing some clearly unspoken piece of data as he starts out across the showroom.*)

SALESMAN: We have about thirty other models in our garage if you'd like to throw them in.

MEYER: No thanks, I was just interested. Thanks very much.

SALESMAN: Not at all.

MEYER takes one last look and, hands in pockets, walks out the door. He moves along a side street in mid-town. He is confronted suddenly by a youngish, middle-aged woman, flanked by two similar companions, who is pointing into his face.

SALLY: You're Meyer Shine!

MEYER: Agh...

SALLY: You are, aren't you?

RHODA: *I* don't think he...

SALLY: (*furiously at her friend, holding out a* Time *magazine*) What are you talking about! *Look* at him! (*We glimpse the cover of* Time *which she is showing her friend, and there is Meyer's picture, and under it, "NEW KING OF BROADWAY."*)

BESS: Could we have your autograph? I saw all your three plays in the last two weeks! (*She is grubbing in her purse for a pen.*)

SALLY: Please, under your picture. (MEYER *takes out his pen, writes his name.*) Could you put "To Doris"? – for my daughter.

BESS: I have nothing to write on...here, do it on here. (*She offers her stuffed Korvette's shopping bag and as* MEYER *starts awkwardly to write on it a round carton of cheese falls out and rolls along the sidewalk, followed by a cylindrical can of hairspray which rolls in the other direction, plus cartons of stockings, a bathing suit and other items, which* MEYER *has to help retrieve and stuff back into the bag, as...*)

RHODA: (*she stands a little apart, appraising him*) *I* don't think he looks like...

BESS: (*grabbing up items from the sidewalk*) It's him, I know it's him!

RHODA: (*to* BESS, *whose shopping bag is now full again*) Where's my brassiere?

MEYER is adroitly slipping backwards and away from this happy distraction.

BESS: I didn't take your brassiere.

RHODA: I told you to put it in your bag!

BESS: It must be still on the counter!

RHODA: (*near tears*) How could you have done such a thing! I told you to put it in your bag. I didn't even keep the sales ticket!

BESS: Well, will you stop screaming?

We follow MEYER, *who moves along the street and through the door of a restaurant. Beyond the bar the tables are rapidly filling up now, the start of the dinner hour.* MEYER *sits on a stool and glances down the bar at the half-dozen customers, all nicely dressed for the new evening.* VINNY, *the bartender, is glancing over at* MEYER *and is already making him a Scotch and soda which he sets before him with a warm, welcoming look.*

VINNY: All packed?

MEYER: Packed! Vinny, I don't leave till Thursday.

VINNY: Boy, if it was me I'd be packed for a week. D'ja buy the suits?

MEYER: They'll be ready tomorrow.

VINNY: How many?

MEYER: Well, two.

VINNY: What about a tuxedo?

MEYER: One of them is a tuxedo.

VINNY: So you got one suit?

MEYER: I'm going there to work, I'm not entering high society.

VINNY: Meyer, the man is the greatest motion picture director in Italy. I get the Italian magazines – Guadalieri is the top in Europe. These guys live like kings, you can't hang out there with one suit. They'll mark you for some kind of kook.

MEYER: Well . . . maybe I'll get another jacket.

VINNY: Look, get yourself another jacket and at least two more suits. You're an important personality, Meyer. I mean it. You can't walk around like this anymore.

PEPE, *a bearded waiter with tinted glasses, comes up to the bar with a tray.*

PEPE: Two Scotch, gin-tonic. (VINNY *makes the drinks as* PEPE *turns to* MEYER.) What d'ya say, Meyer, want to get back into uniform?

MEYER: How's business, Pepe?

PEPE: Not bad. Whyn't you get that *Time* cover framed? I'll hang it on the wall over your old station. No kiddin', be a conversation piece . . . where Meyer Shine used to work, y'know?

MEYER: Whyn't you just remember me in spirit?

PEPE: (*loading drinks on his tray as received from* VINNY) You're the pride of the Waiters' Union, baby – including that you never got an order straight. (*Jabs* MEYER'S *arm*) Watch out with the Roman broads, kid. (PEPE *exits.*)

VINNY: What about the movie contracts – everything settled?

MEYER: (*nods*) I signed the last one today. Had sixty-three pages.

VINNY: For which play?

MEYER: *Mostly Florence.*

VINNY: And how much for that?

MEYER: Well, let's see . . . on that I get six hundred thousand over ten years.

VINNY: How come? You got six hundred and fifty for *Imperial Café.* And . . . what? – seven for *The Clown Sandwich.*

MEYER: I don't know, I guess *Mostly Florence* wouldn't make as commercial a movie or something. My agent does it, I don't understand it.

VINNY: What about a financial manager?

MEYER: They're getting me one when I get back from Italy.

VINNY: 'Cause on top of the movie money you got the royalties every week.

MEYER: Oh yeah.

VINNY: How much is that?

MEYER: Well on the three plays it's . . . around eighteen thousand a week.

VINNY: Not counting London.

MEYER: No, plus London . . . and Paris and

Rome...and Germany. They're opening in Japan, next month, I think.

VINNY: *Mama mia* – Why don't you buy something?

MEYER: I can't think of anything. I bought a new typewriter...

VINNY: Typewriter! Whyn't you buy like a car or a...

MEYERS: Matter of fact, I stopped in at the Rolls-Royce place over on Third Avenue just before.

VINNY: You're going to buy a Rolls-Royce!

MEYER: Oh, no, but they had three cars on the floor, and it suddenly came to me that I could have bought all of them. (*VINNY, enthralled, shakes his head.*) On the bus before I started thinking to myself – I could buy this bus.

VINNY: You're still riding the bus?

MEYER: I don't know for how long, though – people are looking at me.

VINNY: Well, sit back and enjoy it.

MEYER: I do...but it's uncomfortable. It's hard to get used to.

VINNY: Relax, for Pete's sake. I tell you the truth, Meyer, you look to me in a constant state of tension.

MEYER: Well there's something so unreal – like everybody's so *nice* to me. I have to keep reminding myself that very few people used to like me. In fact, practically nobody. Now, I start to speak and everybody waits to see what's going to come out of my mouth. I ask what time it is, they die laughing, it's so witty.

VINNY: Must be a big advantage with the broads, though.

MEYER: (*slight pause*) That's true, yes. That's the best part of it. But even there – like I was with this girl the other night. And I looked at her, and I suddenly had the feeling there were three of us: me, her, and my fame. It does something to the intimacy.

VINNY: That's the one trouble I wish I had. Whyn't you grow a beard? A nice bushy beard.

MEYER: (*with a wry look*) But nobody'd recognize me! (*He starts to laugh when a tall, distinguished-looking man comes up.*)

PROFESSOR: I have to tell you, Mr. Shine, that in your three plays you have three American classics. Not only are they marvellously funny, but what's more important, they are profound moral observations.

MEYER: Well...thanks very much. What's your name?

PROFESSOR: Douglas Jennings. I teach at Yale.

MEYER: (*as they shake hands*) Well I'm...I don't know what to say.

PROFESSOR: You've said it. Thank you.

He goes. MEYER *is inflated, high, shaking his head with wonder.*

VINNY: *Now* what's the complaint?

MEYER: Nothing. But he's talking about my writing, not my publicity.

PEPE comes up to the bar with his tray.

PEPE: Dry martini, Scotch, two gin-tonic.

VINNY makes the drinks. MEYER, *floating on his cloud, now relaxes and looks about with an air of success and satisfaction. A few yards away a clot of people are standing, waiting to be escorted in by the* MAÎTRE D'. *A couple enters from the street,* MR. *and* MRS. WILLIAM DORFMAN. MRS. DORFMAN *is pretty, forty, distorted by a thick mink jacket.* ABE *is short, a little shorter than his wife. His dress – a midnight blue topcoat and grey fedora – announces pride, infinite success, and minor hauteur. He is fit, ruddy, and on top of a very shaky world. Their arrival naturally attracts* MEYER's *attention, as nemesis usually does. So inevitably his eyes momentarily meet* DORFMAN's, *but he –* MEYER – *instantly turns away.* DORFMAN, *however, keeps staring at him with a quizzical expression. He starts across the intervening space and* MRS. DORFMAN *follows, with a quick movement revealing that her husband often forgets she is with him.*

MRS. DORFMAN: Billy . . . ?

DORFMAN: (*over his shoulder, hardly pausing*) Stay there. (*He continues on to* MEYER *and she comes to a halt close enough to hear the conversation, but distant enough to be out of Billy's way. On* DORFMAN*'s approach,* MEYER, *sensing a blatant fan, swivels about his stool to face the bar.*) 'Scuse me. (MEYER *lets a second go by before looking up at him.*) You're not Meyer Shine by any chance?

MEYER: (*with a forced simplicity; that is, simple acknowledgment plus a subtle signal that he is being intruded on*) I am, yeah.

DORFMAN: (*a grin comes onto his face, combining an unearned familiarity and a ineffable condescension*) You're kidding.

MEYER: I wish I was, after a remark like that.

DORFMAN: (*something approaching genuine warmth seems to spring into his voice as he points at* MEYER) You're Meyer Shine?

MEYER: (*with a strained laugh: he is playing a bit to* VINNY) You know when you put it like that I'm beginning to wonder myself.

DORFMAN: (*inoculated against satire, he is filling with some obscure pleasure*) From the Bronx.

MEYER: (*nodding; in fact, over-nodding*) Right, right. (*He turns away from* DORFMAN *to glance at* VINNY.)

DORFMAN: Remember me?

MRS. DORFMAN *is looking on, excitedly smiling.*

MEYER: (*surprise; with a tweak of minor guilt*) Do I know you?

DORFMAN: (*incredulously; a scratch on his pride*) You don't remember me?

MEYER: (*honestly*) Who are you?

DORFMAN: (*hurt*) Who am I!

MEYER: Well, I don't remember you so I have to ask who you are.

DORFMAN: Meyer! (*as though they had lived together until this morning*) I'm Billy Dorfman.

MEYER: (*frowning into the mists of the past — and growing embarrassed*) Billy Dorfman.

DORFMAN: (*spreading his arms out as though presenting his total identity*) Billy Dorfman!

MEYER: (*a little alarmed by both the man's driving need for recognition and the total blank in his own mind*) Geez, forgive me, I just don't have any . . .

DORFMAN: We sat next to each other in English for three years in high school!

MEYER: No kidding.

DORFMAN: Meyer, we were best friends!

MEYER: (*guilty for his own success, he reaches out and touches* DORFMAN*'s sleeve*) You'll have to forgive me, Billy, I have a terrible memory and I . . .

DORFMAN: You remember me now, don't you?

MEYER: What's the difference, I'm glad to see you anyway. . . .

DORFMAN: You don't remember Billy Dorfman with the curly red hair? (*He removes his hat, revealing a stone bald head.*)

MEYER: (*pouring out kindness*) Right. But you *have* changed. . . .

DORFMAN: But I didn't change *that* much.

MEYER: Billy, I'm not trying to . . . put you down. You know it's a long time ago.

DORFMAN: But after you sit next to a person for three years . . . how can you?

MEYER: Well that's the way I am, I forget everything. That's why I have to make it all up.

DORFMAN: (*to remind* MEYER) You were always losing something.

MEYER: Sounds like me. (*to assuage the hurt he feels he had caused*) You look very well.

DORFMAN: Oh, I'm in great shape. What's the matter — you tired? You look kind of tired.

MEYER: A little, yeah. But I've been pretty

busy. You know...(*He spreads his elbows back on the bar and his last button hangs precariously*.)

DORFMAN: You're going to lose that.

MEYER awkwardly covers the button. Their eyes meet, and MEYER sees in DORFMAN a mixture of condescension and pity for his apparent condition.

MEYER: (*with a gesture toward DORFMAN's elegance*) You look terrific. What do you do?

DORFMAN: I'm in shoulder pads. (*It stops MEYER cold – particularly the suddenness with which DORFMAN has adopted an eminence, a stance of position, one eyebrow even creeping higher than the other*.)

MEYER: ...Really! Shoulder pads.

DORFMAN: You know, like...(*touching his own shoulders*) Coats, and dresses.

MEYER: (*for DORFMAN's sake*) Right. Geez, I never imagined there was a whole industry for shoulder pads.

DORFMAN: (*a bit put-out*) Of course. We're on the Stock Exchange. Acme International?

MEYER: That so!

DORFMAN: We're the largest in the country. In the world, in fact.

MEYER: That's marvellous.

DORFMAN: (*with weight*) I'm vice-president.

MRS. DORFMAN looks on benignly, glancing down at the bar where a Time *magazine lies.*

DORFMAN: I'm in charge of everything east of the Mississippi.

MEYER: (*shaking his head*) Boy! (*laughing*) That must be a lot of shoulder pads!

DORFMAN: (*it isn't funny*) You're darned tootin!

MEYER: Well, it was awfully nice to see you again, Billy. (*extending his hand*) Good luck to you.

DORFMAN: Likewise. (*He holds MEYER's hand and glances at his jacket, his wan, stubbled face, unable to speak without registering his own glittering fate....*) And what do *you* do? (*Several things happen. MEYER's breathing stops. VINNY's eyes pop and he looks down to busy himself to ward off the coming disaster. Unmitigated horror blazes onto MRS. DORFMAN's pretty face. DORFMAN remains waiting for MEYER's reply, so filled with his victory in life that he feels a magnanimous pity for his old friend. He pats MEYER's hand with his free one, adds confidentially.*) Forget it, kid, I shouldn't have been nosey. Look, here's my card. If you need anything...I'm serious, Meyer... just give me a ring. I mean that, kid.

MEYER: (*the card in his hand*) That's okay, I'm...I don't need anything.

DORFMAN: Don't be bashful; I'm serious. I'm going to expect your call, you understand?

MEYER: (*his expression hardens; a resentful edge in his voice*) I don't need any help, Billy.

DORFMAN: Kid, now, don't be offended....

MEYER: (*offended*) I'm not offended.

DORFMAN: What *do* you do?

MEYER: I'm a writer.

DORFMAN: (*the news amuses him, for some reason*) You don't say. Like what kind? What do you write?

MEYER: Well, ah...stories, sometimes...

DORFMAN: (*even more amused*) Don't say! Get any published?

MRS. DORFMAN's hand is going to her mouth.

MEYER: Yeah, I get published.

DORFMAN: I don't get much time for reading, although my wife does to some degree. You do that for a living, or...?

MEYER: Ya, for a living.

MRS. DORFMAN breaks out of her assigned position and, near hysteria, breaks in.

MRS. DORFMAN: (*with the delicacy of the long-crushed ego*) Billy dear, I think our table is ready...

DORFMAN: Want to meet Dotty, my wife. Honey, this is Meyer Shine. Sat next to each in English.

MRS. DORFMAN: Oh, I know all about you!

MEYER: Hi!

MRS. DORFMAN: We'd better get the table, dear...(*She takes his arm to draw him away*.)

DORFMAN: (*starting to move with her*) Whyn't you write plays? There's the real money.

MEYER: I've written plays.

DORFMAN: (*this is even more amusing, his eyebrows rise superciliously*) Plays?

MRS. DORFMAN: Darling, this is Meyer Shine.

DORFMAN: (*with her stupidity he has no patience at all*) What do you mean, it's Meyer Shine? I just introduced you to him.

MRS. DORFMAN: (*dreading his reaction, pumping all the kindness she can into her near-whisper*) He wrote the play we're seeing tonight.

True metamorphosis sweeps over DORFMAN. First he is appalled as he stands for a moment staring into her wracked face. He is growing smaller and smaller by the second. He turns to MEYER with eyes that see a miracle − a common human having been turned before his eyes into a statue, a monument, a sort of god. And his right hand weakly rises just a few inches, the index finger pointing at MEYER.

DORFMAN: Are you...Meyer Shine?

MEYER: (*it's like killing a man and it has its pleasure and it is terrible, too*) I am, yeah.

DORFMAN: Well! (*His manner is that of a total stranger; a mixture of formality and gratitude and utter despair.*) I'm very honored to meet you.

MRS. DORFMAN: (*apologizing, she draws DORFMAN, step by step, away*) We're seeing *Mostly Florence* tonight.

MEYER: I hope you enjoy it.

MRS. DORFMAN: We already saw *Imperial Café* and your other one.

MEYER: Oh good, good...

DORFMAN has paralytically nodded confirmation of her two declarations and now the MAÎTRE D' comes up to them.

MAÎTRE D': I have your table, Mr. Dorfman. (*He walks sideways to lead them into the restaurant, but DORFMAN changes course as he turns from MEYER and, ahead of MRS. DORFMAN, walks − flees − through the door to the street, she behind him. We study the mixture of wonder and pain − yes, and secret victory − on MEYER's face as he stares after the departing DORFMANS.*)

VINNY: Beautiful, Meyer − you crippled him.

MEYER: (*pained*) Don't say that...

VINNY: Why? He was asking for it, he was walking on your face.

MEYER: The whole thing is insane. You see the look that came over him when he...?

VINNY: Well, that's fame, baby.

MEYER: I should never have told him.

VINNY: You see? If you'd been wearing a good suit that would never have happened; he thought you were dying of hunger. You gotta start acting like who you are. Meyer-the-waiter is dead and gone; you bury him, kid, or you won't have a happy day.

MEYER: (*putting money on the bar*) See you when I get back, Vinny.

VINNY: And by the way − when you get to Italy − they've been kidnapping rich people for ransom over there.

MEYER: Ah, come on now!

VINNY: I'm serious, Meyer. You got three shows running in Rome? You're probably famous over there.

MEYER: Yeah, yeah, okay...I'll buy a machine gun.

VINNY: And be careful with the broads − they're famous for blackmail.

MEYER: (*turning*) Keep it up, I'll go home and lock the door and never come out.

VINNY: I'm just telling you it's a new ballgame, Meyer; everybody wants a piece of you so stay awake over there.

42 MEYER: Right, right. See ya, Vinny – if I live through it.

He walks outside and down the street. A passing cab driver leans out through his window and waves.
CABBY: Hey, Meyer, how's it goin'?
MEYER: Great, great...(*He changes course to escape the cab, walking faster than usual, and his expression shows a certain dawn of new determination. He halts at the window of a men's clothing store which displays expensive suits bathed in expensive lights. He stares at the clothes. To himself.*) Why not? I've worked for it. I'm Meyer Shine... or something...

Robert Collins

Wayne and Shuster: Canada's Stay-at-Home Clowns

On stage and off, Wayne and Shuster fare
is an amiable mixture of slapstick,
pantomime, visual tricks, sheer corn....

44

By May 1958, most comedians in North America would have given a year's joke-books to be in Johnny Wayne and Frank Shuster's old soft-shoes. The pair had just emerged from their first appearance on *The Ed Sullivan Show* – then the most coveted TV showcase on the continent – to rave reviews. Their thirteen-minute spoof of *Julius Caesar* was, said the *New York Times*, a "harbinger of literate slapstick." In bars everywhere, Wayne and Shuster fans were ordering the "martinus" ("Gimme a martinus." "You mean a martini?" "If I want *two*, I'll *order* two!"). And now Sullivan had offered an unprecedented twenty-six-week contract at his top fee of $7500 a show – on their own terms.

"People down here may try to change your style," he warned. "Resist them. Do it your own way."

"What if *you* try to make us change?" cautioned Shuster.

"If you think I'm wrong, say no," insisted Sullivan. "Do it your way!"

Wayne and Shuster did. Fearing overexposure, they refused the twenty-six-week offer in favor of sixteen appearances the first year and they insisted on using their full-length sketches – ten to twenty minutes – although Sullivan restricted most performers to three or four minutes. Then Wayne had a silver medallion engraved: "Do it your way, Ed Sullivan." For twelve years he carried it throughout the twosome's record-breaking sixty-five appearances on *The Ed Sullivan Show*. In times of disagreement he plunked down the medal, grinning wickedly, and the Sullivan crew always gave in.

Today, after twenty-eight years in the

most precarious kind of show business, Wayne and Shuster are still doing it "their way." Now in their mid-fifties, Shuster – the gracious, patient straight man – and Wayne – the irrepressible cutup – are as much a Canadian institution as the Mounties or the maple leaf. They've twice been voted the top comedy team in North America, and once won the Silver Rose of Montreux for the second-best TV variety show in the world. Their Gulf Oil commercials have won eleven awards in the past five years. U.S. schools use their recorded spoofs of Shakespeare in English appreciation classes.

Choosy Comedians. Yet Frank and Johnny have consistently broken the rules of show-business success, resisting countless overtures to change their style, get rich quick, "go Hollywood," or appear on Broadway. Although their four annual CBC specials alone gross them an estimated six-figure annual income, Shuster says, "We could make a lot more money but we'd rather set our own pace and enjoy life." Adds Wayne, "We have staying power, because we're choosy about what we do."

Thus they rejected the script for Broadway's *A Funny Thing Happened on the Way to the Forum* because "it wasn't right for us" and refused starring roles in another New York play, *The Golden Fleecing*. "If you can guarantee the show will flop we'll take it," Shuster told the astonished producers. "About two weeks in this town is all we could stand!" After their first appearance on *The Ed Sullivan Show*, NBC offered them a $600,000 contract for a weekly TV comedy show. "We turned it down in seven seconds," says Shuster. "We'd have had no time for our families, our friends, ourselves."

Similarly, they're adamant about staying in Canada. Once a talent agent trying to lure them to the States found Wayne in the swimming pool of his comfortable home in Toronto's Forest Hill. "Tell me," urged the comedian, "are you gonna get me some kind of TV job so I can buy a house with a pool?"

On stage or off, Wayne and Shuster fare is an amiable mixture of slapstick, pantomime, visual tricks, sheer corn, and sometimes ingenious twists on classic situations: the meek little man whose blundering brother-in-law happens to be Superman (he keeps bursting in through the window, and when you want a quart of milk he brings back the whole refrigerator), and the bumbling German U-boat commander who has sunk thirty-two ships (all German), but can't be fired because he's Hitler's nephew.

Such a potpourri doesn't always please the critics. It was, said one commentator, best suited to "someone who is simultaneously watching TV, giving a party, and washing the car. They hardly demand undivided attention...." But critic Bob Blackburn perhaps summed it up best a few years ago in the now-defunct *Toronto Telegram*. "Often you'll find a flash of almost brilliant wit snuggled up beside a line which would be banal even for *Comedy Crackers*. I suppose they are trying to be all things to all men."

"We don't try to please the critics," says their CBC executive producer, Leonard Starmer. "Our duty is to a big audience, including children. Anyway, contemporary comedy of any decade is faddish. Traditional comedy is timeless."

D-Day Shows. Weaned on the humor of such old masters as Chaplin, Laurel and Hardy, the Marx Brothers, and Jack Benny, Wayne and Shuster are content to be classified as traditionals. Fifty years ago, Shuster's father owned and operated a silent-movie theatre in Niagara Falls. His mother sold tickets, so five-year-old Frank sat in the projection booth every night, learning to read from the subtitles. Wayne was one of seven children of a Toronto clothing manufacturer who wrote Hebrew poetry in his spare time.

The two met at Toronto's Harbord Collegiate. After producing a Boy Scout play that netted forty dollars for their troop, they starred as writers, singers, and actors in Harbord's annual revue. They kept right on at the University of Toronto, producing college shows and developing a commercial radio program, *Wife Preservers* – household hints mixed with humor – that paid them each $12.50 a week. Amid all this they got B.A.'s, majoring in English. "What I like about you, Wayne," said Claude Bissell, then an English lecturer and later president of the University of Toronto, "is you don't let your studies interfere with your education!"

Even World War II couldn't keep them off stage. They enlisted as infantrymen but were soon writing the music, book, and lyrics for a show called *Invasion Review*. It played to troops all over Canada and Britain, and for a while after D-day they presented five shows a day from a cave in France. "Doing that show for men from every province gave us our first real sense of Canada," Wayne says.

They came home to start families and the chancy business of professional comedy. ("I know he's a very funny boy," Shuster's father-in-law told his daughter, "but what does he do for a *living*?")

Their first radio show was a humorous look at servicemen's rehabilitation problems. By 1947 they had a regular CBC program – and were doing it *their* way. The CBC saw no need for studio audiences, but Wayne and Shuster had seen how audience response was buoying up U.S. radio comedians. After their second performance in an empty studio they threatened to quit unless the CBC provided a live audience and enough studio microphones to pick up the laughter. They got both.

Cast of Characters. Soon NBC offered them the summer replacement spot for *The Life of Riley* radio show. Fine, said the Canadians, but why do it in New York? NBC was puzzled: didn't *everybody* want to work in New York? But Toronto's facilities proved satisfactory and the U.S. network show was produced in Canada.

In 1950 Wayne and Shuster were guest stars on a U.S. television show sponsored by Toni Home Permanents. Toni promptly offered them their own show, but though TV hadn't yet come to Canada, Wayne and Shuster refused. Toni's president then offered them vice presidencies in charge of his company's entire U.S. TV programming. They politely heard him out, sitting on a quiet Toronto lawn, then turned him down. "Why should we leave all this," said Wayne with a wave of an arm, "to spend our lives on airplanes?"

Starting regular CBC television work in 1954, they began honing their style, quickening their pace and building a cast of characters: The Brown Pumpernickel (like the Scarlet Pimpernel, he helps the downtrodden, but the trademark he leaves is a loaf of bread); Professor Waynegartner, a nutty old scientist with runaway white hair (the professor's rocket ship has a crew of 120. Shuster: "That's a large crew!" Professor: "Too large. The first time we flew it, some of us had to go by train."); and Tex Rorschach, Frontier Psychiatrist ("Your husband's problem iss all in his mind, he can valk if he vants to. Goodbye, Mrs. Sitting Bull.").

There were contemporary twists on classics: in *The Picture of Dorian Wayne*, a glutton gorges himself on food and stays thin, while his portrait grows fat. And there were the popular Shakespearean spoofs. In *The Elsinore Kid*, a horse-opera Hamlet swaggers into a bar: "Gimme a shot of whiskey and don't cut the liquor. I want the uncuttest kind of all!" In the *Julius Caesar* skit, a line uttered by Caesar's nagging widow – "If I told him once, I told him a thousand times. I said 'Julie, don't go!'" – became an international "in" phrase.

In 1957, millions of British viewers watched them perform in *Chelsea at Nine*. Critics were enthusiastic, actor Charles Laughton said it was "bloody good," and Granada TV offered them a thirteen-week show. As usual, they refused; "You can't do a weekly show and keep up standards." A few months later, after a guest appearance on *The Rosemary Clooney Show*, they turned down an NBC invitation to take over *that* series. "What *do* you guys want?" demanded a frustrated agent. They wanted what Ed Sullivan finally gave them: major U.S. network appearances on their terms, with freedom to live and continue working in Canada.

Time for the Family. Now the industry courted Wayne and Shuster harder than ever. There was a guest spot on *The Dinah Shore Show*, another on *The Red Skelton Show*, and records for Columbia. The St. Louis Municipal Opera wanted them for a musical comedy. Comedians like Jack E. Leonard, Jack Carter, and Ernie Kovacs visited rehearsals, to kibitz and accord the respect of fellow professionals.

Wayne and Shuster loved it, but gratefully hurried home after every performance. Then as now, they saved time for their families – Shuster has two children; Wayne, three – who generally accompanied them on New York or Hollywood assignments. "We embarrass the show biz crowd because we still have the wives we started with," chuckles Shuster. "Once at a party Groucho

Marx told us, 'How dare you flaunt your own wives at a Hollywood gathering! Do you want to undermine the social structure?'"*

In their spare time they do benefit shows, patronize the basement pub of Toronto's Celebrity Club, spend an evening at the theatre or lunch with friends. Shuster is a golfer, Wayne a rabid hockey fan and rare-book collector. "I suppose I'm an intellectual," he says, "but if people ever find out, I'm dead!"

Unlike most comics, they continue to write most of their material. Ideas come from all around them. Antismoking campaigns inspired a routine about the smoking addict who phones for help from Cigarettes Anonymous; they send over a drunk to sit up with him. Once, riding an aircraft economy class with his wife, Wayne began to fantasize about the "orgy" going on in first class: "They're eating *turkey* up there...hey, *they've* got *wine*! I guess *I'll* go back and pump a glass of water from the well...hey, there's a girl in a bathing suit, they must have a *pool* up there..." From this came a skit which helped win the Montreux award.

They work at one or the other's home, taking turns at the typewriter and acting out the material until the lines come right. Once a blood-curdling scream issued from the Wayne study. "It's all right," a Wayne child assured a startled friend. "It just Daddy, writing."

"Our Best Shot, Always." The show then goes into a week and a half of rehearsal, during which the two argue vehemently, still polishing the script. "I'm really a bad-tempered guy," says Wayne. "I don't know how Shuster puts up with me." Shuster, always patient, shows his annoyance only with the occasional sarcastic plea, "Will *somebody* please tell my partner..."

"It's all for the good of the show, and nobody takes it seriously," says actor Paul Kligman, who has worked with them for twenty-three years with nothing more binding than a handshake. "Johnny is really a genius. And few people realize that, behind the straight-man routine, Frank is a highly talented actor."

Hundreds of hours of work from the germ of an idea, the show goes into the studio for taping. "We give it our best shot, always," Wayne says simply. "We owe the people our best possible show."

Wayne and Shuster now produce their CBC specials as well as writing and performing in them. Because they are uncommonly versatile, the death of *The Ed Sullivan Show* in 1970 caused scarcely a ripple in their careers. They have produced and narrated a filmed series on great comedians of our time. They've collaborated on a script, satirizing Canadian politics, which may become a feature film. They have appeared on educational television and next fall will host on the CBC a British series on Gilbert and Sullivan. "We're experimenting," Wayne says. "The biggest danger in our business is in getting complacent."

Not long ago Shuster was sitting with their New York manager who was again trying to lure them to the United States. For ten minutes he wheedled and cajoled to no avail. Finally the agent snapped in frustration, "You know, Frank, there's more to life than happiness!"

Judging by the roar of laughter it got, that line may show up some day in a Wayne and Shuster skit.

---

*Editors' note: Johnny Wayne's wife died in 1980.

J. Paul Getty

The World Is Mean to Millionaires

But can
really rich people
live completely
normal lives?

Reprinted from *The Saturday Evening Post*. © 1965
The Curtis Publishing Co.

Never have the burdens of wealth been greater than they are today, and never have its rewards been slimmer. Rich people once lived in a world apart; today almost the only difference between the multimillionaire and the reasonably well-to-do man earning fifteen thousand to twenty-five thousand a year is that the millionaire works harder, relaxes less, is burdened with greater responsibilities, and is exposed to the constant glare of publicity.

The greatest difference lies in the exposure to publicity. As soon as this is published, I know my mail will increase from an average low of fifty letters a day to three hundred, four hundred or even a thousand. My two secretaries will be working overtime for weeks dealing with long letters from complete strangers, usually written in crabbed, almost indecipherable handwriting, and headed "Dear Paul" – so that they *might* conceivably be from old friends, long lost sight of. Some will be from cranks and religious maniacs, urging me to give away my riches for the good of my soul; but mostly they'll be from people who genuinely need – or at any rate claim to need – financial assistance for themselves or their families, or from perfectly well-to-do people who wish me to contribute to their pet charities. A few, like one I received recently, will demand "one million dollars by return mail since you have so much of the stuff."

I have received up to two thousand letters a day. Obviously, if I read them all, I'd have time for nothing else. And if I acted on them, I'd be bankrupt very quickly. Calculating the average request at five hundred dollars, with an average of two hundred letters a day, I would hand out about $100 000 a day for the rest of my life if I obliged every request for funds that is imposed on me.

I want to make it clear that I don't resent

this state of affairs. I accept it as part of the penalty of being rich and known. I don't resent such publicity as comes my way. On the contrary, I feel that throughout my life the press has been overwhelmingly fair, even friendly to me. Like the publicity, the letters are part of the price I pay for being a millionaire. I hate rudeness, but I can't reply personally to all the letters I receive. So I have a polite printed reply, a "Mr. Getty regrets," which my secretaries use in most cases.

But this is not to say that I am indifferent to all the unwanted attention. Indeed, it often annoys me. Perhaps it's the lack of consideration of the well-to-do solicitors for charities that irks me most: It doesn't seem to occur to these people that I, too, have charities I'm interested in, and that I'd never dare to do indiscriminate fund-raising among acquaintances of mine, let alone total strangers. As Groucho Marx once said, in an unforgettable hotel-lobby scene: "Boy, what are you shouting my name for? Do I go around shouting your name?"

The charity solicitors, and those who write straightforward begging letters, display an elementary ignorance of the basic financial facts of life which is almost touching. They seem to think that all my wealth is in cash, ready for distribution. It never occurs to them that, as an active businessman, I invest my money, or that I'm in competition, in the oil business, with some of the world's largest corporations. Even successful corporations have to borrow money for expensive, essential development, and no successful corporation, to my knowledge, has ever had a surplus of liquid cash. Why should these people assume that I do?

I first became aware of the penalties of being rich when my father died. I was thirty-seven. My father's affairs had never been publicized during his lifetime, and he died a very wealthy man. The size of his estate was commented on in the press. The effect was instantaneous. My mother, Sarah Catharine Getty, his widow, then aged seventy-eight, received hundreds of proposals of marriage from total strangers from all over the world. Acquaintances who had never paid particular attention to me would come up and say, "You related to that rich oil man who died the other day?" When I explained, they'd say, "You mean to say he was your *father*?" and I could see in their eyes a sinister glint that hadn't been there before. Constant exposure to this sort of thing has, I suppose, made me wary of the "old friend" who calls up, just because – or so I first suppose – he is glad to see me. I am glad to see him, but I become depressed when I realize that he doesn't really want to see me at all: What he wants is a loan. I have become gun-shy about such people, to the extent of never carrying on my person any sizable amounts of cash.

If I were convinced that by giving away my fortune I could make a real contribution toward solving the problems of world poverty, I'd give away 99.5 percent of all I have immediately. But a hard-eyed appraisal of the situation convinces me this is not the case. The best form of charity I know is the act of meeting a payroll. If I turned over my entire fortune to a charitable foundation, would it do any more good than I do with it? The answer is no. However admirable the work of the best charitable foundation, it would accustom people to the passive acceptance of money – and incidentally deprive of their jobs thousands of hard-working people associated with me.

I disagree, now more than ever, with Scott Fitzgerald's often-quoted remark to Ernest Hemingway: "The rich are different from us." Take the case of the man earning twenty thousand a year and compare him with the multimillionaire. Looking at them, more often than not, you simply can't tell the difference. They wear the same clothes, drive the same cars, and live in more or less the same style. In fact, most multimillionaires I've known have been rather frugal in their personal expenditure. I doubt whether many of them spend more on groceries than the man with ten thousand a year. The limousine was once a status symbol. It isn't any longer. Neither are yachts, private planes or world tours. Look at the hundreds of thousands of Americans today who own small yachts (the only kind worth having, in my view) or fly private planes or travel round the world.

One of the few status symbols left to the really rich is art collecting, but even in this field the true value of the picture isn't necessarily in its price. I can prove my point: the best picture I ever acquired was a Raphael, picked up in a sale for $112. Not many modern painters will acquire Raphael's stature, but a small investment in a picture can get you a great picture, if you have taste and a certain amount of luck. The connoisseurs who recognized the genius of Jackson Pollock before he became famous did not only acquire great paintings. They also made a fortune.

When I was a boy, multimillionaires owned huge steam yachts, with large crews. I had one – until 1936. It gave me so much trouble I felt I was in the shipping business. If I ever buy a yacht again, it'll be a small one I can handle – and enjoy handling – myself. As far as I'm concerned, the transatlantic liner of today is more comfortable than the most luxurious private yacht, and the scheduled airliner as comfortable as – and a good deal safer than – the most expensive private plane.

Since multimillionaires have been stripped of so many status symbols and must live very much as other people do, they should, I think, be entitled to the same courtesies. If I go to a doctor, I should be charged the regular fee. If I go to a hotel, I should pay the standard charge for a room. And when I tip, I shouldn't be expected to tip more than the average man. It's rude and inconsiderate to overtip. It only makes things difficult – and embarrassing – for people who are not as rich as I am.

But can really rich people live completely normal lives? It isn't easy. Speaking personally, I find it necessary to insulate myself so I can keep away from professional hangers-on – and I've got awfully good at spotting them. I'm always slight wary about meeting strangers. Most of my social life revolves round old friends whom I know really well. Not all of them are wealthy – but none of them is obsessed with money. For some years, in Paris, I lived in a hotel room, partly because a hotel provides the same kind of protection from strangers as that afforded by a fleet of servants in a mansion.

I must concede that I'm not overcharged systematically, but some restaurants do inflate my bill, and so do some hotels – and a doctor or two. When that happens, I retaliate very simply by crossing the place, or the specialist, off my list. It isn't quite so easy to cope with the unwarranted attention given to little things I do, especially if money is involved. There was this business of the pay phone I had installed in my country house in England to be used by my guests. When *I'm* staying with friends and have to make long-distance calls, I make a point of making them from a pay phone in the nearest town or village. I had the pay phone installed in my place because I knew that guests preferred it that way. It saved them the trouble of settling with me afterward, or of attempting to pay for their phone calls. It saved them trouble. And yet a spate of letters and cartoons resulted. You might have thought I was pathologically inclined, instead of taking the simple, rational step.

Just as a millionaire has to be wary about hangers-on, he has to be wary about the feminine company he keeps. This is where the rich man is penalized enormously for being rich. The penalty he pays for divorce makes many a rich man unwilling to marry in the first place. Whereas it's generally assumed that the multimillionaire should pay no more than the next man for a meal, a hotel room or a doctor's bill, it's regarded as normal for a judge in an American divorce court to impose the maximum settlement the husband can afford. Old-established family fortunes, usefully invested for the benefit of society, have been broken by excessive divorce judgments. The multimillionaire who marries is always possible prey. His wife may not be the classic gold digger, but she may become neurotically intent on obtaining the maximum settlement, either to humiliate her husband or as a kind of revenge. And lawyers will egg her on and encourage her wildest demands.

We all know of women who make life unbearable for their husbands, in little ways which can never be proved in court. I find it incredible that such women can obtain millions of dollars for having suffered the misfortune of being married to multimillionaires. It is offensive that the more spendthrift and extravagant such a woman has been during her marriage, the more she can legitimately claim as being commensurate to her standard of living. I also find it strange that a woman can claim huge sums of money earned by her husband's creative talent and without her help during their marriage.

Most very rich people who end up in the divorce courts have very unpleasant experiences, and this is perhaps why millionaires often marry women who have money of their own, and generally mix with people of comparable incomes. There is less risk of an unpleasant situation arising. Most ordinary wives have nothing to gain from divorce. In the case of the millionaire, women have every incentive to behave unscrupulously.

With all these problems, why bother to become a millionaire in the first place? In my case, I inherited a certain amount of wealth and was determined to use this wealth constructively. I take a certain pride in running a corporation, if not more successfully than other people, at any rate just as successfully as most. I could have turned all my assets into liquid cash, instead of working at the drilling business as I do, an average of twelve hours a day – longer hours, incidentally, than your average-income business executive or salary earner. But that, to my mind, would have been running up the white flag and admitting that the responsibilities were too much for me. And I've never felt tempted to give my fortune away to buy my way into a better mood. There are people, of course, who have been destroyed, physically and morally, by their wealth. The same people, born poor, would probably have become alcoholics or thieves.

Though our rewards may be small, we are, if our society is to remain in its present form, essential to the nation's prosperity. We provide others with incentives which would not exist if we were to disappear. As active businessmen, we find it useful to have money simply because a tolerable margin of financial security makes for increased efficiency and competitiveness. If I were not using my fortune usefully, I would have little justification for having it in the first place. And if you then took it away, it wouldn't make all that much difference to me. At least I wouldn't be getting all those letters.

Peter McLaren

The Blue-Eyed Mistress of the Keys

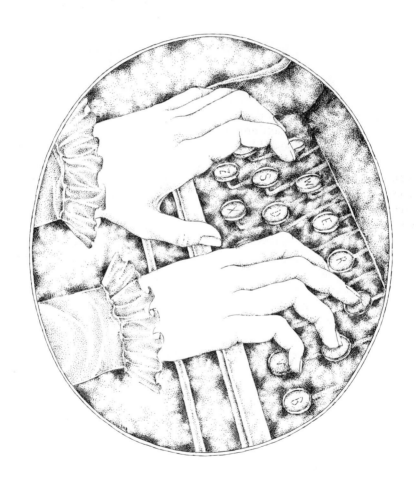

"I can't really define the feeling,
but I knew instantly that somehow the typewriter
was going to play a major part in my life."

The year: 1928. The place: civic arena in Sacramento, California. Twenty top-ranked male and female competitors from two continents are gathered for the world championship. As they quietly take their positions on the stage, a hush falls over the standing-room-only audience.

One of the youngest contestants is Irma Wright, an attractive twenty-eight-year-old from Toronto. Nervously, she rubs the tips of her fingers with her "good luck" cotton handkerchief. She has trained 540 hours for this moment, but, as always, she is worried; in training she's lost three pounds from sheer nervous tension. She feels a rush of adrenalin as the announcer calls her name, and she prays she won't lose her concentration – not even for an instant.

The competitors sit in three rows facing their oiled and polished machines. Bodies erect and poised, elbows at sides, fingers gingerly touching the keys. Finally the signal is given, and they loose themselves with fury.

Thirty minutes later, Irma Wright, diamond medalist and five times Canadian professional champion, has become the Amateur Typewriting Champion of the World. Her speed: 116 words per minute. From this night on, she will be known internationally as "Canada's typing tornado," "Queen of Dominion typists," and "the blue-eyed mistress of the keys."

After the contest, Irma Wright soaks her swollen fingers in a bucket of ice and leans back in her chair with a sigh. "It's all in the rhythm," she says to the reporters.

Irma Wright was born in Hamilton in 1900. In 1913 her father, Charles, who had moved his family to Toronto the previous year for

business reasons, died after a long bout with the bottle, and Irma enrolled in a business course at Toronto's Wellesley Public School. When she plunked out her first word on the typewriter, she had a strange feeling that, for her, typing would become more than just an acquired skill. "There was something eerie, almost supernatural about my first session at the typewriter," she recalled years later. "I can't really define the feeling, but I knew instantly that somehow the typewriter was going to play a major part in my life."

Even in her early teens, Wright stood over six feet. She was often ridiculed by her classmates because of her height and awkward gait. But, while only an average student, she quickly excelled at the keyboard, earning praise from her fellow students. Less than six months after she started to type she won a silver medal at an annual Toronto business show. Her instructors were at a loss to explain her victory, since only thirty-five minutes of the school day were given over to typing. Already there was something phenomenal about this girl who had just turned fourteen.

Ten years later, Wright's name flashed across the typing firmament when she won both the Canadian Open and the Quebec Bilingual crowns of 1924. She owed much of her success to Fred Jarrett, manager of the United Typewriter Company's educational department and holder of the Canadian Professional Championship for fifteen years. She had joined United two years earlier as an understudy to Jarrett, who took a special interest in her extraordinary prowess.

Typing soon became Wright's entire world. Relatives remember that whenever she came to visit, she brought her typewriter along. "When she babysat me as a boy," one great-nephew recalls, "she would enthrall me with stories of strange, faraway places she had visited giving typing demonstra-

54 tions. Later in the evening, when I was safely tucked in bed, she would go into the den. The next sound would be the steady, metallic beat of the keys. Aunt Irma was practising. It would go on for hours."

By now, Irma Wright had blossomed into an attractive woman with a flair for clothes. Sporting a marcel hairstyle, and with the latest New York fashions draped on her tall, slender frame, she became the public ideal of a secretary: attractive, intelligent, well mannered, and an expert typist. Her pastel suits became her trademark. "Never refer to pastel as a *color*," she would chide her friends. "Pastel is a *tint*."

In 1925, and in each of the four subsequent years, she won the Canadian Professional Typing Championship, shattering all existing records. The fastest speed she ever officially attained, in a measured one-minute test, was 157 words. This in the hard, slow days of manual machines, when electronic keyboards belonged to the realm of science fiction.

Everyone, it seemed, tried to capitalize on Wright's success. She turned down dozens of offers from advertisers who wanted her to promote their products. The exception was Lux; this one she accepted because she did use Lux and felt it wouldn't be dishonest to promote the detergent.

After her world win in 1928, a lifelong dream of Wright's was fulfilled when she was invited to visit the Metro-Goldwyn-Mayer studios in Hollywood. She could hardly believe being whisked away in a sleek limousine to meet screen idols Norma Shearer and Johnny Mack Brown. She wrote to her family that Norma Shearer was "charm itself, so beautiful too; very small, about up to my shoulder, I would say. She got such a kick out of everything, and you would imagine those people to be bored stiff all the time."

Soon Wright was travelling the continent giving demonstrations of her lightning sprints on the keys, leaving thousands popeyed. She boosted her demonstrations with a genuine show-business flair, electrifying audiences by typing blindfolded and wearing gloves *and* with a silk handkerchief over the keyboard – at the astonishing rate of 126 error-free words per minute.

If these antics seem a little bizarre now, they were not unique in the pioneer days of speed typing. Joe Pinson of Clarksville, Texas, was making headlines by typing almost seventy words a minute with one hand. E. B. Peterson of Pocatello, Idaho, received wide acclaim after dismantling and reassembling a standard typewriter and typing a line in a record two minutes and fifty-three seconds. Cortez W. Peters of Washington, D.C., the world's portable-typewriter champion, did 130 words a minute while reciting something entirely different. Margaret Hamma (appropriately named, perhaps) of Brooklyn, New York, typed twenty carbons at one time. Tom Breen of Richmond Hill, New York, did sprints on the keys with his toes, and a U.S. Army sergeant who'd lost his hands and the sight in both eyes made history by typing twenty words a minute with an artificial hand.

But life on the demonstration circuit was not always roses. Wright wrote to her family: "We arrived Saturday morning, tired and travel-stained and I thought: Now here is a chance to get to a hotel and have a bath. But no – more pictures to be taken and that meant a delay of another two hours. Such is fame. In the evening I went up to see myself in moving pictures. I got a kick out of that, but I looked rather sad because my hair had just been washed and I could not get a marcel any place in Sacramento before three o'clock that day and the pictures were taken at one."

Wright avoided strenuous sports in order to protect her hands. But she trained like an athlete – a certain diet, so many hours typing a day, lots of sleep, and, above all, quiet nerves. "Those nerves are the typist's greatest worry," she said. "One can freeze to the fingertips and be unable to move a key. That is where training of the mind counts." As for training of the fingers, Wright typed the entire text of *Gone with the Wind* over and over again.

Wright always took along her own favorite typewriter (an Underwood) and a custom-made table and chair. During one contest she was inexplicably thrown off her rhythm. It turned out that her chair had not been assembled properly and was a quarter-inch too short.

Not only did she possess uncanny mechanical skills when it came to typing, she developed an almost psychic ability as well. She knew how fast others were typing by merely *listening*. She could even tell *what* they were typing. During serious competition, though, she had to suppress this talent because it interfered with her own concentration.

By the time she retired from competition in 1936, Irma Wright had achieved her goal of one hundred million words or five hundred million strokes. She estimated that she'd trained no less than 540 hours for each of the twelve major contests in her career and had typed an average 6,500 words per hour. That made 42,120,000 words in training alone.

Once retired from contests, Wright became head of the speed department for United Typewriter, and later director of education for Royal Typewriter Co. Ltd. She was also a guest instructor at various business and commercial colleges throughout the country. On a typical day, she would take her position at the front of a room full of junior business boys and girls.

"Sit up straight," she would begin, "feet flat, wrists relaxed. Correct posture and relaxation are the keys to good speed work." When the students were ready, she would write a number of odd combinations on the blackboard: *fif, juj, jyj, aba, szs, d3d, k8k*, etc. Then she would crank up a record player.

"Now," she would say, to the strains of the *Star-Spangled Banner*, "please keep in rhythm, no matter what speed it is." In later years, she would sometimes surprise and delight the class by putting on an Elvis Presley record.

At the end of a lesson, she often gave a demonstration. Her show business flair never left her and the new electric typewriters made possible one of her most thrilling feats: since she didn't have to raise her hand to shift the carriage, Wright would ask a volunteer to place a glass of water on top of each of her hands; then she would speed type without making an error or spilling a drop.

Irma Wright was billed by the nation's press as "Canada's top secretary," but she was not content to remain in that role. A forceful woman, she kept her maiden name after marriage when it was unfashionable to do so and encouraged secretaries to seek executive positions. On tours she would tell young women training to become secretaries not to reply to advertisements for a "Girl Friday" or an "Office Wife." She would recall how she had refused to make coffee for her bosses when she was a budding secretary. She once told a male audience that the average typist expends as much energy during the day as a man digging ditches. And, in fact, tests at the National Business School in Chicago in 1933 proved that a speed typist works harder than a coal miner.

Like many coal miners and ditchdiggers, Irma Wright died young, at fifty-nine.

John Updike

Ex-Basketball Player

Pearl Avenue runs past the high school lot,
Bends with the trolley tracks, and stops, cut off
Before it has a chance to go two blocks,
At Colonel McComsky Plaza. Berth's Garage
Is on the corner facing west, and there,
Most days, you'll find Flick Webb, who helps Berth out.

Flick stands tall among the idiot pumps —
Five on a side, the old bubble-head style,
Their rubber elbows hanging loose and low.
One's nostrils are two S's, and his eyes
An E and O. And one is squat, without
A head at all — more of a football type.

Once, Flick played for the high school team, the Wizards.
He was good: in fact, the best. In '46,
He bucketed three hundred ninety points,
A county record still. The ball loved Flick.
I saw him rack up thirty-eight or forty
In one home game. His hands were like wild birds.

He never learned a trade; he just sells gas,
Checks oil, and changes flats. Once in a while,
As a gag, he dribbles an inner tube,
But most of us remember anyway.
His hands are fine and nervous on the lug wrench.
It makes no difference to the lug wrench, though.

Off work, he hangs around Mae's Luncheonette.
Grease-grey and kind of coiled, he plays pinball,
Sips lemon cokes, and smokes those thin cigars;
Flick seldom speaks to Mae, just sits and nods
Beyond her face towards bright applauding tiers
Of Necco Wafers, Nibs, and Juju Beads.

Janice Tyrwhitt

Remembering "The Chief"

He blew into Ottawa
like a chinook,
heated and unsettling.

THE MAN WHO WOULD BE KING

"They never thought that I would be Prime Minister," John Diefenbaker used to say. "Only one man ever predicted that someday my fellow Canadians would elect me to the highest office in the land. He was a fellow called Davidson, a Conservative organizer in Saskatchewan, back in the '40s when western Tories were almost as scarce as Grits in heaven. It was election night, and all our candidates had lost their deposits.

"Remembering 'The Chief'" by Janice Tyrwhitt. © 1980 The Reader's Digest Magazines Limited. Reprinted by permission.

"That terrible night in his committee room, a shabby little second-floor room with an old desk and a few kitchen chairs, Davidson sat with a bottle of rye in one hand and a tumbler in the other, contemplating the devastation, every one of his candidates wiped out. And he sighed, and he filled his glass, and he swirled his whiskey round, and he said, 'They never sent that money from Toronto for my campaign, the way they promised.' And he sighed again, and he sipped his whiskey, and it was right then that he predicted that I would become Prime Minister. Right there in that little room he looked at me and he said, 'Diefenbaker, if I only had that money, I could make you or any other damn fool Prime Minister of Canada.'"

It wasn't a story Diefenbaker told often. Becoming Prime Minister was his childhood dream, never taken lightly. One summer evening in 1950, after a dinner party at his house in Prince Albert, he was entertaining friends with a wicked imitation of Mackenzie King when a local radio station called: King had just died. Sir John A. Macdonald was Diefenbaker's official hero, but King was the politician he envied. Though he joked about King's mysticism, he devoured *Hansard*, searching for the secret of the wily old Liberal's success. Instantly solemn, Diefenbaker turned to his guest of honor, David Walker, and whispered, "Dave, my future now has just begun."

His time had been so long coming that only he was sure it would come. Even after he won the Conservative leadership in 1956 few expected him to win the country. An editorial in *Maclean's*, written ahead of publication, reflected Gallup Poll indications and Press Gallery expectations of Liberal victory: "For better or for worse, we Canadians have once more elected one of the most powerful governments ever created by the

58 free will of a free electorate." When it appeared the morning after the 1957 election, Diefenbaker had it framed to hang over his bed. At his first news conference as Prime Minister he greeted *Maclean's* Ottawa editor, Blair Fraser, "Good morning... Prophet."

Yet, for all his confidence, he was awed by his achievement. A week after the election, which was close enough to make the Liberals hesitate before relinquishing power, Louis St. Laurent summoned his successor to tell him of his intention to resign. Pierre Sévigny was waiting in Diefenbaker's office when he returned, pale and tense. He asked a secretary to telephone his wife and sat waiting for the call, wrapped in thought. Then he said, more to himself than to Sévigny, "It is so strange that such a great honor should come to a small man like me."

MR. AVERAGE CANADIAN

He blew into Ottawa like a chinook, heated and unsettling. He was a wholly new force in Canadian government, a Westerner more at home in a general store than in a board room, an outsider with a German name raised in a frontier province where poverty, immigration and the Depression years had bred a spirit of fierce independence. He saw the Liberals as the party of big business, the New Democrats as the voice of organized labor, and he was determined that the Conservatives should represent the common folk of Canada who had no power base. His touchstone for any issue was how it would affect *them*.

He was perhaps the last politician with complete confidence in the railways, the postal system, and the ordinary citizen. "If you can't explain something to a station agent," he once said, "forget it." His concern for his grass-roots constituency brought a ceaseless flood of letters from across Canada.

He read them all, and often astonished his correspondents with long personal replies. Children were his soft spot, and he invited so many to "Come and see me if you're in Ottawa," that his staff had to curb his habit of leaving Cabinet ministers and industrialists cooling their heels while he swept his young visitors on a pilgrimage through Parliament.

Occasionally he even answered *other* people's letters. When he was over 80, a woman in Nova Scotia wrote to a reporter who had praised him. "Canada's greatest Prime Minister," she called him, and the journalist showed the letter to the old Chief. "I'll answer it myself," said Diefenbaker. "A letter from me will be something she'll cherish."

Those who asked his help usually got it. A lad in Nova Scotia wrote to ask why the government proposed to slaughter the wild ponies on Sable Island; instantly Diefenbaker rose to defend the ponies in the House. A 70-year-old man in Halifax complained of being cut off unemployment insurance, while his wife was pregnant. When officials protested that he was too old to receive it, Diefenbaker roared, "How are they going to feed that child?" and an aide scurried to find an obsolete regulation to channel funds to the needy father. While he was in office – and long after – pensioners, veterans, Indians, the poor, and the dispossessed found in Diefenbaker an ombudsman with both the will and the power to slash red tape.

His sympathy with the "average Canadian" sprang from his illusion that he *was* one. When he was visiting a friend who lived in the country, near Ottawa, a neighboring farmer dropped in. Apart from three and a half childhood years on his father's homestead, Diefenbaker's only experience of farming was one wretched summer when he worked as a hired hand, but he immediately struck up a knowledgeable discussion of crops and livestock. "Ordie," he said as he left, "us farmers have got to stick together."

THE FAMILY MAN

Any politician counts himself lucky to have a good marriage. Diefenbaker had *two*. His first wife, Edna, was a joyous, witty woman who won the hearts of newsmen and voters. When she died of leukemia in 1951, everyone who knew her mourned. James Gardiner, the notoriously unsentimental architect of the Saskatchewan Liberal machine, wept at the news, though he recovered from his grief in time to redraw the boundaries of Lake Centre in an attempt to eliminate Diefenbaker in the next election. Shattered by his wife's death, Diefenbaker considered giving up politics. Later he claimed that only his fury at the Liberal gerrymandering persuaded him to switch to Prince Albert and run there in 1953.

By then he was courting his second wife, Olive, with such propriety that, after a weekend holiday with David Walker who was later their best man, Mrs. Walker reported sadly, "No romance there." But the romance lasted the rest of his life. Though Olive never shared his relish in campaigning, her appetite for his stories was unquenchable. When a weary reporter asked, "Don't *you* find it tiresome to hear him give the same speech over and over?" she corrected him gently: "Tiring, yes; tiresome, never."

Carolyn Weir, Olive's daughter by her first marriage, had five children, and Diefenbaker excelled as an indulgent grandfather. He had grown up in a family close-knit by frequent moves and shared responsibilities. His father, a gentle schoolteacher, taught him to revere Parliament; his strong-willed mother was determined that he should be *in* Parliament. And no one worked harder to get

him there and keep him there than his younger brother Elmer, who travelled Saskatchewan for the Retail Merchants' Association and sent John daily reports of his constituency. When Elmer's letter arrived, the Chief dropped everything to read it.

THE CAMPAIGNER

He was the last of the whistle-stop campaigners, a born Main Streeter who got high on a handshake. In the House or on the hustings, he delivered his well-polished one-liners with the timing of a stand-up comedian. Before a major speech he fretted like an opera star, unable to eat, convinced the hall would be empty, querulous with his staff: "Where's my stuff? You never give me any good stuff." When they gave him his "stuff," neatly packaged research, he would tear it into strips, pin it with straight pins, strew it about like confetti and somehow miraculously reassemble it in his head. Then, exhilarated by an audience, he would cast out ideas like trout flies, till his listeners rose to a theme. His voice swelling like an organ, he would spin that theme into a vision. "Roads to resources!" he would cry, and the crowd would see a rainbow at the end of the roads, and a pot of gold at the end of the rainbow.

After a successful speech, euphoric, dripping with sweat, he sometimes had to be wrenched from the platform. In the 1965 campaign his aides, Gregor Guthrie and Tom Van Dusen, carried a towel and dry sweat shirt. Backstage, they would strip off his shirt and rub him down like a tough old fighter. In Winnipeg, Mrs. Diefenbaker begged them to get him out quickly after his speech because he was exhausted. When the crowd closed in, as eager to shake his hand as he was to shake theirs, Guthrie, an ex-Army officer, took command. Seizing Diefenbaker by the arms, he manhandled him out the door and into his car. "The major must have been a great soldier," muttered the Chief. "How his men must have loved him."

He never gave up. In 1972, his friend Max Carment took him vote-gathering near Prince Albert. A sleety autumn snow was falling, flakes big as half dollars, as they passed a field where three men struggled to start a tractor. "Stop the car!" cried the Chief. Turning up the collar of his trench coat, he trudged through the soggy stubble. Fifteen minutes later, soaking wet, he returned in triumph. "I had to talk to those fellows," he told Carment. "They weren't with me last time, but they are now."

To the end of his life he drew crowds – and they drew him. At eighty-three, he was flying by helicopter to a meeting when he saw a knot of people below, and told the pilot to land. "That's not where we're going," said the pilot. "Land anyway!" Diefenbaker ordered, and down he came, an unexpected but welcome guest at a wedding.

THE TASKMASTER

Working for the Chief was no sinecure. His staff had to be companions, advisors, trouble-shooters and dogsbodies. Jim Nelson's first assignment as press secretary was guarding the Prime Minister's briefcase on a flight to Toronto; on landing he peeked inside and discovered it held one clean shirt.

His aides soon learned that anything mechanical was alien to him. John Fisher, his special assistant in the early '60s, persuaded him to buy an automatic signature machine for signing letters; he detested and discarded it. Appalled to find there was no lock on the door of the Prime Minister's office to protect him from cranks and assassins, Fisher installed an electric lock, controlled from the desk. When a visitor arrived Fisher would buzz the Chief to release the lock, but the sound always confused Diefenbaker who

would then grab a telephone, sometimes a hotline to Washington, while Fisher gave up and banged on the door.

For all his charm, Diefenbaker had a quick-fire temper. Almost without warning his voice would rise, his head would shake, his face would grow pale, and his blue eyes would glitter so icily that one man swore they turned green. His invective was never profane and seldom specific. When it stopped soon and suddenly, those who had incurred his wrath sometimes slunk out without knowing how they had offended. Once, when a drunken Conservative ended an ugly encounter with a taxi driver by giving a false name, the driver complained to Diefenbaker who then castigated the wrong politician. Mystified, the innocent member brooded for weeks over his possible sins until Diefenbaker was persuaded to apologize.

THE PRIVATE MAN

When Diefenbaker was first elected he smoked and drank moderately and enjoyed playing bridge and poker. He gave up cigarettes because the Ottawa climate troubled his breathing, and whiskey because he had seen too many careers ruined by alcohol. One evening a western member stumbled in drunk to complain that the Chief never sought his advice. With his arm round the man's shoulder, Diefenbaker told him, "I'm glad you came in, there's nobody's thinking I value more." When he left, the Chief said, "He's a good lad." "I thought you had a deep prejudice against drink," said a friend. "If I had had such a prejudice," he answered, "I wouldn't have got very far."

But his Baptist propriety, reinforced by Olive's, sometimes inhibited his hospitality. At the leadership convention of 1956 he refused to serve liquor; his campaign managers, George Hees and Allister Grosart, took delegates to meet him, then wheeled them into Hees' suite for a drink.

In private, however, the Chief liked an excuse for a beer. Once when deep-sea fishing in rough weather, he was offered seasick pills by his host. "I don't want one," Diefenbaker said. Then his eye fell on the tray of canned beer that accompanied the pills. Ten minutes later he said, "Maybe I will have one of those pills, just to be on the safe side. And," clutching a beer, "course I'll need something to wash it down."

He loved eating. Crackers and milk were his solace in times of trouble, ice-cream cones his favorite treat, lobster his rare extravagance. Once, after lunching and dining on lobster, he said wistfully, "I wish I could have lobster for breakfast."

Olive forbade chocolates, but his secretaries cached bars in desk drawers, and he picked them up in airports and hotels. Since he had no credit cards and didn't like carrying money, an aide would tag behind, paying for his purchases. In London, Ontario, Olive spied him emerging alone from a Laura Secord shop with a five-pound box. "I bought them for you," he improvised. "But John," she protested, "you know I don't eat chocolates. And where did you get the money?" "I found it," he said. "In that jar in the pantry." "Oh John," Olive said, "that was the money I left for the housekeeper!"

Diefenbaker's sense of the value of money was frozen in the mid-1930s, and he professed astonishment at all but the most meager expense accounts. He scorned the trappings of office, and boasted that he spent only $18 000 on 24 Sussex while he was Prime Minister. When the Liberals increased MP salaries from $12 000 to $18 000 a year, he refused to accept the supplement until after the next election on the grounds that it had to be ratified by the taxpayers. He never applied for an old-age pension and never

touched the money – more than $450 000 – that accumulated in a trust fund set up for him in 1960 by a group of affluent Tories; in fact, he claimed he didn't know of its existence until 1973. Altogether he left more than a million dollars; the rest came from royalties on his published memoirs and the value of land around his father's homestead.

He drove others hard, himself even harder. He rose about 5:30, worked for an hour, walked two kilometres, breakfasted with his wife, and reached his office before eight. The only time he really relaxed was when he went fishing. Stalking into a slough in windbreaker and hip waders, battling a steelhead on a gravel bar on Vancouver Island, reeling in a shark off Bermuda, he came as close as he ever could to forgetting politics. Yet even at remote Lac La Ronge in northern Saskatchewan, after winning the biggest majority in Canadian history in 1958, when his fishing partner Harry Houghton exulted, "Now you've got the world by the tail!" he answered, "Yes, and I've got 207 Tory members gunning for my job."

He occasionally hunted ducks and geese, though never animals. One morning David Walker said, "Chief, let's go hunting. I've got a new gun." A little embarrassed, Diefenbaker said, "Dave, I can't hunt today. I promised my mother I wouldn't hunt on Sunday, and I never have."

THE LEGEND

Diefenbaker wanted to be remembered as a statesman who had fought for one Canada, an independent nation where citizens of every race and color had equal rights, and as a Conservative who restored his party to power, barring the Liberals from majority rule all through his leadership. He couldn't leave at his own time, in his own way, so he went down fighting.

Before the Conservative convention of 1967, he encouraged his supporters Mike Starr and Alvin Hamilton to contest the leadership. Just before the convention he called Starr to his suite in the Royal York. "Mike, do you think I should run?" he asked. Starr was astonished; he knew his slight chance of winning would vanish if the Chief split the vote. Diefenbaker hung in an agony of indecision. Before making the keynote address he ate oyster stew, vomited it up, and composed himself to deliver a stirring repudiation of the "two nations" policy which he considered divisive for Canadians, disastrous for Conservatives. Even David Walker, dragged from a hospital bed to head his strategy committee, told him, "Chief, you haven't a chance of winning." He knew it. He ran anyway.

When he lost, dropping steadily to 114 votes on the third ballot, he scribbled his withdrawal and told his wife, "I guess I'm all washed up, Olive." "You'll never be washed up, Chief," his driver broke in. And suddenly, as they drove back to the hotel, Diefenbaker's voice lifted in song, "When you come to the end of a perfect day..."

Stubbornly he refused retirement, and just as stubbornly thousands of Canadians refused to forget him. As 1970 ended, a Victoria hot-line host asked his listeners to phone in nominations for Man of the Year. Pierre Trudeau, an early favorite, was soon overtaken by a dark horse as the creaky voices of scores of pensioners spoke up for John Diefenbaker. "But Diefenbaker didn't do anything in 1970," sputtered the host. "He wasn't even in power!" "Maybe not," one caller acknowledged, "but if he hadda been, he would of done!"

At 80 he published the first volume of his memoirs, and his legions of loyalists rushed to buy it. At a luncheon at Simpson's in Toronto before his first autographing, a phone call interrupted dessert: more than a thousand people were already lined up to meet him. Instantly he leaped to his feet, "We can't keep those poor people waiting!" As he rode down on the escalator, a sea of faces turned to him, hands stretched out, and a cheer rose from the crowd. He signed all afternoon, and when time ran out he persuaded Simpson's to send crates of books to Ottawa to be autographed for those still in line. When women asked for an inscription, he insisted on their full names, preferably prefaced by Mrs. or Miss. "If I just put the first name," he said primly, "it might be misinterpreted."

He was already a legend, and he knew it. He set about planning his last campaign, the most elaborate funeral ever staged in Canada. There would be guards of honor, gun salutes, military bands with muffled drums. From Ottawa to Saskatoon the train would carry his body – and that of his beloved Olive, who had died in 1976 – a solemn procession no mourner would ever forget. The pallbearers would be friends he wished to honor, the flag that wrapped him would be the old Red Ensign he had defended as "ennobled by heroes' blood." Learning that the Maple Leaf flag was mandatory for state funerals, he said cheerfully. "That'll drive the chief of protocol crazy." In the end the two flags were stitched together round his coffin.

He talked about his funeral with a certain delight. "They'll line the streets," he would say. "They'll come from miles around to see the train go by. The railway crossings will be filled with people waving." Everything happened as he had planned it. And when at last he was buried on a hillside by the South Saskatchewan, as the Indians' lament for a fallen warrior cut suddenly across the wail of the pipes, it was all he could have wanted.

Crimes,
Criminals,
and Detectives.

Anonymous

Great Detectives: Ageless Fictions

Everybody loves a mystery.

It has been said, though with no such definitive proof as the subject himself would demand, that Sherlock Holmes is the best-known character in all of English literature.

He is a member of that most exclusive group of imaginative creations who have outlived not only their creators, but their era. Through films, radio, television, and comic strips, the peculiarities of Holmes's personality are known to vast numbers of people who have never read the original Holmes stories. In what must be the ultimate test of immortality, many madmen evidently believe they are Sherlock Holmes.

Reprinted by permission of The Royal Bank of Canada.

This probably would have pleased his creator, Arthur Conan Doyle, a spiritualist who dabbled in the ways of immortality. Conan Doyle hugely enjoyed the game of persuading readers that Holmes was a real, if somewhat shadowy, human being. He did this by deftly scattering references to actual persons and events throughout his stories. Their tongues in their cheeks, Holmes scholars are only too happy to keep the game going to this day.

The first thing they will tell you is that the Holmes stories were not written by Conan Doyle at all, but by a rather stuffy but good-natured chap named Dr. Watson. Sherlock Holmes societies everywhere (and they *are* everywhere) operate on the elementary premise that Holmes and his apostle really did make their headquarters in their lodgings at 221B Baker Street. The address does not exist now, but they explain that is because of demolition and rebuilding since Holmes's and Watson's heyday.

It is reported that the firm which occupies the nearest number to 221B regularly receives mail addressed to Sherlock Holmes.

So, long after the last hackney vanished from the gaslit streets of London, Sherlock Holmes still strides conceitedly across the stage of fancy, practising what Watson called his speciality – omni-science.

Since Conan Doyle's copyright finally lapsed a few years ago, new books and films about Holmes's adventures by other authors have been appearing regularly, supposedly culled from hitherto undiscovered documents. Holmes is still capable of bowling over readers and audiences with the might of his mental processes. He is doing very well for a man 125 years of age.

What is it that makes fictional detectives, above all literary figures, live on agelessly in our imaginations? A conversation among any group of mystery story fans – which means almost any group of people who like to read for relaxation – will turn up endless minutiae about the lives of characters who never existed in the strict sense of the word.

You might hear about how Charlie Chan not only has a number of sons but a daughter; about how Hercule Poirot once failed to tell someone who thought he was French that he was really Belgian; about how Nero Wolfe might just be Sherlock Holmes's illegitimate son, the issue of the liaison between the great detective and a forgotten lady long ago in Montenegro (the clue is the similarity in the spelling of the two names; note the identical vowels).

Obviously the lasting appeal of the imaginary detectives has much to do with the type of story in which they are the leading players. Everybody loves a mystery.

In common with characters in comic strips and television serials and situation comedies, fictional sleuths owe at least part of their familiarity to the fact that they keep appearing in one story after another. But while the other types soon fade from memory when their stint in the limelight is over, the detectives retain their prominence through constant retellings of their adventures in reprinted paperback books and fresh adaptations for television, film, and the stage.

Yet, despite the fact that no lesser a literary figure than Edgar Allan Poe is credited with writing the first modern detective stories and such splendid writers as Dashiell Hammett and Raymond Chandler have specialized in them, detective fiction is still not fully recognized as a serious art form. The more earnest literary critics frown upon mysteries. Only recently a historian of the detective genre put it down as "preeminently the literature of the sick-room and the railway carriage."

But if art is any reflection of the preoccupations of society, then the persistent demand for crime fiction in all media should make it an important variety of art.

Our paper detectives really are modern knights errant. It is difficult to picture Agatha Christie's Miss Marple or G. K. Chesterton's Father Brown riding in on horseback to rout villains and vandals, but that is basically the tradition they followed every time they applied marvellous intellects to the question of who disturbed the social order by exterminating another human being.

In addition to the fact that detective stories are fun and make excellent harmless tranquillizers, they would indeed seem to owe some of their enduring popularity to a human need for knight errant images.

Moral philosophers have said that knights errant represent the conscience. Even Don Quixote tilting ridiculously at the windmills is an expression of the latent nobility of man coming out to confront the dark forces that trouble the soul.

The question of why we should want to believe in these mythical creatures to the extent of pretending they actually exist leads us back into the comforting, tobacco-scented presence of Chief Inspector Maigret of the Paris police. Maigret is good, strong, simple, wise, and understanding. Who would not want to believe in a man like that?

The same goes for all the other great detectives (take your pick) suspended in time as they strive in their own particular ways to accomplish justice. For without the possibility that people with the will and skill to deliver us from evil walk the earth, where would we be?

We can only hope that such people exist not only on paper – that somewhere there really are heroes fighting for the freedom from molestation that is the basis of everyday civilized life.

Sir Arthur Conan Doyle

The Man with the Twisted Lip

The window was open,
and she distinctly saw his face....
He waved his hands frantically to her....

Isa Whitney, brother of the late Elias Whitney, D.D., Principal of the Theological College of St. George's, was much addicted to opium. The habit grew upon him, as I understand, from some foolish freak when he was at college, for having read De Quincey's description of his dreams and sensations, he had drenched his tobacco with laudanum in an attempt to produce the same effects. He found, as so many more have done, that the practice is easier to attain than to get rid of, and for many years he continued to be a slave to the drug, an object of mingled horror and pity to his friends and relatives. I can see him now, with yellow, pasty face, drooping lids and pinpoint pupils, all huddled in a chair, the wreck and ruin of a noble man.

One night – it was in June, '89 – there came a ring to my bell, about the hour when a man gives his first yawn, and glances at the clock. I sat up in my chair, and my wife laid her needlework down in her lap and made a little face of disappointment.

"A patient!" said she. "You'll have to go out."

I groaned, for I was newly come back from a weary day.

We heard the door open, a few hurried words, and then quick steps upon the linoleum. Our own door flew open, and a lady, clad in some dark-colored stuff with a black veil, entered the room.

"You will excuse my calling so late," she began, and then, suddenly losing her self-control, she ran forward, threw her arms about my wife's neck, and sobbed upon her shoulder. "Oh! I'm in such trouble!" she cried. "I do so want a little help."

"Why," said my wife, pulling up her veil, "it is Kate Whitney. How you startled me, Kate! I had not an idea who you were when you came in."

"I didn't know what to do, so I came straight to you." That was always the way. Folk who were in grief came to my wife like birds to a lighthouse.

"It was very sweet of you to come. Now, you must have some wine and water, and sit here comfortably and tell us all about it. Or should you rather that I sent James off to bed?"

"Oh, no, no. I want the Doctor's advice and help too. It's about Isa. He has not been home for two days. I am so frightened about him!"

It was not the first time that she had spoken to us of her husband's trouble, to me as a doctor, to my wife as an old friend and school companion. We soothed and comforted her by such words as we could find. Did she know where her husband was? Was it possible that we could bring him back to her?

It seemed that it was. She had the surest information that of late he had, when the fit was on him, made use of an opium den in the farthest east of the City. Hitherto his orgies had always been confined to one day, and he had come back, twitching and shattered, in the evening. But now the spell had been upon him eight-and-forty hours, and he lay there, doubtless, among the dregs of the docks, breathing in the poison or sleeping off the effects. There he was to be found, she was sure of it, at the "Bar of Gold," in Upper Swandam Lane. But what was she to do? How could she, a young and timid woman, make her way into such a place, and pluck her husband out from among the ruffians who surrounded him?

There was the case, and of course there was but one way out of it. Might I not escort her to this place? And then, as a second thought, why should she come at all? I was Isa Whitney's medical adviser, and as such I had influence over him. I could manage it better if I were alone. I promised her on my word that I would send him home in a cab within two hours if he were indeed at the address which she had given me. And so in ten minutes I had left my armchair and cheery sitting room behind me, and was speeding eastward in a hansom on a strange errand, as it seemed to me at the time, though the future only could show how strange it was to be.

But there was no great difficulty in the first stage of my adventure. Upper Swandam Lane is a vile alley lurking behind the high wharves which line the north side of the river at the east of London Bridge. Between a slop shop and a gin shop, approached by a steep flight of steps leading down to a black gap like the mouth of a cave, I found the den of which I was in search. Ordering my cab to wait, I pressed down the steps, worn hollow in the centre by the ceaseless tread of drunken feet, and by the light of a flickering oil lamp above the door I found the latch and made my way into a long, low room, thick and heavy with the brown opium smoke, and terraced with wooden berths, like the forecastle of an emigrant ship.

Through the gloom one could dimly catch a glimpse of bodies lying in strange fantastic poses, bowed shoulders, bent knees, heads thrown back and chins pointing upwards, with here and there a dark, lacklustre eye turned upon the newcomer. Out of the black shadows there glimmered little red circles of light, now bright, now faint, as the burning poison waxed or waned in the bowls of the metal pipes. The most lay silent, but some muttered to themselves, and others talked together in a strange, low, monotonous voice, their conversation coming in gushes, and then suddenly tailing off into silence, each mumbling out his own thoughts, and paying little heed to the words of his neighbor. At the farther end was a small brazier of burning charcoal, beside which on a three-legged wooden stool there sat a tall, thin old man, with his jaw resting upon his two fists, and his elbows upon his knees, staring into the fire.

As I entered, a sallow Malay attendant had hurried up with a pipe for me and a supply of the drug, beckoning me to an empty berth.

"Thank you, I have not come to stay," said I. "There is a friend of mine here, Mr. Isa Whitney, and I wish to speak with him."

There was a movement and an exclamation from my right, and peering through the gloom, I saw Whitney, pale, haggard, and unkempt, staring out at me.

"My God! It's Watson," he said. He was in a pitiable state of reaction, with every nerve in a twitter. "I say, Watson, what o'clock is it?"

"Nearly eleven."

"Of what day?"

"Of Friday, June 19th."

"Good heavens! I thought it was Wednesday. It is Wednesday. What d'you want to frighten a chap for?" He sank his face on to his arms, and began to sob in a high treble key.

"I tell you that it is Friday, man. Your wife has been waiting this two days for you. You should be ashamed of yourself!"

"So I am. But you've got mixed, Watson, for I have only been here a few hours, three pipes, four pipes — I forget how many. But I'll go home with you. I wouldn't frighten Kate — poor little Kate. Give me your hand! Have you a cab?"

"Yes, I have one waiting."

"Then I shall go in it. But I must owe something. Find what I owe, Watson. I am all off color. I can do nothing for myself."

I walked down the narrow passage between the double row of sleepers, holding my breath to keep out the vile, stupefying fumes of the drug, and looking about for the manager. As I passed the tall man who sat by the brazier I felt a sudden pluck at my skirt, and a low voice whispered, "Walk past me, and then look back at me." The words fell quite distinctly upon my ear. I glanced down. They could only have come from the old man at my side, and yet he sat now as absorbed as ever, very thin, very wrinkled, bent with age, an opium pipe dangling down from between his knees, as though it had dropped in sheer lassitude from his fingers. I took two steps forward and looked back. It took all my self-control to prevent me from breaking out into a cry of astonishment. He had turned his back so that none could see him but I. His form had filled out, his wrinkles were gone, the dull eyes had regained their fire, and there, sitting by the fire, and grinning at my surprise, was none other than Sherlock Holmes. He made a slight motion to me to approach him, and instantly, as he turned his face half round to the company once more, subsided into a doddering, loose-lipped senility.

"Holmes!" I whispered "what on earth are you doing in this den?"

"As low as you can," he answered, "I have excellent ears. If you would have the great kindness to get rid of that sottish friend of yours, I should be exceedingly glad to have a little talk with you."

"I have a cab outside."

"Then pray send him home in it. You may safely trust him, for he appears to be too limp to get into any mischief. I should recommend you also to send a note by the cabman to your wife to say that you have thrown in your lot with me. If you will wait outside, I shall be with you in five minutes."

It was difficult to refuse any of Sherlock Holmes's requests, for they were always so exceedingly definite, and put forward with such an air of mastery. I felt, however, that when Whitney was once confined in the cab, my mission was practically accomplished; and for the rest, I could not wish anything better than to be associated with my friend in one of those singular adventures which were the normal condition of his existence. In a few minutes I had written my note, paid Whitney's bill, led him out to the cab, and seen him driven through the darkness. In a very short time a decrepit figure had emerged from the opium den, and I was walking down the street with Sherlock Holmes. For two streets he shuffled along with a bent back and an uncertain foot. Then, glancing quickly round, he straightened himself out and burst into a hearty fit of laughter.

"I suppose, Watson," said he, "that you imagine that I have added opium-smoking to cocaine injections and all the other little weaknesses on which you have favored me with your medical views."

"I was certainly surprised to find you there."

"But not more so than I to find you."

"I came to find a friend."

"And I to find an enemy!"

"An enemy?"

"Yes, one of my natural enemies, or, shall I say, my natural prey. Briefly, Watson, I am in the midst of a very remarkable inquiry, and I have hoped to find a clue in the incoherent ramblings of these sots, as I have done before now. Had I been recognized in that den my life would not have been worth an hour's purchase, for I have used it before now for my own purposes, and the rascally Lascar who runs it has sworn vengeance upon me. There is a trapdoor at the back of that building, near the corner of Paul's Wharf, which could tell some strange tales of what has passed through it upon the moonless nights."

"What! You do not mean bodies?"

"Aye, bodies, Watson. We should be rich men if we had a thousand pounds for every poor devil who has been done to death in that den. It is the vilest murder-trap on the whole riverside, and I fear Neville St. Clair has entered it never to leave it more. But our trap should be here!" He put his two fore-fingers between his teeth and whistled shrilly, a signal which was answered by a similar whistle from the distance, followed shortly by the rattle of wheels and the clink of horse's hoofs. "Now, Watson," said Holmes, as a tall dog-cart dashed up through the gloom, throwing out two golden tunnels of yellow light from its side-lanterns, "you'll come with me, won't you?"

"If I can be of use."

"Oh, a trusty comrade is always of use. And a chronicler still more so. My room at the Cedars is a double-bedded one."

"The Cedars?"

"Yes; that is Mr. St. Clair's house. I am staying there while I conduct the inquiry."

"Where is it, then?"

"Near Lee, in Kent. We have a seven-mile drive before us."

"But I am all in the dark."

"Of course you are. You'll know all about it presently. Jump up here! All right, John, we shall not need you. Here's half-a-crown. Look out for me tomorrow about eleven. Give her her head! So long, then!"

He flicked the horse with his whip, and we dashed away through the endless succession of sombre and deserted streets, which widened gradually, until we were flying across a broad balustraded bridge, with the murky river flowing sluggishly beneath us. Beyond lay another broad wilderness of bricks and mortar, its silence broken only by the heavy, regular foot-fall of the policeman,

or the songs and shouts of some belated party of revellers. A dull wrack was drifting slowly across the sky, and a star or two twinkled dimly here and there through the rifts of the clouds. Holmes drove in silence, with his head sunk upon his breast, and the air of a man who is lost in thought, whilst I sat beside him curious to learn what this new quest might be which seemed to tax his powers so sorely, and yet afraid to break in upon the current of his thoughts. We had driven several miles, and were beginning to get to the fringe of the belt of suburban villas, when he shook himself, shrugged his shoulders, and lit up his pipe with the air of a man who has satisfied himself that he is acting for the best.

"You have a grand gift of silence, Watson," he said. "It makes you quite invaluable as a companion. 'Pon my word, it is a great thing for me to have someone to talk to, for my own thoughts are not over-pleasant. I was wondering what I should say to this dear little woman tonight when she meets me at the door."

"You forget that I know nothing about it."

"I shall just have time to tell you the facts of the case before we get to Lee. It seems absurdly simple, and yet, somehow, I can get nothing to go upon. There's plenty of thread, no doubt, but I can't get the end of it in my hand. Now, I'll state the case clearly and concisely to you, Watson, and maybe you may see a spark where all is dark to me."

"Proceed, then."

"Some years ago – to be definite, in May, 1884 – there came to Lee a gentleman, Neville St. Clair by name, who appeared to have plenty of money. He took a large villa, laid out the grounds very nicely, and lived generally in good style. By degrees he made friends in the neighborhood, and in 1887 he married the daughter of a local brewer, by whom he has now had two children. He had no occupation, but was interested in several companies, and went into town as a rule in the morning, returning by the 5:14 from Cannon Street every night. Mr. St. Clair is now thirty-seven years of age, is a man of temperate habits, a good husband, a very affectionate father, and a man who is popular with all who know him. I may add that his whole debts at the present moment, as far as we have been able to ascertain, amount to £88 10s., while he has £220 standing to his credit in the Capital and Counties Bank. There is no reason, therefore, to think that money troubles have been weighing upon his mind.

"Last Monday Mr. Neville St. Clair went into town rather earlier than usual, remarking before he started that he had two important commissions to perform, and that he would bring his little boy home a box of bricks. Now, by the merest chance his wife received a telegram upon this same Monday, very shortly after his departure, to the effect that a small parcel of considerable value which she had been expecting was waiting for her at the offices of the Aberdeen Shipping Company. Now, if you are all well up in your London, you will know that the office of the company is in Fresno Street, which branches out of Upper Swandam Lane, where you found me tonight. Mrs. St. Clair had her lunch, started for the City, did some shopping, proceeded to the Company's office, got her packet, and found herself exactly at 4:35 walking through Swandam Lane on her way back to the station. Have you followed me so far?"

"It is very clear."

"If you remember, Monday was an exceedingly hot day, and Mrs. St. Clair walked slowly, glancing about in the hope of seeing a cab, as she did not like the neighborhood in which she found herself. While she walked in this way down Swandam Lane she suddenly heard an exclamation or cry, and was struck cold to see her husband looking down at her, and, as it seemed to her, beckoning to her from a second-floor window. The window was open, and she distinctly saw his face, which she describes as being terribly agitated. He waved his hands frantically to her, and then vanished from the window so suddenly that it seemed to her that he had been plucked back by some irresistible force from behind. One singular point which struck her quick feminine eye was that, although he wore some dark coat, such as he had started to town in, he had on neither collar nor necktie.

"Convinced that something was amiss with him, she rushed down the steps – for the house was none other than the opium den in which you found me tonight – and, running through the front room, she attempted to ascend the stairs which led to the first floor. At the foot of the stairs, however, she met this Lascar scoundrel, of whom I have spoken, who thrust her back, and, aided by a Dane, who acts as assistant there, pushed her out into the street. Filled with the most maddening doubts and fears, she rushed down the lane, and, by rare good fortune, met, in Fresno Street, a number of constables with an inspector, all on their way to their beat. The inspector and two men accompanied her back, and, in spite of the continued resistance of the proprietor, they made their way to the room in which Mr. St. Clair had last been seen. There was no sign of him there. In fact, in the whole of that floor there was no one to be found, save a crippled wretch of hideous aspect, who, it seems, made his home there. Both he and the Lascar stoutly swore that no one else had been in the front room during that afternoon. So determined was their denial that the inspector was staggered, and had almost come to believe that Mrs. St. Clair had been deluded when, with a cry, she sprang at a small deal box which lay upon the table, and tore the lid from it. Out there fell a cascade of children's bricks. It was the toy which he had promised to bring home.

"This discovery, and the evident confusion which the cripple showed, made the inspector realize that the matter was serious. The rooms were carefully examined, and results all pointed to an abominable crime. The front room was plainly furnished as a sitting room, and led into a small bedroom, which looked out upon the back of one of the wharves. Between the wharf and the bedroom window is a narrow strip, which is dry at low tide, but is covered at high tide with at least four and a half feet of water. The bedroom window was a broad one, and opened from below. On examination traces of blood were to be seen upon the window sill, and several scattered drops were visible upon the wooden floor of the bedroom. Thrust away behind a curtain in the front room were all the clothes of Mr. Neville St. Clair, with the exception of his coat. His boots, his socks, his hat, and his watch – all were there. There were no signs of violence upon any of these garments, and there were no other traces of Mr. Neville St. Clair. Out of the window he must apparently have gone, for no other exit could be discovered, and the ominous bloodstains upon the sill gave little promise that he could save himself by swimming, for the tide was at its very highest at the moment of the tragedy.

"And now as to the villains who seemed to be immediately implicated in the matter. The Lascar was known to be a man of the vilest antecedents, but as by Mrs. St. Clair's story he was known to have been at the foot of the stair within a few seconds of her husband's appearance at the window, he could hardly have been more than an accessory to the crime. His defence was one of absolute ignorance, and he protested that he had no knowledge as to the doings of Hugh Boone, his lodger, and that he could not account in any way for the presence of the missing gentleman's clothes.

"So much for the Lascar manager. Now for the sinister cripple who lives upon the second floor of the opium den, and who was certainly the last human being whose eyes rested upon Neville St. Clair. His name is Hugh Boone, and his hideous face is one which is familiar to every man who goes much to the City. He is a professional beggar, though in order to avoid the police regulations he pretends to a small trade in wax vestas. Some little distance down Threadneedle Street upon the left-hand side there is, as you may have remarked, a small angle in the wall. Here it is that the creature takes his daily seat, cross-legged, with his tiny stock of matches on his lap, and as he is a piteous spectacle a small rain of charity descends into the greasy leather cap which lies upon the pavement before him. I have watched this fellow more than once, before ever I thought of making his professional acquaintance, and I have been surprised at the harvest which he has reaped in so short a time. His appearance, you see, is so remarkable that no one can pass him without observing him. A shock of orange hair, a pale face disfigured by a horrible scar, which, by its contraction, has turned up the outer edge of his upper lip, a bulldog ch:n, and a pair of very penetrating dark eyes, which present a singular contrast to the color of his hair, all mark him out from amid the common crowd of mendicants, and so, too, does his wit, for he is ever ready with a reply to any piece of chaff which may be thrown at him by the passersby. This is the man whom we now learn to have been the lodger at the opium den, and to have been the last man to see the gentleman of whom we are in quest."

"But a cripple!" said I. "What could he have done single-handed against a man in the prime of life?"

"He is a cripple in the sense that he walks with a limp; but, in other respects, he appears to be a powerful and well-nurtured man. Surely your medical experience would tell you, Watson, that weakness in one limb is often compensated for by exceptional strength in the others."

"Pray continue your narrative."

"Mrs. St. Clair had fainted at the sight of the blood upon the window, and she was escorted home in a cab by the police, as her presence could be of no help to them in their investigations. Inspector Barton, who had charge of the case, made a very careful examination of the premises, but without finding anything which threw any light upon the matter. One mistake had been made in not arresting Boone instantly, as he was allowed some few minutes during which he might have communicated with his friend the Lascar, but this fault was soon remedied, and he was seized and searched, without anything being found which could incriminate him. There were, it is true, some bloodstains upon his right shirt-sleeve, but he pointed to his ring finger, which had been cut near the nail, and explained that the bleeding came from there, adding that he had been to the window not long before, and that the stains which had been observed there came doubtless from the same source. He denied strenuously having ever seen Mr. Neville St. Clair, and swore that the presence of the clothes in his room was as much a mystery to him as to the police. As to Mrs. St. Clair's assertion, that she had actually seen her husband at the window, he declared that she must have been either mad or dreaming. He was removed, loudly protesting, to the police station, while the inspector remained upon the premises in the hope that the ebbing tide might afford some fresh clue.

"And it did, though they hardly found upon the mudbank what they had feared to find. It was Neville St. Clair's coat, and not Neville St. Clair, which lay uncovered as the tide receded. And what do you think they found in the pockets?"

"I cannot imagine."

"No, I don't think you will guess. Every pocket stuffed with pennies and halfpennies – four hundred and twenty-one pennies, and two hundred and seventy halfpennies. It was no wonder that it had not been swept away by the tide. But a human body is a different matter. There is a fierce eddy between the wharf and the house. It seemed likely enough that the weighted coat had remained when the stripped body had been sucked away into the river."

"But I understand that all the other clothes were found in the room. Would the body be dressed in a coat alone?"

"No, sir, but the facts might be met speciously enough. Suppose that this man Boone had thrust Neville St. Clair through the window, there is no human eye which could have seen the deed. What would he do then? It would of course instantly strike him that he must get rid of the telltale garments. He would seize the coat then, and be in the act of throwing it out when it would occur to him that it would swim and not sink. He has little time, for he had heard the scuffle downstairs when the wife tried to force her way up, and perhaps he has already heard from his Lascar confederate that the police are hurrying up the street. There is not an instant to be lost. He rushes to some secret hoard, where he has accumulated the fruits of his beggary, and he stuffs all the coins upon which he can lay his hands into the pockets to make sure of the coat's sinking. He throws it out, and would have done the same with the other garments had not he heard the rush of steps below, and only just had time to close the window when the police appeared."

"It certainly sounds feasible."

"Well, we will take it as a working hypothesis for want of a better. Boone, as I have told you, was arrested and taken to the station, but it could not be shown that there had ever before been anything against him. He had for years been known as a professional beggar, but his life appeared to have been a very quiet and innocent one. There the matter stands at present, and the questions which have to be solved, what Neville St. Clair was doing in the opium den, what happened to him when there, where he is now, and what Hugh Boone had to do with his disappearance, are all as far from solution as ever. I confess that I cannot recall any case within my experience which looked at the first glance so simple, and yet which presented such difficulties."

Whilst Sherlock Holmes had been detailing this singular series of events we had been whirling through the outskirts of the great town until the last straggling houses had been left behind, and we rattled along with a country hedge upon either side of us. Just as he finished, however, we drove through two scattered villages, where a few lights still glimmered in the windows.

"We are on the outskirts of Lee," said my companion. "We have touched on three English counties in our short drive, starting in Middlesex, passing over an angle of Surrey, and ending in Kent. See that light among the trees? That is the Cedars, and beside that lamp sits a woman whose anxious ears have already, I have little doubt, caught the clink of our horse's feet."

"But why are you not conducting the case from Baker Street?" I asked.

"Because there are many inquiries which must be made out here. Mrs. St. Clair has most kindly put two rooms at my disposal, and you may rest assured that she will have nothing but a welcome for my friend and colleague. I hate to meet her, Watson, when I have no news of her husband. Here we are. Whoa, there, whoa!"

We had pulled up in front of a large villa which stood within its own grounds. A stable-boy had run out to the horse's head, and, springing down, I followed Holmes up the small, winding gravel drive which led to the house. As we approached the door flew open, and a little blonde woman stood in the opening, clad in some sort of light *mousseline-de-soie*, with a touch of fluffy pink chiffon at her neck and wrists. She stood with her figure outlined against the flood of light, one hand upon the door, one half raised in eagerness, her body slightly bent, her head and face protruded, with eager eyes and parted lips, a standing question.

"Well?" she cried, "well?" And then, seeing that there were two of us, she gave a cry of hope which sank into a groan as she saw that my companion shook his head and shrugged his shoulders.

"No good news?"

"None."

"No bad?"

"No."

"Thank God for that. But come in. You must be weary, for you have had a long day."

"This is my friend, Dr. Watson. He has been of most vital use to me in several of my cases, and a lucky chance has made it possible for me to bring him out and associate him with this investigation."

"I am delighted to see you," said she, pressing my hand warmly. "You will, I am sure, forgive anything which may be wanting in our arrangements, when you consider the blow which has come so suddenly upon us."

"My dear madam," said I, "I am an old campaigner, and if I were not, I can very well see that no apology is needed. If I can be of any assistance, either to you or to my friend here, I shall be indeed happy."

"Now, Mr. Sherlock Holmes," said the lady as we entered a well-lit dining-room, upon the table of which a cold supper had been laid out. "I should very much like to ask you one or two plain questions, to which I beg that you will give a plain answer."

"Certainly, madam."

"Do not trouble about my feelings. I am not hysterical, nor given to fainting. I simply wish to hear your real, real opinion."

"Upon what point?"

"In your heart of hearts, do you think that Neville is alive?"

Sherlock Holmes seemed to be embarrassed by the question. "Frankly now!" she repeated, standing upon the rug, and looking keenly down at him, as he leaned back in a basket chair.

"Frankly, then, madam, I do not."

"You think that he is dead?"

"I do."

"Murdered?"

"I don't say that. Perhaps."

"And on what day did he meet his death?"

"On Monday."

"Then perhaps, Mr. Holmes, you will be good enough to explain how it is that I have received this letter from him today?"

Sherlock Holmes sprang out of his chair as if he had been galvanized.

"What!" he roared.

"Yes, today." She stood smiling, holding up a little slip of paper in the air.

"May I see it?"

"Certainly."

He snatched it from her in his eagerness, and smoothing it out upon the table, he drew over the lamp, and examined it intently. I had left my chair, and was gazing at it over his shoulder. The envelope was a very coarse one, and was stamped with the Gravesend postmark, and with the date of that very day, or rather of the day before, for it was considerably after midnight.

"Coarse writing!" murmured Holmes. "Surely this is not your husband's writing, madam."

"No, but the enclosure is."

"I perceive also that whoever addressed the envelope had to go and inquire as to the address."

"How can you tell that?"

"The name, you see, is in perfectly black ink, which has dried itself. The rest is of the greyish color which shows that blotting paper has been used. It if had been written straight off, and then blotted, none would be of a deep black shade. This man has written the name, and there has then been a pause before he wrote the address, which can only mean that he was not familiar with it. It is, of course, a trifle, but there is nothing so important as trifles. Let us now see the letter! Ha! There has been an enclosure here!"

"Yes, there was a ring. His signet ring."

"And you are sure that this is your husband's hand?"

"One of his hands."

"One?"

"His hand when he wrote hurriedly. It is very unlike his usual writing, and yet I know it well."

"'Dearest, do not be frightened. All will come well. There is a huge error which it may take some little time to rectify. Wait in patience. – Neville.' Written in pencil upon a flyleaf of a book, octavo size, no watermark. Posted today in Gravesend by a man with a dirty thumb. Ha! And the flap has been gummed, if I am not very much in error, by a person who has been chewing tobacco. And you have no doubt that it is your husband's hand, madam?"

"None. Neville wrote those words."

"And they were posted today at Gravesend. Well, Mrs. St. Clair, the clouds lighten, though I should not venture to say that the danger is over."

"But he must be alive, Mr. Holmes."

"Unless this is a clever forgery to put us on the wrong scent. The ring, after all, proves nothing. It may have been taken from him."

"No, no; it is, it is, it is his very own writing!"

"Very well. It may, however, have been written on Monday, and only posted today."

"That is possible."

"If so, much may have happened between."

"Oh, you must not discourage me, Mr. Holmes. I know that all is well with him. There is so keen a sympathy between us that I should know if evil came upon him. On the very day that I saw him last he cut himself in the bedroom, and yet I in the dining room rushed upstairs instantly with the utmost certainty that something had happened. Do you think that I would respond to such a trifle, and yet be ignorant of his death?"

"I have seen too much not to know that the impression of a woman may be more valuable than the conclusion of an analytical reasoner. And in this letter you certainly have a very strong piece of evidence to corroborate your view. But if your husband is alive and able to write letters, why should he remain away from you?"

"I cannot imagine. It is unthinkable."

"And on Monday he made no remarks before leaving you?"

"No."

"And you were surprised to see him in Swandam Lane?"

"Very much so."

"Was the window open?"

"Yes."

"Then he might have called to you?"

"He might."

"He only, as I understand, gave an inarticulate cry?"

"Yes."

"A call for help, you thought?"

"Yes. He waved his hands."

"But it might have been a cry of surprise. Astonishment at the unexpected sight of you might cause him to throw up his hands."

"It is possible."

"And you thought he was pulled back?"

"He disappeared so suddenly."

"He might have leaped back. You did not see anyone else in the room?

"No, but this horrible man confessed to having been there, and the Lascar was at the foot of the stairs."

"Quite so. Your husband, as far as you could see, had his ordinary clothes on?"

"But without his collar or tie. I distinctly saw his bare throat."

"Had he ever spoken of Swandam Lane?"

"Never."

"Had he ever shown any signs of having taken opium?"

"Never."

"Thank you, Mrs. St. Clair. Those are the principal points about which I wished to be abolutely clear. We shall now have a little supper and then retire, for we may have a very busy day tomorrow."

A large and comfortable double-bedded room had been placed at our disposal, and I was quickly between the sheets, for I was weary after my night of adventure. Sherlock Holmes was a man, however, who when he had an unsolved problem upon his mind would go for days, and even for a week, without rest, turning it over, rearranging his facts, looking at it from every point of view, until he had either fathomed it, or convinced himself that his data were insufficient. It was soon evident to me that he was now preparing for an all-night sitting. He took off his coat and waistcoat, put on a large blue dressing gown, and then wandered about the room collecting pillows from his bed, and cushions from the sofa and armchairs. With these he constructed a sort of Eastern divan, upon which he perched himself crosslegged, with an ounce of shag tobacco and a box of matches laid out in front of him. In the dim light of the lamp I saw him sitting there, an old brier pipe between his lips, his eyes fixed vacantly upon the corner of the ceiling, the blue smoke curling up from him, silent, motionless, with the light shining upon his strong-set aquiline features. So he sat as I dropped off to sleep, and so he sat when a sudden exclamation caused me to wake up, and I found the summer sun shining into the apartment. The pipe was still between his lips, the smoke still curled upwards, and the room was full of a dense tobacco haze, but nothing remained of the heap of shag which I had seen upon the previous night.

"Awake, Watson?" he asked.

"Yes."

"Game for a morning drive?"

"Certainly."

"Then dress. No one is stirring yet, but I know where the stable-boy sleeps, and we shall soon have the trap out." He chuckled to himself as he spoke, his eyes twinkled, and he seemed a different man to the sombre thinker of the previous night.

As I dressed I glanced at my watch. It was no wonder that no one was stirring. It was twenty-five minutes past four. I had hardly finished when Holmes returned with the news that the boy was putting in the horse.

"I want to test a little theory of mine," said he, pulling on his boots. "I think, Watson, that you are now standing in the presence of one of the most absolute fools in Europe. I deserve to be kicked from here to Charing Cross. But I think I have the key of the affair now."

"And where is it?" I asked, smiling.

"In the bathroom," he answered. "Oh, yes, I am not joking," he continued, seeing my look of incredulity. "I have just been there, and I have taken it out, and I have got it in this Gladstone bag. Come on, my boy, and we shall see whether it will not fit the lock."

We made our way downstairs as quietly as possible; and out into the bright morning sunshine. In the road stood our horse and trap, with the half-clad stable-boy waiting at the head. We both sprang in, and away we dashed down the London road. A few country carts were stirring, bearing in vegetables to the metropolis, but the lines of villas on either side were as silent and lifeless as some city in a dream.

"It has been in some points a singular case," said Holmes, flicking the horse on into a gallop. "I confess that I have been as blind as a mole, but it is better to learn wisdom late, than never to learn it at all."

In town, the earliest risers were just beginning to look sleepily from their windows as we drove through the streets of the Surrey side. Passing down the Waterloo Bridge Road we crossed over the river, and dashing up Wellington Street wheeled sharply to the right, and found ourselves in Bow Street. Sherlock Holmes was well known to the Force, and the two constables at the door saluted him. One of them held the horse's head while the other led us in.

"Who is on duty?" asked Holmes.

"Inspector Bradstreet, sir."

"Ah, Bradstreet, how are you?" A tall, stout official had come down the stone-flagged passage, in a peaked cap and frogged jacket. "I wish to have a word with you, Bradstreet."

"Certainly, Mr. Holmes. Step into my room here."

It was a small office-like room, with a

huge ledger upon the table, and a telephone projecting from the wall. The inspector sat down at his desk.

"What can I do for you, Mr. Holmes?"

"I called about that beggar-man, Boone – the one who was charged with being concerned in the disappearance of Mr. Neville St. Clair, of Lee."

"Yes. He was brought up and remanded for further inquiries."

"So I heard. You have him here?"

"In the cells."

"Is he quiet?"

"Oh, he gives no trouble. But he is a dirty scoundrel."

"Dirty?"

"Yes, it is all we can do to make him wash his hands, and his face is as black as a tinker's. Well, when once his case has been settled he will have a regular prison bath; and I think, if you saw him, you would agree with me that he needed it."

"I should like to see him very much."

"Would you? That is easily done. Come this way. You can leave your bag."

"No, I think I'll take it."

"Very good. Come this way, if you please." He led us down a passage, opened a barred door, passed down a winding stair, and brought us to a whitewashed corridor with a line of doors on each side.

"The third on the right is his," said the inspector. "Here it is!" He quietly shot back a panel in the upper part of the door, and glanced through.

"He is asleep," said he. "You can see him very well."

We both put our eyes to the grating. The prisoner lay with his face toward us, in a very deep sleep, breathing slowly and heavily. He was a middle-sized man, coarsely clad as became his calling, with a colored shirt protruding through the rent in his tattered coat. He was, as the inspector had said, extremely dirty, but the grime which covered his face could not conceal its repulsive ugliness. A broad weal from an old scar ran across it from eye to chin, and by its contraction had turned up one side of the upper lip, so that three teeth were exposed in a perpetual snarl. A shock of very bright red hair grew low over his eyes and forehead.

"He's a beauty, isn't he?" said the inspector.

"He certainly needs a wash," remarked Holmes. "I had an idea that he might, and I took the liberty of bringing the tools with me." He opened his Gladstone bag as he spoke, and took out, to my astonishment, a very large bath sponge.

"He! he! You are a funny one," chuckled the inspector.

"Now, if you will have the great goodness to open that door very quietly, we will soon make him cut a much more respectable figure."

"Well, I don't know why not," said the inspector. "He doesn't look a credit to the Bow Street cells, does he?" He slipped his key into the lock, and we all very quietly entered the cell. The sleeper half turned, and then settled down once more into a deep slumber. Holmes stooped to the water jug, moistened his sponge, and then rubbed it twice vigorously across and down the prisoner's face.

"Let me introduce you," he shouted, "to Mr. Neville St. Clair, of Lee, in the county of Kent."

Never in my life have I seen such a sight. The man's face peeled off under the sponge like the bark from a tree. Gone was the coarse brown tint! Gone, too, the horrid scar which had seamed it across, and the twisted lip which had given the repulsive sneer to the face! A twitch brought away the tangled red hair, and there, sitting up in his bed, was a pale, sad-faced, refined-looking man, black-haired and smooth-skinned, rubbing his eyes, and staring about him with sleepy bewilderment. Then suddenly realizing the exposure, he broke into a scream, and threw himself down with his face to the pillow.

"Great heaven!" cried the inspector, "it is, indeed, the missing man. I know him from the photograph."

The prisoner turned with the reckless air of a man who abandons himself to his destiny. "Be it so," said he. "And pray what am I charged with?"

"With making away with Mr. Neville St. – Oh, come, you can't be charged with that, unless they make a case of attempted suicide of it," said the inspector, with a grin. "Well, I have been twenty-seven years in the Force, but this really takes the cake."

"If I am Mr. Neville St. Clair, then it is obvious that no crime has been committed, and that, therefore, I am illegally detained."

"No crime, but a very great error has been committed," said Holmes. "You would have done better to have trusted your wife."

"It was not the wife, it was the children," groaned the prisoner. "God help me, I would not have them ashamed of their father. My God! What an exposure! What can I do?"

Sherlock Holmes sat down beside him on the couch, and patted him kindly on the shoulder.

"If you leave it to a court of law to clear the matter up," said he, "of course you can hardly avoid publicity. On the other hand, if you convince the police authorities that there is no possible case against you, I do not know that there is any reason that the details should find their way into the papers. Inspector Bradstreet would, I am sure, make notes upon anything which you might tell us, and submit it to the proper authorities. The case would then never go into court at all."

"God bless you!" cried the prisoner passionately. "I would have endured imprison-

ment, aye, even execution, rather than have left my miserable secret as a family blot to my children.

"You are the first who have ever heard my story. My father was a schoolmaster in Chesterfield, where I received an excellent education. I travelled in my youth, took to the stage, and finally became a reporter on an evening paper in London. One day my editor wished to have a series of articles upon begging in the metropolis, and I volunteered to supply them. There was the point from which all my adventures started. It was only by trying begging as an amateur that I could get the facts upon which to base my articles. When an actor I had, of course, learned all the secrets of making up, and had been famous in the greenroom for my skill. I took advantage now of my attainments. I painted my face, and to make myself as pitiable as possible I made a good scar and fixed one side of my lip in a twist by the aid of a small slip of flesh-colored plaster. Then with a red head of hair, and an appropriate dress, I took my station in the busiest part of the City, ostensibly as a match-seller, but really as a beggar. For seven hours I plied my trade, and when I returned home in the evening I found, to my surprise, that I had received no less than twenty-six shillings and fourpence.

"I wrote my articles, and thought little more of the matter until, some time later, I backed a bill for a friend, and had a writ served upon me for £25. I was at my wits' end where to get the money, but a sudden idea came to me. I begged a fortnight's grace from the creditor, asked for a holiday from my employers, and spent the time in begging in the City under my disguise. In ten days I had the money, and had paid the debt.

"Well, you can imagine how hard it was to settle down to arduous work at two pounds a week, when I knew that I could earn as much in a day by smearing my face with a little paint, laying my cap on the ground, and sitting still. It was a long fight between my pride and the money, but the dollars won at last, and I threw up reporting, and sat day after day in the corner which I had chosen, inspiring pity by my ghastly face and filling my pockets with coppers. Only one man knew my secret. He was the keeper of a low den in which I used to lodge in Swandam Lane, where I could every morning emerge as a squalid beggar and in the evening transform myself into a well-dressed man about town. This fellow, a Lascar, was well paid by me for his rooms, so that I knew that my secret was safe in his possession.

"Well, very soon I found that I was saving considerable sums of money. I do not mean that any beggar in the streets of London could earn seven hundred pounds a year — which is less than my average takings — but I had exceptional advantages in my power of making up, and also in a facility in repartee, which improved by practice, and made me quite a recognized character in the City. All day a stream of pennies, varied by silver, poured in upon me, and it was a very bad day upon which I failed to take two pounds.

"As I grew richer I grew more ambitious, took a house in the country, and eventually married, without anyone having a suspicion as to my real occupation. My dear wife knew that I had business in the City. She little knew what.

"Last Monday I had finished for the day, and was dressing in my room above the opium den, when I looked out of the window, and saw, to my horror and astonishment, that my wife was standing in the street, with her eyes fixed full upon me. I gave a cry of surprise, threw up my arms to cover my face, and rushing to my confidant, the Lascar, entreated him to prevent anyone from coming up to me. I heard her voice downstairs, but I knew that she could not ascend. Swiftly

I threw off my clothes, pulled on those of a beggar, and put on my pigments and wig. Even a wife's eyes could not pierce so complete a disguise. But then it occurred to me that there might be a search in the room and that the clothes might betray me. I threw open the window, re-opening by my violence a small cut which I had inflicted upon myself in the bedroom that morning. Then I seized my coat, which was weighted by the coppers which I had just transferred to it from the leather bag in which I carried my takings. I hurled it out of the window, and it disappeared into the Thames. The other clothes would have followed, but at that moment there was a rush of constables up the stairs, and a few minutes after I found, rather, I confess, to my relief, that instead of being identified as Mr. Neville St. Clair, I was arrested as his murderer.

"I do not know that there is anything else for me to explain. I was determined to preserve my disguise as long as possible, and hence my preference for a dirty face. Knowing that my wife would be terribly anxious, I slipped off my ring, and confided it to the Lascar at a moment when no constable was watching me, together with a hurried scrawl, telling her that she had no cause to fear."

"That note only reached her yesterday," said Holmes.

"Good God! What a week she must have spent."

"The police have watched this Lascar," said Inspector Bradstreet, "and I can quite understand that he might find it difficult to post a letter unobserved. Probably he handed it to some sailor customer of his, who forgot all about it for some days."

"That was it," said Holmes, nodding approvingly, "I have no doubt of it. But have you never been prosecuted for begging?"

"Many times; but what was a fine to me?"

"It must stop here, however," said Bradstreet. "If the police are to hush this thing up, there must be no more of Hugh Boone."

"I have sworn it by the most solemn oaths which a man can take."

"In that case I think that it is probable that no further steps may be taken. But if you are found again, then all must come out. I am sure, Mr. Holmes, that we are very much indebted to you for having cleared the matter up. I wish I knew how you reach your results."

"I reached this one," said my friend, "by sitting upon five pillows and consuming an ounce of shag. I think, Watson, that if we drive to Baker Street we shall just be in time for breakfast."

Agatha Christie

Wasps' Nest

There was, perhaps,
something a little sinister
in the stillness,
like the lull before a storm.

From *Poirot's Early Cases* by Agatha Christie. Reprinted by permission of Hughes Massie Limited, London, England.

Out of the house came John Harrison and stood a moment on the terrace looking out over the garden. He was a big man with a lean, cadaverous face. His aspect was usually somewhat grim but when, as now, the rugged features softened into a smile, there was something very attractive about him.

John Harrison loved his garden, and it had never looked better than it did on this August evening, summery and languorous. The rambler roses were still beautiful; sweet peas scented the air.

A well-known creaking sound made Harrison turn his head sharply. Who was coming in through the garden gate? In another minute, an expression of utter astonishment came over his face, for the dandified figure coming up the path was the last he expected to see in this part of the world.

"By all that's wonderful," cried Harrison. "Monsieur Poirot!"

It was, indeed, the famous Hercule Poirot whose renown as a detective had spread over the whole world.

"Yes," he said, "it is. You said to me once: 'If you are ever in this part of the world, come and see me.' I take you at your word. I arrive."

"And I'm obliged," said Harrison heartily. "Sit down and have a drink."

With a hospitable hand, he indicated a table on the veranda bearing assorted bottles.

"I thank you," said Poirot, sinking down into a basket chair. "You have, I suppose, no *sirop*? No, no. I thought not. A little plain soda water then – no whisky." And he added in a feeling voice as the other placed the glass beside him, "Alas, my moustaches are limp. It is this heat!"

"And what brings you into this quiet spot?" asked Harrison as he dropped into another chair. "Pleasure?"

"No, *mon ami*, business."

"Business? In this out-of-the-way place?"

Poirot nodded gravely. "But yes, my friend, all crimes are not committed in crowds, you know?"

The other laughed. "I suppose that was rather an idiotic remark of mine. But what particular crime are you investigating down here, or is that a thing I mustn't ask?"

"You may ask," said the detective. "Indeed, I would prefer that you asked."

Harrison looked at him curiously. He sensed something a little unusual in the other's manner. "You are investigating a crime, you say?" he advanced rather hesitatingly. "A serious crime?"

"A crime of the most serious there is."

"You mean..."

"Murder."

So gravely did Hercule Poirot say that word that Harrison was quite taken aback. The detective was looking straight at him and again there was something so unusual in his glance that Harrison hardly knew how to proceed. At last, he said, "But I have heard of no murder."

"No," said Poirot, "you would not have heard of it."

"Who has been murdered?"

"As yet," said Hercule Poirot, "nobody."

"What?"

"That is why I said you would not have heard of it. I am investigating a crime that has not yet taken place."

"But look here, that is nonsense."

"Not at all. If one can investigate a murder before it has happened, surely that is very much better than afterwards. One might even – a little idea – prevent it."

Harrison stared at him. "You are not serious, Monsieur Poirot."

"But yes, I am serious."

"You really believe that a murder is going to be committed? Oh, it's absurd!"

Hercule Poirot finished the first part of the sentence without taking any notice of the exclamation.

"Unless we can manage to prevent it. Yes, *mon ami*, that is what I mean."

"We?"

"I said we. I shall need your co-operation."

"Is that why you came down here?"

Again Poirot looked at him, and again an indefinable something made Harrison uneasy.

"I came here, Monsieur Harrison, because I – well – like you."

And then he added in an entirely different voice, "I see, Monsieur Harrison, that you have a wasps' nest there. You should destroy it."

The change of subject made Harrison frown in a puzzled way. He followed Poirot's glance and said in a bewildered voice, "As a matter of fact, I'm going to. Or rather, young Langton is. You remember Claude Langton? He was at that same dinner where I met you. He's coming over this evening to take the nest. Rather fancies himself at the job."

"Ah," said Poirot. "And how is he going to do it?"

"Petrol and the garden syringe. He's bringing his own syringe over; it's a more convenient size than mine."

"There is another way, is there not?" asked Poirot. "With cyanide of potassium?"

Harrison looked a little surprised. "Yes, but that's rather dangerous stuff. Always a risk having it about the place."

Poirot nodded gravely. "Yes, it is deadly poison." He waited a minute and then repeated in a grave voice, "Deadly poison."

"Useful if you want to do away with your mother-in-law, eh?" said Harrison with a laugh.

But Hercule Poirot remained grave. "And you are quite sure, Monsieur Harrison,

84 that it is with petrol that Monsieur Langton is going to destroy your wasps' nest?"

"Quite sure. Why?"

"I wondered. I was at the chemist's in Barchester this afternoon. For one of my purchases I had to sign the poison book. I saw the last entry. It was for cyanide of potassium and it was signed by Claude Langton."

Harrison stared. "That's odd," he said. "Langton told me the other day that he'd never dream of using the stuff; in fact, he said it oughtn't to be sold for the purpose."

Poirot looked out over the garden. His voice was very quiet as he asked a question. "Do you like Langton?"

The other stared. The question somehow seemed to find him quite unprepared. "I – I – well, I mean – of course, I like him. Why shouldn't I?"

"I only wondered," said Poirot placidly, "whether you did."

And as the other did not answer, he went on. "I also wondered if he liked you?"

"What are you getting at, Monsieur Poirot? There's something in your mind I can't fathom."

"I am going to be very frank. You are engaged to be married, Monsieur Harrison. I know Miss Molly Deane. She is a very charming, a very beautiful girl. Before she was engaged to you, she was engaged to Claude Langton. She threw him over for you."

Harrison nodded.

"I do not ask what her reasons were: she may have been justified. But I tell you this, it is not too much to suppose that Langton has not forgotten or forgiven."

"You're wrong, Monsieur Poirot. I swear you're wrong. Langton's been a sportsman; he's taken things like a man. He's been amazingly decent to me – gone out of his way to be friendly."

"And that does not strike you as unusual? You use the word *amazingly*, but you do not seem to be amazed."

"What do you mean, M. Poirot?"

"I mean," said Poirot, and his voice had a new note in it, "that a man may conceal his hate till the proper time comes."

"Hate?" Harrison shook his head and laughed.

"The English are very stupid," said Poirot. "They think that they can deceive anyone but that no one can deceive them. The sportsman – the good fellow – never will they believe evil of him. And because they are brave, but stupid, sometimes they die when they need not die."

"You are warning me," said Harrison in a low voice. "I see it now – what has puzzled me all along. You are warning me against Claude Langton. You came here today to warn me...."

Poirot nodded. Harrison sprang up suddenly. "But you are mad, Monsieur Poirot. This is England. Things don't happen like that here. Disappointed suitors don't go about stabbing people in the back and poisoning them. And you're wrong about Langton. That chap wouldn't hurt a fly."

"The lives of flies are not my concern," said Poirot placidly. "And although you say Monsieur Langton would not take the life of one, yet you forget that he is even now preparing to take the lives of several thousand wasps."

Harrison did not at once reply. The little detective in his turn sprang to his feet. He advanced to his friend and laid a hand on his shoulder. So agitated was he that he almost shook the big man, and, as he did so, he hissed into his ear, "Rouse yourself, my friend, rouse yourself. And look – look where I am pointing. There on the bank, close by that tree root. See you, the wasps returning home, placid at the end of the day? In a little hour, there will be destruction, and they know it not. There is no one to tell them. They have not, it seems, a Hercule Poirot. I tell you, Monsieur Harrison, I am down here on business. Murder is my business. And it is my business before it has happened as well as afterwards. At what time does Monsieur Langton come to take this wasps' nest?"

"Langton would never..."

"At what time?"

"At nine o'clock. But I tell you, you're all wrong. Langton would never..."

"These English!" cried Poirot in a passion. He caught up his hat and stick and moved down the path, pausing to speak over his shoulder. "I do not stay to argue with you. I should only enrage myself. But you understand, I return at nine o'clock?"

Harrison opened his mouth to speak, but Poirot did not give him the chance. "I know what you would say: 'Langton would never,' et cetera. Ah, Langton would never! But all the same I return at nine o'clock. But, yes, it will amuse me – put it like that – it will amuse me to see the taking of a wasps' nest. Another of your English sports!"

He waited for no reply but passed rapidly down the path and out through the door that creaked. Once outside on the road, his pace slackened. His vivacity died down, his face became grave and troubled. Once he drew his watch from his pocket and consulted it. The hands pointed to ten minutes past eight. "Over three quarters of an hour," he murmured. "I wonder if I should have waited."

His footsteps slackened; he almost seemed on the point of returning. Some vague foreboding seemed to assail him. He shook it off resolutely, however, and continued to walk in the direction of the village. But his face was still troubled, and once or twice he shook his head like a man only partly satisfied.

It was still some minutes off nine when he once more approached the garden door. It was a clear, still evening; hardly a breeze stirred the leaves. There was, perhaps, something a little sinister in the stillness, like the lull before a storm.

Poirot's footsteps quickened ever so lightly. He was suddenly alarmed – and uncertain. He feared he knew not what.

And at that moment the garden door opened and Claude Langton stepped quickly out into the road. He started when he saw Poirot.

"Oh – er – good evening."

"Good evening, Monsieur Langton. You are early."

Langton stared at him. "I don't know what you mean."

"You have taken the wasps' nest?"

"As a matter of fact, I didn't."

"Oh," said Poirot softly. "So you did not take the wasps' nest. What did you do then?"

"Oh, just sat and yarned a bit with old Harrison. I really must hurry along now, Monsieur Poirot. I'd no idea you were remaining in this part of the world."

"I had business here, you see."

"Oh! Well, you'll find Harrison on the terrace. Sorry I can't stop."

He hurried away. Poirot looked after him. A nervous young fellow, good-looking with a weak mouth!

"So I shall find Harrison on the terrace," murmured Poirot. "I wonder." He went in through the garden door and up the path. Harrison was sitting in a chair by the table. He sat motionless and did not even turn his head as Poirot came up to him.

"Ah! *Mon ami*," said Poirot. "You are all right, eh?"

There was a long pause and then Harrison said in a queer, dazed voice, "What did you say?"

"I said – are you all right?"

"All right? Yes, I'm all right. Why not?"

"You feel no ill effects? That is good."

"Ill effects? From what?"

"Washing soda."

Harrison roused himself suddenly. "Washing soda? What do you mean?"

Poirot made an apologetic gesture. "I

infinitely regret the necessity, but I put some in your pocket."

"You put some in my pocket? What on earth for?"

Harrison stared at him. Poirot spoke quietly and impersonally like a lecturer coming down to the level of a small child.

"You see, one of the advantages, or disadvantages, of being a detective is that it brings you into contact with the criminal classes. And the criminal classes, they can teach you some very interesting and curious things. There was a pickpocket once – I interested myself in him because for once in a way he has not done what they say he has done – and so I get him off. And because he is grateful he pays me in the only way he can think of – which is to show me the tricks of his trade.

"And so it happens that I can pick a man's pocket if I choose without his ever suspecting the fact. I lay one hand on his shoulder, I excite myself, and he feels nothing. But all the same I have managed to transfer what is in his pocket to my pocket and leave washing soda in its place.

"You see," continued Poirot dreamily, "if a man wants to get at some poison quickly to put in a glass, unobserved, he positively must keep it in his right-hand coat pocket; there is nowhere else. I knew it would be there."

He dropped his hand into his pocket and brought out a few white, lumpy crystals. "Exceedingly dangerous," he murmured, "to carry it like that – loose."

Calmly and without hurrying himself, he took from another pocket a wide-mouthed bottle. He slipped in the crystals, stepped to the table and filled up the bottle with plain water. Then carefully corking it, he shook it until all the crystals were dissolved. Harrison watched him as though fascinated.

Satisfied with his solution, Poirot stepped across to the nest. He uncorked the bottle, turned his head aside, and poured the solution into the wasps' nest, then stood back a pace or two watching.

Some wasps that were returning alighted, quivered a little and then lay still. Other wasps crawled out of the hole only to die. Poirot watched for a minute or two and then nodded his head and came back to the veranda.

"A quick death," he said. "A very quick death."

Harrison found his voice. "How much do you know?"

Poirot looked straight ahead. "As I told you, I saw Claude Langton's name in the book. What I did not tell you was that almost immediately afterwards, I happened to meet him. He told me he had been buying cyanide of potassium at your request – to take a wasps' nest. That struck me as a little odd, my friend, because I remember that at that dinner of which you spoke, you held forth on the superior merits of petrol and denounced the buying of cyanide as dangerous and unnecessary."

"Go on."

"I knew something else. I had seen Claude Langton and Molly Deane together when they thought no one saw them. I do not know what lovers' quarrel it was that originally parted them and drove her into your arms, but I realized that misunderstandings were over and that Miss Deane was drifting back to her love."

"Go on."

"I knew something more, my friend. I was in Harley Street the other day, and I saw you come out of a certain doctor's house. I know the doctor and for what disease one consults him, and I read the expression on your face. I have seen it only once or twice in my lifetime, but it is not easily mistaken. It was the face of a man under sentence of death. I am right, am I not?"

"Quite right. He gave me two months."

"You did not see me, my friend, for you

had other things to think about. I saw something else on your face – the thing that I told you this afternoon men try to conceal. I saw hate there, my friend. You did not trouble to conceal it, because you thought there was none to observe."

"Go on," said Harrison.

"There is not much more to say. I came down here, saw Langton's name by accident in the poison book as I tell you, met him, and came here to you. I laid traps for you. You denied having asked Langton to get cyanide, or rather you expressed surprise at his having done so. You were taken aback at first at my appearance, but presently you saw how well it would fit in and you encouraged my suspicions. I knew from Langton himself that he was coming at half past eight. You told me nine o'clock, thinking I should come and find everything over. And so I knew everything."

"Why did you come?" cried Harrison. "If only you hadn't come!"

Poirot drew himself up. "I told you," he said, "murder is my business."

"Murder? Suicide, you mean."

"No." Poirot's voice rang out sharply and clearly. "I mean murder. Your death was to be quick and easy, but the death you planned for Langton was the worst death any man can die. He bought the poison; he comes to see you, and he is alone with you. You die suddenly, and the cyanide is found in your glass, and Claude Langton hangs. That was your plan."

Again Harrison moaned.

"Why did you come? Why did you come?"

"I have told you, but there is another reason. I liked you. Listen, *mon ami*, you are a dying man; you have lost the girl you loved, but there is one thing that you are not; you are not a murderer. Tell me now: are you glad or sorry that I came?"

There was a moment's pause and Harrison drew himself up. There was a new dignity in his face – the look of a man who has conquered his own baser self. He stretched out his hand across the table.

"Thank goodness you came," he cried. "Oh, thank goodness you came."

John Wilson Murray

John Dobbin, from Beyond the Quicksands

I felt myself slowly settling,
"Name your own price," I said.

Wild Dobbin was a name given by some to John Dobbin of Bracebridge, when he skipped out of the District of Muskoka and settled across the Red River in the western country, away out in Manitoba, seventy miles beyond Winnipeg. He won the nickname by flying into fits of rage and chasing those near him helter-skelter, while he pursued with club or gun or whatsoever he laid his hands upon. Dobbin was about fifty years old, five feet nine inches tall, with a sandy beard. He was a wiry fellow with an ungovernable temper.

"The reason for his skipping out of the District of Muskoka," says Murray, "was his treatment of John Breckenridge, a Scotchman, who came from the old country. Breckenridge had some money, but knew nothing of farming. He went to the District of Muskoka and settled near Bracebridge. He wanted to buy a farm. John Dobbin heard of it and went to see him and sold him a farm. Breckenridge paid Dobbin part cash and gave him a note for the balance, pending the arrival of a remittance from the old country. When the note came due, Dobbin told Breckenridge he had lost it, and made an affidavit to that effect. Thereupon Breckenridge paid him the amount of the note. Dobbin went away and was seen no more. After he disappeared it transpired that, instead of losing the note, he had sold it to a man who gave it to another man to collect, and this man sued Breckenridge for the value of the note and got judgment. The Scotchman saw he had been swindled by Dobbin, and applied for assistance to the Government. He was directed to me.

"I went to Dobbin's old home at Bracebridge. I could find no trace of him. I nosed around until I learned that his sister had gone away some time before and had bought a ticket to Winnipeg. Through a friend of the sister in Winnipeg I learned that she had gone to Morris, at that time the end of that branch of the Canadian Pacific Railroad, and at Morris she had disappeared. I got my warrant and went to Winnipeg. There I got an officer, Mackenzie, now a private detective, and went to Morris, where the railroad ended. I arrived in Morris on a stifling hot day in July, 1883. I inquired right and left for trace of John Dobbin, but no one seemed to know of him. I decided to try the open country beyond the Red River. I walked for three miles down the river, asking at every house if they knew John Dobbin. No one knew him. After trudging another mile and finding no way to cross the river I sat down in the shade to cool. The river was not so wide but you could be heard on the other side, so while I sat in the shade I bellowed at the top of my voice, at frequent intervals. I became interested in the echoes and shouted lustily. Then I whistled and listened for the echoes and finally I screeched and roared. I was lying flat on my back.

"Suddenly I heard an answering screech. I sat up and looked across the river. On the opposite bank stood a woman screaming to know what was the matter.

"'I want to cross the river,' I shouted.

"'How much will you give if I take you over?' she screamed.

"'I'll give you a dollar,' roared I.

"'All right! I'll call my man from the field!' she shouted.

"I waited. She moved back into a field and presently I saw a man at the water's edge and he pushed off in a boat and paddled over. He stood off shore about fifteen feet and I looked him over. He was a funny little Frenchman, burned almost black by the sun.

"'Give dollair,' he said, keeping his boat away from the shore.

"I stood up, took out a paper dollar, and was about to walk down the sandy shore to the water's edge, when he let out a terrific whoop and waved me back with frantic flourishes of the paddle.

"'Queeksand! Queeksand!' he yelled.

"I stopped short on the very edge of a treacherous pit of quicksand. I tested it cautiously with one foot and while it looked like dry sand it yielded readily and sucked in the foot greedily. The little Frenchman all the while shrieked for me to keep back. He would not come nearer shore but motioned for me to give him the dollar first. I cut a long stick from a tree and fastened the dollar to an end of the stick, then climbed out on a limb of a tree overhanging the water and tried to hand the money to him in this way. The limb bent and suddenly broke clean off and down I went in a quicksand by the water's edge. I began to sink. My ankles had disappeared in the sand and my knees were vanishing. I had struggled to an upright position as I fell. The Frenchman backed his boat over near me, but just beyond my reach.

"'Back in here quick and let me get hold!' I shouted.

"He smiled at me with a sweetness born of the angels.

"'How much you give?' he asked.

"'Back in here! Name your price later but give me a grip of the boat!' I said, for I could feel myself settling and I knew that to struggle would involve me all the deeper.

"My little Frenchman paddled a foot nearer but still kept beyond reach, even if I had flung myself forward with outstretched arms.

"'How much you give?' he asked again, with a voice that seemed to tremble with divine pity. Then, as a thought struck him, he added: 'You give to me, not to her,' and he nodded to the woman who calmly waited on the opposite shore.

"'Yes, yes!' I roared. 'Back the boat in, you fool!'

"'But how much you give?' he insisted, holding himself just out of reach.

"Figures flashed through my head. A goodly sum trembled on the tip of my tongue. I felt myself slowly settling.

"'Name your own price,' I said.

"The Frenchman eyed me with sparkling eyes.

"'It must be one dollar! No less!' he cried.

"You could have knocked me down with a feather. I had been thinking of hundreds.

"'All right! Back in!' I said.

"'But please give it me,' he said sweetly. 'Give me please the dollar!'

"I was sinking well up the hips and beginning to settle fast, too, but I had to go down in my pocket and dig up another dollar, and toss it out to the little Frenchman, who had rescued the first dollar when the limb broke and the stick fell in the water. The Frenchman whirled his boat around and shot the light end in to where I could reach it. I clutched it and kicked and heaved while the little boatman paddled valiantly. I came up like a cork out of a bottle and the boat shot out into the stream with me dragging along in the water behind it. I clambered in and the Frenchman, with the perspiration pouring down his shining face, paused in his paddling to take the two one-dollar bills out of his mouth. He folded one in a tiny wad and tucked it into his left ear. The other he rolled in a ball and as he was about to hide it in his mouth, under his tongue, he smiled to me and said:

"'Please, you do not tell her,' and as if to make doubly sure of my good will he added, 'If you had not been in such hurry I would have done it for feefty cents – maybe.'

"I smiled, and he paddled us to shore. The

woman was waiting and the little French-man took the dollar out of his ear and gave it to her. She shouted at him to give her what he had in his mouth, but he darted beyond reach and defied her. I told her I was buying farms.

"'I understand a man named Dobbin lives near here and has a farm to sell,' I said.

"'Buy ours,' she said.

"'I'll buy a lot of farms,' said I. 'But I must see Dobbin's first. Where does he live?'

"'The only Dobbin I know is four miles back cutting hay,' she said.

"'Can your man show me?' I asked.

"The commercial instinct popped out again instantly.

"'For one-fifty,' she said.

"I paid her the money then and there. She shouted to the Frenchman and he nodded, and away we started to find the man Dobbin, who might or might not be my Dobbin. The little Frenchman walked ahead and I followed. We trudged along in the blazing sun for an hour through brush and across prairie. At last we came upon a man in a field cutting beaver hay.

"'There's Dobbin,' said the Frenchman, keeping aloof, for it seemed all thereabouts feared Dobbin.

"Dobbin stopped mowing as we drew near. He was dripping wet and his face was crimson from his labor.

"'Are you John Dobbin who lived near Bracebridge?' I asked, while the Frenchman listened intently.

"'Yes, why?' said Dobbin.

"'Dobbin,' said I, 'I have a warrant for your arrest.'

"'Arrest me!' exclaimed Dobbin, and then slowly he turned on the little Frenchman. 'And you brought him here to arrest me? You French...!'

"With a roar of rage Dobbin went after the little Frenchman with the scythe. With a shriek of terror the little Frenchman sped away, Dobbin in hot pursuit and I after Dobbin. As the little Frenchman ran he squealed with fright, and as Dobbin ran he bellowed in fury. I began to laugh. The ludicrous side of it struck me. There scooted my little Frenchman like a rabbit, bounding over ditch and bush, while Dobbin thundered after him like a savage hound or an avenging demon. They ran until Dobbin dropped the scythe and settled down into steady chase. I trailed along for I saw that the Frenchman was heading for the river. The terrific pace was telling on both of them, and their gait fell bit by bit until it was a lagging trot, then a walk, then a stagger. And so they tottered on, not twenty feet apart, both gasping and well-nigh exhausted, the Frenchman unable to go forward and Dobbin unable to overtake him. They ran themselves to a standstill. I came up and caught Dobbin and started him back toward his house, which was beyond the field where he had been mowing. I heard the little Frenchman crying after me piteously. I turned back to see if he were hurt.

"'The dollair!' he lamented. 'I did swallow it!' and his grief burst forth afresh.

"As I started away he cried after me: 'Think, oh think! The queeksand! I save you! I do eat the dollair! Give to me a dollair!'

"Dobbin, furious as he was, laughed scornfully back at the Frenchman.

"Dobbin's wife was out when we arrived at his house, but she came in presently with her sister. She was a terror. The moment she spied the handcuffs on her husband she made a break for the woodpile and the axe. The sister ran down in the cellar. Dobbin and I were in the kitchen, he on a chair in one corner and I on a chair in another corner. In a moment in marched Mrs. Dobbin, axe in hand, and up from the cellar came the sister with a cleaver.

"'What does this mean?' said Mrs. Dobbin to me. 'Explain yourself, or I'll chop you into mincemeat.'

"She was the kind of woman who could have made first-class mincemeat out of a man. I carefully changed my revolver to my left hand, and began to reason with her. But it seemed there was to be no such thing as reason. She advanced toward me with the axe. I drew a second gun.

"'Dobbin,' I said, 'call off your wife. I dislike to shoot a woman. I can arrest her and take her to Winnipeg and lock her up and send her to prison. She's a fool.'

"The woman stopped in the middle of the kitchen floor. There she stood, axe in hand, while her sister guarded the door with the cleaver. It was twilight, and darkness came. I could discern the three figures as they stood. A clock struck nine.

"'Time's up,' I said, rising. 'Strike a light!'

"There was silence. I turned to Dobbin.

"'I've had enough of this,' I said. 'Axe or no axe, woman or no woman, this stops now. Call her off.'

"Mrs. Dobbin burst into furious ragings.

"'I'll die before Dobbin crosses the Red River tonight,' she shouted.

"I'll take him, you, and your sister,' I replied; and I advanced, preparing to dodge the axe and seize it.

"She raised the axe and planted herself to strike. I stepped forward, and with my left hand holding a revolver and my right hand free, I feinted to draw her blow. Dobbin, who had watched it all, saw the beginning of the end, and stood up and called his wife aside and tried to pacify her. The sister sought to slip outdoors, but I called her in, mindful of men who had been shot in the darkness through an open window.

"'Be quick,' I said to Dobbin. 'I've dallied too long. I'll get a boat three miles up the river.'

"'I own a boat on the river,' said Dobbin sullenly.

"'It's mine, not yours,' said Mrs. Dobbin.

"I thought of the commercial instinct.

"'You can make some money out of your boat,' I said to her. 'Dobbin must go over the river with me. Some one will make the money.'

"'What will you pay?' she asked.

"'I'll give you a dollar,' I said.

"I dropped four silver quarters on the kitchen floor, one by one. She leaped for a candle, lighted it, and gazed at the money.

"'Who will bring the boat back?' she asked.

"'You can send for it,' said I.

"She thought it over.

"'For one-fifty I'll do it,' she said.

"I dropped two more quarters on the floor. She clutched them eagerly, and the woman who was going to die before Dobbin should cross the river – and meant it, too – capitulated for six quarters shining in the candlelight on her kitchen floor. Truly, the power of money is magical at times.

"I took Dobbin away in the night, and we crossed the river and hired a team and driver at Morris and drove the seventy miles to Winnipeg, getting a midnight meal on the way. Dobbin kicked in Winnipeg. He employed a lawyer, the famous Fighting Mackenzie. This lawyer took Dobbin before Chief Justice Walbridge on a writ of habeas corpus. I employed the present Judge McMahon to fight the writ. The Chief Justice dismissed the writ, and ordered the prisoner into my custody. I started back with Dobbin. I had to take him by way of the Sault Ste. Marie Canal, and the boat went through the American side. Fighting Mackenzie told Dobbin to keep quiet until the boat was in the Soo; then to yell and demand protection, and he would telegraph the American sheriff to be there and compel me to liberate Dobbin, as I had no papers authorizing me to hold him in American territory.

"Dobbin and I embarked on the steamer *Campana* at Port William, which at that time was Port Arthur. Captain Anderson, now of the steamer *Manitoba*, was her commander. I got a hint of the job put up to save Dobbin in the Soo. I knew everybody aboard ship. The crew and officers all were my friends. I said to Captain Anderson: 'Before we get to Sault Ste. Marie, land me with Dobbin in a small boat above the rapids, and I'll pull for the Canadian shore.' I told him of the job.

"'I know the sheriff myself,' said Captain Anderson, 'and instead of risking it in a small boat above the rapids, I'll put Dobbin in the hold and shut the hatches before we get to the American side.'

"John Burns of Toronto was steward of the boat. Captain Anderson and Burns and I talked it over, and the captain selected a room on the port side farthest from the American shore, and told me to get Dobbin in there and Burns would lock the door.

"'He can yell like a Comanche in there and no one will hear him,' said Captain Anderson.

"Dobbin was all primed for the job. As we drew near the locks he even cleared his throat for the yells that he was to pour forth. The steward came to me.

"'Mr. Murray,' he said, 'would you like a little good whisky?'

"'Yes, indeed,' said I. 'Dobbin, want a drink?'

"Dobbin smacked his lips. He had time, before the boat entered the locks.

"'Why, yes,' he said.

"We went down to the room. It was a little cubbyhole of a place with no window or outlet but a little porthole. A decanter of whisky and glasses were on the table. We went in. The steward stepped out and slammed the door.

"'What did he shut the door for?' asked Dobbin, with sudden suspicion.

"I eyed him.

"'Why don't you holler, Dobbin?' said I.

"He glared at me. I could see the crimson dye his face, the veins swell, the eyes grow small, as his temper rose. He grabbed the decanter. I flipped out my revolver. We stood face to face with the little table between us. I eyed him, look for look.

"'Take a good drink, Dobbin,' I said.

"The boat was in the locks. Dobbin drank.

"'Why don't you holler?' I said.

"He looked at me, at the locked door, at the porthole; then he sank into a chair.

"'Murray, I've lost my voice,' said Dobbin.

"He sat with eyes closed for an hour or more. When we were through the locks and out into Canada waters and away from shore, the steward unlocked the door and said:

"'Dinner, gentlemen!'

"Dobbin awoke, as if from a dream.

"'I'm hungry as hell,' he said, and went in to dinner.

"We landed in Collingwood, and went to Barrie, where, on August 13th, 1883, I turned Dobbin over to the authorities. As I bade him goodbye, he said, 'Just wait till I get back to Red River and meet that Frenchman!' At times, when weird noises sound in the night, I think of Dobbin, and wonder if he has caught the little Frenchman at last."

Sinclair Ross

adapted for television by

Rudi Dorn

One's a Heifer

Characters   the BOY   the MAN   the UNCLE

SCENE 1

Farmhouse. Ext. Day. Blizzard. (Special effects.)

The front of a barn. Snow is drifting past the screen in violent white waves. The door of the barn opens wide. Out of the blackness a boy emerges, leading a sturdy horse by bridle. The horse, upset by the blizzard, rears and tries to back into the safety of the barn. After a short struggle, the boy manages to mount the horse and they are off, into the storm.

SCENE 2

Farm. Ext. Day. Blizzard.

The horse and rider are in the midst of the blizzard. Fences are broken or half covered by snow. Various shots.

Adaptation by Rudi Dorn of "One's a Heifer" from *The Lamp at Noon and Other Stories* by Sinclair Ross. Reprinted by permission of The Canadian Publishers, McClelland and Stewart Limited, Toronto, Ontario.

SCENE 3

Farm. Ext. Day. Blizzard.

Another area close by to facilitate special effects. Another angle of the rider bracing the elements. Passing a half-buried cart or some broken field equipment to show the devastation.
    Sound: Howling storm, rattling shingles. The boy's voice urging on the horse, muffled by the storm.
    Various shots (M.S., C.U.) to establish a sense of motion and thrust against the elements.

SCENE 4

Open country. Snow. Day.

Possibly another angle of the same area. (Still needs some special effects, blizzard.)
    There is a gust of wind. Eddies of snow whirling through the air. Slowly the camera pans into the open field. (L.S.)
    Some distance away the horse and rider are crossing the snow-covered ground, leaving deep tracks in the snow. The blizzard is slowly losing its strength.
    The boy's face, close (C.U.) showing relief. His face is crusted over with snow. He has trouble seeing the terrain ahead of him. His eyes are sore, his lips blue from the intense cold (Make-up). But the blizzard is over.

SCENE 5

Open country. Snow. Day.

The boy pulls the reins of the horse, looks about, then yells. Silence. There is no more sound. The blanket of snow is all around them. Slowly they continue what now obviously seems to be a search.
    There are animal tracks in the snow. (C.U.)
Note: *Animal tracks to be made by special*

effects or staging. The boy rides beside them, looking down and around. (c.u.) Then suddenly the tracks disappear in a snowdrift. Silence. Frustration in the boy's face.

Suddenly he focuses his eyes. A long distance away there is a dark spot in the snow. He swings his horse around. As they are approaching the area the horse stops, seemingly frightened, neighing softly. The boy jumps off the horse and pulling it by the bridle he moves closer. A dead calf is lying half buried in the snow. The boy leans over it, looks at it carefully, when suddenly the sounds from a herd of cattle are reaching him. He gets up startled, looks about. There is nothing at first. Quickly he remounts the horse and rides off in the direction of the sound.

Cut to:

SCENE 6

Farm area. Ext. Snow. Day.

A small herd of cattle is slowly moving toward a few dilapidated farm buildings. (Vickers' farm, also the barn area of Scene 1.)

When the boy sees the cattle he charges across the wide field trying to close in on them. At the last moment a wire fence stops him. Vainly he tries to intercept the herd of cattle by trying to get around the obstacle (fence).

Some of the calves in the herd seem to hold his attention. When he finally catches up with them, they have already entered the farm yard.

Cut to:

SCENE 7

Farmyard. Ext. Day.

Horse and rider are following the herd into the junky farmyard. Suddenly someone (the man) is shouting.

V.O.: Stay where you are!

A tall, ungainly-looking man moves toward them wearing a long black overcoat. He grabs the bridle of the horse. For a moment he looks as if he wants to pull the boy out of the saddle.

MAN: Didn't you hear what I said? Stay out!

BOY: *(steeling himself)* I want my two calves. One's a heifer. They are in there with your cattle.

MAN: That's a lie.

BOY: The two red ones with the white faces. They are mine. They've got lost in the blizzard – they are mine. Listen, if you'll give me a hand getting them out again, I'll start for home right away.

MAN: *(still clutching the bridle)* They are all mine, boy. All mine. I watched every one of them coming in.

Silence. Tension.

BOY: Just let me look. I'll prove it to you.

MAN: *(with a crafty look, shaking his head)* You didn't see any calves of yours.

BOY: *(more upset now)* I know you're trying to steal them. All right, I'll go home and get the police after you, then we'll see whether they are our calves or not.

MAN: *(with a shifty glance at the stable)* All right, look them over. Then maybe you'll be satisfied.

Crossing the yard he is still clutching the bridle. The boy gets off the horse, moves toward the door of the stable.

MAN: *(intercepting him)* Wait here.

And disappears inside the stable. The shuffling of feet of the cows inside. The boy's face is cold and frustrated. The man reappears at the door and is more pleasant now.

MAN: Will your horse stand or do you want to tie him?

Before the boy has time to answer, he takes the horse by the bridle and leads it into the horse stable (beside the cattle if possible). The

*boy's look of mounting frustration as he
follows the stranger.*
Cut to:

SCENE 8

Int. Stable. Horse and cattle. Low key.
*The man has tied up the horse, and motions
the boy to follow him (through a low door
separating the horse stable from the cattle).*

MAN: *(holding a kerosene stable lantern)*
Watch where you are going – it's mighty
dark in here. The blizzard has cut off all
the power.
*As soon as the boy has adjusted his eyes to
the dark he goes straight toward two calves
in a stall. He touches their heads, looking for
their familiar marks. It's not them. The man
watches him with a faint smile.*
*The boy turns and proceeds further into
the darkness of the stable. There is a
boarded-up area (or a low door, etc.). The
boy stops in front of it, turns to face the
stranger.*
BOY: What's in there?
MAN: Oh that. It's just a kind of harness room
now. Until a year ago I kept a stallion.
*He looks as if he is anxious to get the boy
from that ominous area. For a brief moment
his face looks dark and evil (Lighting).*
BOY: Why don't you let me look inside?
*Slowly the stranger is intercepting him,
blocking the door. Sudden stillness. Only the
breathing and shuffling of feet from the
cattle.*
*The boy is managing not to show his
sudden fear and looks squarely into the
stranger's eyes. After what seems an eternity
the stranger speaks.*
MAN: There is a hole in the floor – that's why
I keep the door closed. If you didn't know,
you might step into it, twist your foot.
That's what happened to one of my horses.
The boy nods, as if believing him, and walks

back toward his horse, followed by the man.
BOY: *(trying the saddle girths. His hands are
still numb from the cold.)* You wouldn't
have a cup of hot tea or something?
*He stands very still, hoping the man doesn't
discover his secret designs.*
MAN: *(after a moment of intense scrutiny)*
After supper we can have a game of
checkers. *(Suddenly he puts out his hand.)*
My name is Arthur Vickers.
(Smiles and exits.)

Cut to:

SCENE 9

Int. Vickers' house. Night. Low key.

*It is a large, low-ceilinged room, more like a
shed or granary than a house. The table in the
centre is littered with tools and a harness. On
a cookstove are two steaming pots of bran and
beans. Next to the stove is a grindstone, then a
white iron bed covered with coats and horse
blankets. Weasel and coyote skins are drying.
There are guns and traps on the wall, a horse
collar, rubber boots. The floor is bare and
grimy. Ashes are littered around the stove.*
*The man walks about looking helplessly at
the disorder, then tries to clear the mess.*

MAN: I've been mending harness. You get
careless, living alone like this. It takes a
woman anyway.
*(He is starting to unbuckle the boy's
sheepskin, then takes off his own coat.)*
Beans, that's all I can give you. Maybe a
little bacon.
*The boy nods, feeling quite uneasy about
having accepted the invitation. He warms
his hands at the stove. He watches the man
put some slices of bacon in a frying pan.*
MAN: *(while at the stove)* Yeah. It takes a
woman. If I'd known I'd cleaned things up
a little. *(Pan to boy.)* Some blizzard that
was. But I got off cheap. Just lost a few

shingles. It all needs fixing up anyway.
The boy looks around apprehensively when suddenly the man shoves a plate full of beans at his side.

MAN: Here. That's yours. *(And goes to the table.)*
The boy grabs the plate and moves to the table, sits.

MAN: *(follows with his own plate)* It's even worse in summer. The heat and the flies. Last summer I had a girl cooking for a few weeks, but it didn't last. Just a cow she was – a big stupid cow – and she wanted to stay on. I had to send her home.
His eyes are riveted on the boy trying to read his thoughts. Tension.

MAN: You've heard about it?

BOY: What?

MAN: Never mind. Eat. *(Silence. He swallows a spoonful, then fixes the boy.)* Where-abouts are you from?

BOY: Me? Oh, just from over that way. About ten, fifteen miles.

MAN: *(quickly)* What does your father do?

BOY: I've got no father. My uncle farms – like you, that is.

MAN: Eat. Don't talk so much.

BOY: I sure like this soup. I must be all frozen up inside.

MAN: You are sure nobody told you to come here? *(beat)* What's your name, boy?

BOY: Richard, Richard Welland.

MAN: Welland. Never heard of it. And you said your father was a farmer.

BOY: My uncle. I've *told* you my father was dead. *(silence)* That's very good bacon.

MAN: Hmm?

BOY: The bacon is very good.
The man looks about as if he were hearing something.

BOY: What is it?

MAN: *(startled)* Nothing. *(nods, smiles)*

BOY: *(stops eating, growing unasy)* Maybe I'd better go now. Tim'll be rested.

MAN: *(suddenly alert)* Who's Tim?

BOY: My horse.

MAN *(grunting with relief)* Oh. *(beat)* Eat. I said *(friendlier)*, eat – Richard.

BOY: Listen, Mr. Vickers. It's getting dark out. I've got at least ten miles to go.
The man puts down his spoon firmly and gets up, blocking the door.

MAN: It's no use, boy. You're going to freeze to death out there. Yes, sir, you better stay right here.

BOY: *(trying to conceal his mounting uneasiness)* Thanks, Mr. Vickers, but I have to go. They are waiting for me back home.
Slowly he has tried to make it to the door.

MAN: *(blocking his way with a smile)* You stay right here, okay? I'll look after your horse.
The man exits into the night. The boy alone, stands very still, listening. Then quickly putting on his sheepskin he follows the man outside.

Cut to:

SCENE 10

Ext. Barnyard, stable area. Dusk.

The boy moves quickly toward the stable door. The door is locked from the inside. He rattles the door in frustration. Then moves along the grimy row of windows outside trying to peek inside. It is very dark. But suddenly he sees the man.

Cut to:

SCENE 11

Int. Stable. Night.

The man is standing beside the boarded-up area, very still, almost as if listening to someone. Then he swings around quickly, instinctively feeling that he is being watched. He turns quickly and goes for the door.

Cut to:

SCENE 12

Ext. Stable. Dusk.

The boy races back to the house. The man follows him quickly.

Cut to:

SCENE 13

Int. House. Dusk.

The door swings open, letting in the cold. The man enters, breathing hard.

MAN: *(very quickly)* You don't know how bad it is sometimes. Weeks on end. Nobody to talk to. You just wouldn't know, boy. You're not yourself. You're not sure what you're going to say – or do. *(There is a hint of madness in his speech.)* Do you want to play checkers? *(Without waiting for an answer, he rambles on, smiling, scowling, etc.)* Sometimes I used to ask her to play, but I had to tell her every move to make. If she didn't win she'd upset the board and go off and sulk. She was very stupid. Women talk too much ever to make good checker players. This one, though, couldn't even talk like anybody else. She was a real cow.

The boy is standing a long distance apart from him, almost hugging the stove.

BOY: *(quickly)* Then why don't you get someone else – another woman – to stay with you?

The man goes slowly toward the area where he has stored his game of checkers.

MAN: *(laughingly)* Oh, too many of them want to do that. Too many of the kind you never get rid of again. *(He empties the checkers on the table.)* What do you want, red or black?

BOY: I don't care, Mr. Vickers. I do think –

MAN: *(dividing the checker drafts with a heavy hand)* Red. You take the red ones.

Then he looks straight at the boy.

BOY: *(after a furtive look in the direction of the stable)* Okay. Just one game.

MAN: Sit down. You know how to play it?

The boy nods. They are both sorting out the drafts. Silence.

BOY: Mr. Vickers?

MAN: Yeah?

BOY: Whatever happened to that woman?

MAN: Oh, her. I had to put her out.

BOY: *(quickly)* She liked you maybe?

MAN: She liked me all right. Just two weeks ago she came back and said she was going to stay. She didn't mind even if I couldn't pay her wages. *(beat)* She said her father thought it time that someone married her. *(beat)* Your move.

BOY: She is a funny one.

MAN: *(startled)* Why? Did you know her?

BOY: Me? No.

MAN: Then what's so funny?

BOY: Everyone knows that the man's supposed to ask the girl.

MAN: Ask for what?

BOY: To marry her.

MAN: *(pleased about the remark)* Oh yeah. I told you, didn't I? She was so stupid that at checkers she'd forget whether she was black or red.

Silence. He lowers his eyes on the game. The boy, very self-conscious now, moves one of his red checkers across the board. Silence. The boy feels powerless, sits very still. There is the heavy breathing of the stranger. It's his move. The black drafts are his.

BOY: And when you didn't marry her, what happened *(very slowly)* then?

Silence.

MAN: *(gently)* Why, nothing happened. I just told her she couldn't stay.

BOY: What did she do?

Silence. Pause.

MAN: I went to town for a few days. *(beat)* When I came back she was gone.
Their eyes meet. The boy cannot hold the stare. Silence.

A wind has started outside, rattling the loose shingles. Both of them look up, listening. Suddenly the man gets up, goes to the stove – raking the coals.

MAN: *(his back to the boy)* Go to bed.

BOY: We haven't finished the game.

MAN: Go to bed. *(then with a warm smile)* You need the sleep, boy. Sleep.

The boy gets up and walks towards the bed and sits on the covers. Trying to think of a way out of the situation. The man watches him.

Is there anything else you need? If you have to go to the can . . .

The boy's eyes are reflecting a "hope for escape." He looks quickly at the door.

MAN: *(smiling)* . . . it's right in there.

BOY: *(dejectedly)* No. Not now.

The man turns, walks toward him – then pushes him gently back on the pillow and covers him with the furs.

MAN: *(gently)* A growing boy like you needs a lot of sleep.

BOY: Aren't you going to bed? I can easily sleep somewhere else.

MAN: No. You stay right here. Don't you worry about me.

Slowly the man withdraws from the bed and goes to the door. Locks it firmly. Then sits down in his chair by the table. The boy is watching it all, his face half covered by the furs.

The wind, the shingles are rattling. Otherwise there is not a sound. It is night. The boy turns in his bed, trying to find a more comfortable position. The face of the man. He reacts. From the corner of his eye he watches the boy. The boy, close, very ill at ease.

The window, a strange sound outside it.

Startled, the man looks towards the window. Then his face relaxes again into stoic stupor. Each moment seems to be suspended. There is no peace this night. The man sits very still, contracted, motionless, as if gathering himself to strike. Then his hands are furtively sliding toward some checkers on the table. The boy's face, watching. The man is reaching for the checkers as if they are an invisible weapon. The man clutches the checkers. Slips slowly from the chair and straightens. His movements are sure, stealthy, and silent like a cat's. The boy is blinking his eyes, closing them, hoping it is a dream. The face of the stranger has taken on a desperate, contorted look. Then he raises his hand, slowly. The face of the boy, his eyes now wide open.

Suddenly wrenching himself into action the man hurls the checkers, with such vicious fury that they hit the wall in front of him and are clattering back across the room. The boy has shut his eyes, afraid. He is not sure whether he has really seen all this.

Silence. Dead silence. Only the faint howling of the storm.

The man is standing limp and dazed in the middle of the room. He turns slowly and goes toward the stove. He inserts another log into the fire. His face, close, the dancing flames. The boy is very sleepy now. The man is sitting in his chair, his head slumped forward as if asleep.

The boy, aware of the sudden lack of movement and tension, is opening his eyes. The man sits very still. The boy throws back the furs. He slides out of the bed and slowly picks up his coat and heads for the door. The man opens his eyes. He has never been asleep. The boy stands frozen, not knowing what to do.

MAN: *(very friendly)* I told you it's in there, boy.

The boy swallows hard and crosses the large room, careful not to come too close to the stranger.

SCENE 13A

There is a window in a tiny little room, all frosted over. The boy's face appears. His hands are scratching away at the thin layer of ice. It is black outside. The howling storm. The face of the boy.

MAN: *(V.O.)* Want a cup of tea, boy?
BOY: *(without moving)* Yes, sir.
    Pan off the face into blackness.

Cut to:

SCENE 14

Farm. Ext. Day.

Blackness. Transition. The sound of morning. Animals kicking their stalls. The gentle mooing of the cows.
    Pan into brightness. (L.S.) The farmhouse sitting peacefully in the snow. Faint smoke rising from a chimney.
    The man is emerging from the stable wearing his huge black coat.

MAN: *(jovially)* Did you finish your breakfast?
BOY: *(running up from the house all flustered)* Yes, sir. Thanks for letting me stay the night. *(reaches for his pocket)* And I do want to pay for all your *trouble*.
MAN: Oh never mind. That's quite all right. It was a pleasure to have you. It gets quite lonely here.
    The boy tries to enter the stable.
MAN: *(filling the frame of the door)* I've fed and saddled your horse. Wait! *(And turns.)*
BOY: Well, thanks. You shouldn't have bothered.
MAN: *(still trying to block the entrance to the stable)* I'll get it for you.

As he enters the stable, the boy slips past him quickly, trying to get another look at the ominous area where his calves could be hidden.

Cut to:

SCENE 15

Int. Stable. Day.

The man staggers after him but is not able to catch up with the boy who walks swiftly through the stable.

MAN: *(upset)* Now listen, boy. I do have a lot of chores to do. Maybe next time you come back and we'll go shooting some rabbits and I'll pick up some things in town so that we can have better meals. I'm a pretty good cook you know, if I set my heart at it. *The boy stops abruptly at a stall, walks into it, starts stroking a horse's nose.*
BOY: *(pretending interest)* I like that one. A real nice animal. How much you want for her? My uncle is looking for a horse like that since — I don't know when.
MAN: She ain't for sale. And better be careful. She ain't used to strangers.
BOY: *(trying to pry the horse's mouth open)* Easy. How old would she be?
MAN: About six years, I'd say. Yeah. Six years, or a little less. Listen, I ain't got much time for gabbing —
BOY: I'd say she's ten years at least.
MAN: Ten years! She is six and not a day older.
BOY: Ten. Do you know how I can tell?
MAN: You're not telling me about horses, boy.
BOY: *(very tense)* Come here, I'll show you. *The man moves quickly into the stall on the other side of the horse.*
MAN: What are you talking about? She was born in that stall over there.

Suddenly the boy pulls a knot and slaps the horse on the face. The horse backs up, almost trampling the man, and plunges toward the low entrance. (Action to be staged.)

MAN: *(shouting)* Quick! The gate's open! Try and head her off. *(And he runs after the horse.)*

Instead of helping the man, the boy dashes toward the boarded-up area and starts prying it open. For a moment he panics, dropping the whiffletree, and/or starts kicking at the door.

He forces back to lower bolt and/or picking up the whiffletree he again tries to pry out the door a little at the bottom.

But too late. Suddenly the stranger is upon him. The boy struggles to his feet and fights back desperately. The man has him firmly by the throat. For a moment the boy goes limp and blind. In desperation he kicks him hard. With a blow the man sends the boy staggering to the floor. The eyes of the stranger are wild and frightening. Quickly, the boy gets up and makes a run for his horse, unties it, manages to lead it into the open followed by the crazed stranger.

Cut to:

SCENE 16

Ext. Stable area. Day.

Frantically the boy swings himself into the saddle. The man grabs the horse by the reins, gathering up the ends of the reins. The boy lashes the man across the face. There is no reaction. He hits the man again and again, until finally he manages to break free and with a dash across the yard he is out of the gate.

Cut to:

SCENE 17

Open fields (near farm). Day.

Through the deep snow, he keeps galloping, pommelling the horse with his fists, kicking his heels against its side. Then he stops, turns around.

The farm is now a lonely little smudge against the whiteness. A long distance off. (L.S.)

The boy slumps against the saddle, weakly (out of breath), and lies there until the horse decides to start on again.

Cut to:

SCENE 18

Ext. Barn. Day. Boy's home.

Slowly the boy rides into the yard. The barn door is open. A man (his uncle) emerges, intent on some chores. It is a cold and quiet day.

UNCLE: Where the hell have you been all night? Mother wanted to call the police but I told her you was all right. Where have you been? We've been looking all over the place for you.

BOY: *(stops his horse)* I didn't get the calves, Uncle, but I know where they are.

UNCLE: The calves? What are you talking about? They came home by themselves last night. Now you better get inside and get warm. I'll look after Tim. *(to horse)* Easy, boy.

The boy's face close. He gets off the horse and turns slightly, as if looking back.

BOY: They came home? Then what . . . ?

The small houses of the stranger are but a smudge in the snow. Then the houses closer. Then the stable. Then the door. The stalls. And the forbidden area.

Will R. Bird

Paid-up Member

*He flung the rifle in
beside the dead man
and shovelled hurriedly.*

It was raining a little at noon but Simon Lasher drove out to his corner lot with the disc harrow. He had seen Dickie go up the back road and he meant to intercept him as he returned; he had cleaned and oiled his old army rifle, and he meant to use it.

Simon gritted his teeth as he drove. Jim Dickie had asked for trouble. He had come into the settlement and bought the farm that Simon was on the point of buying. True, he and Hank Wheeler had disagreed on the price, but what right had an outsider to come in and pay more than the land was worth? Then, insult added to injury, Dickie had taken Simon's girl from him. It was carrying things too far.

Simon hurried his horses. He must get to the road corner a few minutes before Dickie came in sight. He held the rifle and a shovel between his knees, and he swung his whip sharply. Folks said Simon never drove without a whip, but how could one hurry horses without it? And where would he be if he had not hurried? In ten years he had paid for his farm, and now had his house in readiness for a bride.

At the corner of the field he stopped his horses. The ground dipped slightly, forming a small hollow, and he dug in the centre of it, scooping a short, shallow trench. He had not got it as deep as he wished when he saw his horses prick up their ears. Someone was coming. He dropped his shovel. Jim Dickie was plodding past, his head down to the fine rain. Simon sneered. No one but Dickie would go in a rain to Hank Wheeler's post office.

"He comes regular," Hank had reported. "He gets soldier magazines and Legion papers. He's a paid-up member if he does live out here."

"Paid-up member!" Simon had jeered. "What good's that to him? Will it help him farm?"

He pretended to be tinkering with the disc harrow. The rifle was on the ground behind the discs.

"Hi," he called. "Been for mail? Come over. I want to show you something."

Dickie turned, his pale face friendly. "Yes, I got something I been expecting, something special for returned men...."

"Come and see where I've been diggin'," interrupted Simon.

He hated soldier stuff as he hated this man who had won Mary Hawkins from him, and the solemn way in which Dickie could recite "In Flanders Fields." Such rot!

Mary and he had quarrelled when he criticized the poem, and Mary had refused him her company. And now, a friend had told Simon in the morning, she and Dickie were to be married as soon as the school term ended. So Simon had cleaned his rifle.

Dickie carefully fished an envelope from his wet jacket as he came to where Simon had dug. "See what the Legion sent me," he said proudly, holding it out. "It's..."

Crack! The sullen report of a rifle. Simon had looped the reins about his wrist before he fired, and for a moment he was busy jerking the horses to a standstill, then he swung them around to where the limp body was pitched, face down, half into the cavity. His aim had been true. A dreadful redness was welling from the collar of Dickie's shirt. "Blast you!" grated Simon. "You kin be a paid-up member of that hole till Kingdom Come."

The horses quieted and Simon caught up the shovel. He had heard the chug-chug of a wheezy motor in the distance. It was Hank Wheeler's car. A twist of his heel buried the envelope Dickie had dropped, a single push straightened the body in the trench. He flung the rifle in beside the dead man and shovelled hurriedly. When the old flivver came in sight Simon was seated on his harrow and had just crossed the spaded earth. Twenty minutes later no one could have found the spot where he had dug.

At six o'clock Wheeler knocked at Simon's door. He was county sheriff as well as postmaster. "Did you see Jim Dickie this afternoon?" he asked bluntly.

"Yes, I did," said Simon. "He passed when I was harrowin'. Why?"

"He ain't been seen since," said Hank, as bluntly as before.

"That's strange." Simon simulated surprise. "Maybe he's at one of the neighbors."

"I been all around," said Hank. "You don't know anything, eh?"

"Me? No, I don't," said Simon smoothly. "I'll send you word if I see him."

Three months had passed since Jim Dickie vanished. Simon went to his hoeing contentedly. Mary was recovering from the shock, had got her color back. He would go and call on her in a few days.

He pulled weeds with a vim. Everything had gone better than he expected. There hadn't been much fuss over Dickie's disappearance, not as much as he had dreaded. And Dickie's Legion had been a joke. An official had come one day and talked with Hank, that was all that had been done. Paid-up member – pooh!

Hank had never seemed the same but perhaps the sheriff's complete failure to find a clue to Dickie's murderer accounted for that. Simon had often looked at the corner lot, now a shimmering green, inches deep. Who would guess its secret? It was good ground and the grain was doing fine. In the fall he would scoop more earth in the hollow at the corner, fill it in.

When he reached the house at suppertime Hank Wheeler and an officer from the city met him. Handcuffs were snapped on Simon's wrists before he could take in what had been said. Hank enlightened him.

"What – me – arrested for murderin' Dickie?" shouted Simon. "You're crazy. I don't know nothin' about him."

"No?" Hank's voice sent shivers up Simon's spine. "You'll have a hard time makin' the judge believe that. You harrowed that field the day Jim was killed – and it was your rifle we found beside him."

"You – you – found – " Simon's face whitened, became ghastly. He seemed to wilt.

"We did," said Hank grimly. "All I been doin' was watch that field of yours. I knowed they'd sprout if they was near the surface."

Simon licked his dry lips. "What – sprouted?" he whispered.

"Poppies," snapped Wheeler as they led Simon to his car. "Poor Jim got an envelope full of seed that day – a special good kind the Legion sent to paid-up members."

Robert Browning

Porphyria's Lover

The rain set early in to-night,
　The sullen wind was soon awake,
It tore the elm-tops down for spite,
　And did its worst to vex the lake:
　I listened with heart fit to break,
When glided in Porphyria; straight
　She shut the cold out and the storm,
And kneeled and made the cheerless grate
　Blaze up, and all the cottage warm;
　Which done, she rose, and from her form
Withdrew the dripping cloak and shawl,
　And laid her soiled gloves by, untied
Her hat and let the damp hair fall,
　And, last, she sat down by my side
　And called me. When no voice replied,
She put my arm about her waist,
　And made her smooth white shoulder bare,
And all her yellow hair displaced,
　And, stooping, made my cheek lie there,
　And spread o'er all her yellow hair,
Murmuring how she loved me – she
　Too weak, for all her heart's endeavor,
To set its struggling passion free
　From pride, and vainer ties dissever,
　And give herself to me for ever.
But passion sometimes would prevail,
　Nor could tonight's gay feast restrain
A sudden thought of one so pale
　For love of her, and all in vain:
　So, she was come through wind and rain.

Be sure I looked up at her eyes
　Happy and proud; at last I knew
Porphyria worshipped me; surprise
　Made my heart swell, and still it grew
　While I debated what to do.
That moment she was mine, mine, fair,
　Perfectly pure and good: I found
A thing to do, and all her hair
　In one long yellow string I wound
　Three times her little throat around,
And strangled her. No pain felt she;
　I am quite sure she felt no pain.
As a shut bud that holds a bee,
　I warily oped her lids: again
　Laughed the blue eyes without a stain.
And I untightened next the tress
　About her neck; her cheek once more
Blushed bright beneath my burning kiss:
　I propped her head up as before,
　Only, this time my shoulder bore
Her head, which droops upon it still:
　The smiling rosy little head,
So glad it has its utmost will,
　That all it scorned at once is fled,
　And I, its love, am gained instead!
Porphyria's love: she guessed not how
　Her darling one wish would be heard.
And thus we sit together now,
　And all night long we have not stirred,
　And yet God has not said a word!

Eddie Collister

Hangman Patiently Waits for Return of the Noose

When carrying out a hanging, he wears a black dress suit, white shirt, and black bow tie.

Reprinted by permission of the *Montreal Gazette*.

KINGSTON

Every other week a man wearing a prison inspector's uniform limps into a jail in southeastern Ontario.

Jail guards assume the heavyset man with thick spectacles and an Australian accent is just another annoying bureaucrat.

But the "inspection" tours are fakes, and the uniform is another cover-up for the man who appears, on the surface, to be rather ordinary.

At home he's a loving, church-going family man. At work, he's a travelling salesman. Philosophically, he's a staunch law-and-order advocate.

Arthur Ellis is Canada's official hangman.

During his jail visits, Ellis, the traditional pseudonym given hangmen to hide their true identity, slips quietly into the prison's execution chamber and spends a couple of hours dropping sandbags through a special trapdoor in the floor.

He's keeping in shape for his calling as public executioner.

"It's like a policeman using his revolver," says Ellis, 58, a Second World War veteran. "He has to go to the [firing] range if he wants to be good at it."

Ellis, who has a bad right leg from an accident in which his vehicle was rammed by "a drunk," has been Canada's public executioner since 1954.

"I've hanged about twenty men, give or take one, in Canada, the United States, and Bermuda," he says in a matter-of-fact voice.

He hasn't hanged anyone in Canada since 1962, when he executed murderers Ronald Turpin and Arthur Lucas in Toronto's Don Jail, but he believes the death penalty, abolished by Parliament in 1976, "will definitely return."

"It was abolished by [Prime Minister

Pierre] Trudeau and his followers," says Ellis during an interview at Kingston's 401 Inn, just off the Macdonald-Cartier Freeway.

"I believe, as do eighty-two percent of the public, that certain people deserve to be hanged, and one day, when they take a public count, hanging will return.

"Abolishing it has put both you and me and everybody else in open season," Ellis says. He's a firm believer in the "eye for an eye and tooth for a tooth" philosophy.

His most recent hanging was in December 1978, when he travelled to Bermuda to hang two men "who boasted of murdering five men in cold blood."

Ellis was paid an undisclosed fee, plus expenses, to travel to Bermuda. His services there had been requested of Canadian officials.

Although he hasn't conducted a hanging in Canada since 1962, the Canadian government still pays Ellis a "reduced retainer" of two hundred dollars a month, he says.

Asked why the retainer is being paid, an aide to federal Justice Minister Marc Lalonde denied any knowledge of Ellis.

The official referred the caller to Solicitor-General Jean-Jacques Blais. His office failed to return a phone call when the question was asked.

Ellis, father of three grown children, earns his living travelling Ontario demonstrating and selling heavy machinery, bulldozers and cranes.

His work often takes him away from home for extended periods, making it easy for him to carry out his moonlighting job as hangman without raising suspicion.

"Only three people in Canada know my real name," said Ellis, a former pilot with the Royal Australian Air Force.

He prefers to use the pseudonym J. Ellis, rather than A. Ellis, for reasons he refused to explain.

Ellis, who came to Canada with his wife five years after the war ended, became hangman to help out a friend, who at the time was a sheriff in the Toronto area.

"We were at a military banquet and the sheriff told me the hangman, a Montreal bricklayer, had had two heart attacks and was in serious physical condition," Ellis recalls, sipping a rum and Coke.

"He brought up the question of where would he find a person to carry on.

"I said: 'Well, I think if I was to go with him [the hangman] as an apprentice, I would be willing to carry on the role of justice.'

"Someone had to be willing to step in. I believe in justice, and if someone takes a life he should be made to pay with his life. I look at myself as just another cog in the wheel of justice."

Ellis says he attended three hangings with the former hangman, Arthur English (his real name), who died in a Montreal hospital at age 73 after dispatching 549 convicted killers.

During his apprenticeship Ellis was taught how to make "the hangman's knot," a knot only he, by law, is allowed to make, and which takes up nine of the fifty feet of rope used in a hanging.

He also "took a course on anatomy, specifically on vertebrae and such things as nerves," he said.

"There's quite a bit to it," he says. "It's not like television, you don't just walk in and string somebody up.

"It's a hanging, not a strangulation. It's supposed to be quick and clean . . . like breaking a stick really.

"Now, lots of people are under the impression that when a man is hanged he struggles, kicks and carries on, but he doesn't if it's done correctly.

"As soon as he hits the end of the rope,

that's it. You may get the odd flicker of a nerve but that's about all.

"Most I've hanged have been pronounced dead within three minutes. Doctors on hand have complimented me on my work."

Ellis says criminals "fear the rope. It's definitely a deterrent to murder."

To back up his "open-season-on-the-public" theory, Ellis says:

"If someone doesn't want to work because he's too lazy, all he has to do is get a gun and shoot someone. He doesn't care if the victim leaves a young widow and children.

"So he gets caught. He's sure of 12 years inside with three meals, in the warm, in the dry with his tobacco supplied, plus he has the chance of earning some money.

"Some stand there [after murdering someone] to get caught, and if acquitted, do it again specifically to get inside because he's a bum. He doesn't want to sleep out in the park. He'd rather sleep inside in the warm.

"I don't call this justice. He should hang. It costs us, the taxpayers, $25 000 a year to keep each convicted killer in prison."

When carrying out a hanging, he wears a black dress suit, white shirt and black bow tie.

From the condemned man's medical report, which gives his height and weight, Ellis figures how much of a drop is needed to do the job cleanly.

He said nobody he has hanged claimed to be innocent before going through the trap door to his death.

But Ellis said he was attacked once by a man with "a wooden spike" that he had fashioned out of the wooden cross-bars of a chair in his cell.

"He was subdued by the three Royal Canadian Mounted Policemen who were with me," Ellis said.

Most of the men he was about to hang took a "let's get on with it attitude."

Not all of them, though.

"Some plead for their lives and others faint dead away," Ellis said. "Guards have had to drag some of them to the execution chamber and prop them up with broomhandles until I sprung the trap," he said.

Ellis remembers one lad "about 20" telling him he wouldn't be facing the noose if he had had a different lawyer.

"He told me he would have gotten off with another lawyer," Ellis said.

The hangman said he doesn't generally get into much of a conversation with the convicted men "unless they want to talk like the postman from Toronto who murdered a young girl.

"He wanted to talk to me, but was shaking so much he couldn't say a word," he said.

"Most just want a last smoke," said Ellis, who smokes the occasional pipe of tobacco himself.

After a hanging, Ellis, conforming to tradition, burns the fifty feet of three-quarter-inch nylon rope, which he imports from Italy, as well as the hood the convicted man wore.

Then he heads back home, perhaps to do a little flying, to go moose or deer hunting, or to read.

Ellis said he has never told his wife about his moonlighting job and sees no need to do so.

If his wife found out he was the hangman, she might stay or go, "depending on whether she loves me enough to believe what I'm doing is right."

Jim Unger

Herman

"The jury has found you not guilty,
but I'm going to give you 2 years
just to be on the safe side."

William Saroyan

The Parsley Garden

"What do you want me to do with him?"
"Leave him with me," the older man said.

One day in August Al Condraj was wandering through Woolworth's without a penny to spend when he saw a small hammer that was not a toy but a real hammer and he was possessed with a longing to have it. He believed it was just what he needed by which to break the monotony and with which to make something. He had gathered some first-class nails from Foley's Packing House where the box-makers worked and where they had carelessly dropped at least fifteen cents' worth. He had gladly gone to the trouble of gathering them together because it had seemed to him that a nail, as such, was not something to be wasted. He had the nails, perhaps a half pound of them, at least two hundred of them, in a paper bag in the apple box in which he kept his junk at home.

Now, with the ten-cent hammer he believed he could make something out of box wood and the nails, although he had no idea what. Some sort of a table perhaps, or a small bench.

At any rate he took the hammer and slipped it into the pocket of his overalls, but just as he did so a man took him firmly by the arm without a word and pushed him to the back of the store into a small office. Another man, an older one, was seated behind a desk in the office, working with papers. The younger man, the one who had captured him, was excited and his forehead was covered with sweat.

"Well," he said, "here's one more of them."

The man behind the desk got to his feet and looked Al Condraj up and down.

"What's *he* swiped?"

"A hammer." The young man looked at Al with hatred. "Hand it over," he said.

From *The Assyrian and Other Stories* by William Saroyan. Reprinted by permission of Laurence Pollinger Limited.

The boy brought the hammer out of his pocket and handed it to the young man, who said, "I ought to hit you over the head with it, that's what I ought to do."

He turned to the older man, the boss, the manager of the store, and he said, "What do you want me to do with him?"

"Leave him with me," the older man said.

The younger man stepped out of the office, and the older man sat down and went back to work. Al Condraj stood in the office fifteen minutes before the older man looked at him again.

"Well," he said.

Al didn't know what to say. The man wasn't looking at him, he was looking at the door.

Finally Al said, "I didn't mean to steal it. I just need it and I haven't got any money."

"Just because you haven't got any money doesn't mean you've got a right to steal things," the man said. "Now, does it?"

"No, sir."

"Well, what am I going to do with you? Turn you over to the police?"

Al didn't say anything, but he certainly didn't want to be turned over to the police. He hated the man, but at the same time he realized somebody else could be a lot tougher than he was being.

"If I let you go, will you promise never to steal from this store again?"

"Yes, sir."

"All right," the man said. "Go out this way and don't come back to this store until you've got some money so spend."

He opened a door to the hall that led to the alley, and Al Condraj hurried down the hall and out into the alley.

The first thing he did when he was free was laugh, but he knew he had been humiliated, and he was deeply ashamed. It was not in his nature to take things that did not belong to him. He hated the young man who had caught him and he hated the manager of the store who had made him stand in silence in the office so long. He hadn't liked it at all when the young man had said he ought to hit him over the head with the hammer.

He should have had the courage to look him straight in the eye and say, "You and who else?"

Of course he *had* stolen the hammer and he had been caught, but it seemed to him he oughtn't to have been so humiliated.

After he had walked three blocks he decided he didn't want to go home just yet, so he turned around and started walking back to town. He almost believed he meant to go back and say something to the young man who had caught him. And then he wasn't sure he didn't mean to go back and steal the hammer again, and this time *not* get caught. As long as he had been made to feel like a thief anyway, the least he ought to get out of it was the hammer.

Outside the store he lost his nerve, though. He stood in the street, looking in, for at least ten minutes.

Then, crushed and confused and now bitterly ashamed of himself, first for having stolen something, then for having been caught, then for having been humiliated, then for not having guts enough to go back and do the job right, he began walking home again, his mind so troubled that he didn't greet his pal Pete Wawchek when they came face to face outside Graf's Hardware.

When he got home he was too ashamed to go inside and examine his junk, so he had a long drink of water from the faucet in the back yard. The faucet was used by his mother to water the stuff she planted every year: okra, bell peppers, tomatoes, cucumbers, onions, garlic, mint, eggplants and parsley.

His mother called the whole business the parsley garden, and every night in the summer she would bring chairs out of the house and put them around the table she had had Ondro, the neighborhood handyman, make for her for fifteen cents, and she would sit at the table and enjoy the cool of the garden and the smell of the things she had planted and tended.

Sometimes she would even make a salad and moisten the flat old-country bread and slice some white cheese, and she and he would have supper in the parsley garden. After supper she would attach the water hose to the faucet and water her plants and the place would be cooler than ever and it would smell real good, real fresh and cool and green, all the different growing things making a green-garden smell out of themselves and the air and the water.

After the long drink of water he sat down where the parsley itself was growing and he pulled a handful of it out and slowly ate it. Then he went inside and told his mother what had happened. He even told her what he had *thought* of doing after he had been turned loose: to go back and steal the hammer again.

"I don't want you to steal," his mother said in broken English. "Here is ten cents. You go back to that man and you give him this money and you bring it home, that hammer."

"No," Al Condraj said. "I won't take your money for something I don't really need. I just thought I ought to have a hammer, so I could make something if I felt like it. I've got a lot of nails and some box wood, but I haven't got a hammer."

"Go buy it, that hammer," his mother said.

"No," Al said.

"All right," his mother said. "Shut up."

That's what she always said when she didn't know what else to say.

Al went out and sat on the steps. His

humiliation was beginning to really hurt now. He decided to wander off along the railroad tracks to Foley's because he needed to think about it some more. At Foley's he watched Johnny Gale nailing boxes for ten minutes, but Johnny was too busy to notice him or talk to him, although one day at Sunday school, two or three years ago, Johnny had greeted him and said, "How's the boy?" Johnny worked with a boxmaker's hatchet and everybody in Fresno said he was the fastest boxmaker in town. He was the closest thing to a machine any packing house ever saw. Foley himself was proud of Johnny Gale.

Al Condraj finally set out for home because he didn't want to get in the way. He didn't want somebody working hard to notice that he was being watched and maybe say to him, "Go on, beat it." He didn't want Johnny Gale to do something like that. He didn't want to invite another humiliation.

On the way home he looked for money but all he found was the usual pieces of broken glass and rusty nails, the things that were always cutting his bare feet every summer.

When he got home his mother had made a salad and set the table, so he sat down to eat, but when he put the food in his mouth he just didn't care for it. He got up and went into the three-room house and got his apple box out of the corner of his room and went through his junk. It was all there, the same as yesterday.

He wandered off back to town and stood in front of the closed store, hating the young man who had caught him, and then he went along to the Hippodrome and looked at the display photographs from the two movies that were being shown that day.

Then he went along to the public library to have a look at all the books again, but he didn't like any of them, so he wandered around town some more, and then around half-past eight he went home and went to bed.

His mother had already gone to bed because she had to be up at five to go to work at Inderrieden's, packing figs. Some days there would be work all day, some days there would be only half a day of it, but whatever his mother earned during the summer had to keep them the whole year.

He didn't sleep much that night because he couldn't get over what had happened, and he went over six or seven ways by which to adjust the matter. He went so far as to believe it would be necessary to kill the young man who had caught him. He also believed it would be necessary for him to steal systematically and successfully the rest of his life. It was a hot night and he couldn't sleep.

Finally, his mother got up and walked barefooted to the kitchen for a drink of water and on the way back she said to him softly, "Shut up."

When she got up at five in the morning he was out of the house, but that had happened many times before. He was a restless boy, and he kept moving all the time every summer. He was making mistakes and paying for them, and he had just tried stealing and had been caught at it and he was troubled. She fixed her breakfast, packed her lunch and hurried off to work, hoping it would be a full day.

It was a full day, and then there was overtime, and although she had no more lunch she decided to work on for the extra money, anyway. Almost all the other packers were staying on, too, and her neighbor across the alley, Leeza Ahboot, who worked beside her, said, "Let us work until the work stops, then we'll go home and fix a supper between us and eat it in your parsley garden where it's so cool. It's a hot day and there's no sense not making an extra fifty or sixty cents."

When the two women reached the garden it was almost nine o'clock, but still daylight, and she saw her son nailing pieces of box wood together, making something with a hammer. It looked like a bench. He had already watered the garden and tidied up the rest of the yard, and the place seemed very nice, and her son seemed very serious and busy. She and Leeza went straight to work for their supper, picking bell peppers and tomatoes and cucumbers and a great deal of parsley for the salad.

Then Leeza went to her house for some bread which she had baked the night before, and some white cheese, and in a few minutes they were having supper together and talking pleasantly about the successful day they had had. After supper, they made Turkish coffee over an open fire in the yard. They drank the coffee and smoked a cigarette apiece, and told one another stories about their experiences in the old country and here in Fresno, and then they looked into their cups at the grounds to see if any good fortune was indicated, and there was: health and work and supper out of doors in the summer and enough money for the rest of the year.

Al Condraj worked and overheard some of the things they said, and then Leeza went home to go to bed, and his mother said, "Where you get it, that hammer, Al?"

"I got it at the store."

"How you get it? You steal it?"

Al Condraj finished the bench and sat on it. "No," he said. "I didn't steal it."

"How you get it?"

"I worked at the store for it," Al said.

"The store where you steal it yesterday?"

"Yes."

"Who give you job?"

"The boss."

"What you do?"

"I carried different stuff to the different counters."

"Well, that's good," the woman said. "How long you work for that little hammer?"

"I worked all day," Al said. "Mr. Clemmer gave me the hammer after I'd worked one hour, but I went right on working. The fellow who caught me yesterday showed me what to do, and we worked together. We didn't talk, but at the end of the day he took me to Mr. Clemmer's office and he told Mr. Clemmer that I'd worked hard all day and ought to be paid at least a dollar."

"That's good," the woman said.

"So Mr. Clemmer put a silver dollar on his desk for me, and then the fellow who caught me yesterday told him the store needed a boy like me every day, for a dollar a day, and Mr. Clemmer said I could have the job."

"That's good," the woman said. "You can make it a little money for yourself."

"I left the dollar on Mr. Clemmer's desk," Al Condraj said, "and I told them both I didn't want the job."

"Why you say that?" the woman said. "Dollar a day for eleven-year-old boy good money. Why you not take job?"

"Because I hate the both of them," the boy said. "I would never work for people like that. I just looked at them and picked up my hammer and walked out. I came home and I made this bench."

"All right," his mother said. "Shut up."

His mother went inside and went to bed, but Al Condraj sat on the bench he had made and smelled the parsley garden and didn't feel humiliated any more.

But nothing could stop him from hating the two men, even though he knew they hadn't done anything they shouldn't have done.

James Michael Ullman

The Dinner Party

" . . .so long as he's saddled with her, he's gone as far in this business as he'll ever go."

When the facts were finally pieced together, it became apparent that a critical point in the commission of the crime came on a Thursday afternoon in the quiet walnut-panelled office of J.J. McGill, board chairman of Midwest Enterprises, Inc. At 3:17 P.M., McGill leaned back in his leather chair, put a match to the tip of a fifty-cent cigar and said, "I'm sure Blake can handle the job. The question is – what kind of wife does he have?"

"Frankly," Don Cosegrove replied, "I don't know much about her."

Cosegrove, Midwest's president and McGill's right-hand man, sat across from McGill, fingering Blake's personnel file. Where McGill was bald, bullnecked and heavy-set, the white-thatched Cosegrove was lean and angular, his waist measurement unchanged from the days when he had captained his college golf team. Both men were in their fifties, garbed in blue, vested suits and conservatively-striped grey ties.

Reprinted by special permission of Samuel French, Inc.

"And now that you mention it," Cosegrove went on, putting the file aside, "it's odd. Blake's never brought his wife to a company affair. I've never seen her, don't even know her name. It's as though he's hiding the woman."

"In that case," McGill drawled, "we'd better find out about her. So long as Blake's head of our accounting department, it doesn't matter who or what she is. But if he's promoted to controller and elected to the board, it'll matter a lot. She'll be representing top management then, just as he'll be. They have children?"

"No."

"I don't like that. Our top men should have families. It makes for a more wholesome corporate image."

"The Blakes," Cosegrove pointed out, "are still young. They've been married only a few years, and I understand she's under thirty."

"Uh-huh. Well, how do you suggest we handle it?"

Cosegrove thought it over. "A dinner party," he concluded. "At my place. I'll invite some of the others. We'll see how she handles herself, and what our wives think of her – if she'd fit in with our kind of people or not."

"Fair enough." McGill puffed on his cigar and swivelled in his chair, gazing out of a floor-to-ceiling window at his empire, the sprawling plant over which he exercised what he regarded as an iron but benevolent rule. "Blake," McGill went on, "is a brilliant man. He's a team player who gets along with others in the organization, but he also has the guts to innovate, to assume responsibility and to speak up when he thinks he's right, even against me. He's personable, he never gets rattled, and his new accounting system has saved us thousands. Be a shame if he lost the promotion he deserves just because he picked the wrong wife – but then, business is business."

116

Carefully, Edmund Blake eased his low-priced sedan up the curved driveway and parked behind an Imperial, which huddled at the end of a row of other large, expensive cars. A tall, thin, prematurely greying man in his early thirties, he turned the engine off and dropped the car keys into his jacket pocket. His features were hawklike; his eyes were wide-spaced and strangely bright, as though harboring thoughts far removed from his mundane existence as chief accountant for a firm that made refrigerators and washing machines.

"If things go right tonight," Blake mused, "we'll be driving a car like those soon."

"Don't remind me." Scowling into a pocket mirror, Jane Blake performed a final touch-up job with her lipstick. "I'm nervous enough as it is."

"Relax. There's nothing special about these people."

"That's easy for you to say. But it's me they'll be watching tonight, not you." Jane angrily tossed the lipstick into her purse. "And I don't like it. Pretending to be something I'm not, in front of those rich men and their snooty Social Register women."

"We've known all along it might come to this." In a pensive way, Blake studied Jane. She was short and blonde, with a good figure and round, reasonably attractive features, but obviously she had dressed in questionable taste. Her gown was too laden with beads and plastic spangles; her costume jewellry was too large and garish.

"Midwest," Blake went on, "never promotes a man into the highest echelon without considering his wife first. An executive's wife has to entertain business contacts, to accompany her husband at all sorts of functions. I'm the obvious choice for controller and the vacant directorship – so now McGill and Cosegrove want a look at you."

Apprehensively, Jane gazed at the man-

sion looming at the driveway's end. "I feel like a slave about to be displayed at the auction. Who'll be in there, anyhow?"

"All the top brass. Plus some outside directors. Their wives, of course...."

"Some fun...."

Blake gave her hand a reassuring squeeze. "Chin up. In a few hours, it'll be over. And then..."

"Never mind the 'and then.'" Jane reached for the door handle. "I'll tell you one thing, though. If I live to be a hundred, I'll never let you make me go through anything like this again."

The Cosegroves met the Blakes at the entrance to an immense living room. Behind them, about two dozen people stood or sat in small groups, drinking and talking. Cosegrove's wife, a brunette, was tall and in her forties, her slim figure encased in an elegantly simple gown that contrasted sharply with the frilly garment Jane wore.

"Jane, it's so nice to meet you."

"My pleasure," Jane murmured hoarsely. Awkwardly, she opened her purse and fumbled for a cigarette. As Cosegrove lit it for her, the tip wobbled. Jane puffed a few times, her face twisted in an ugly grimace, before she took the cigarette out of her mouth. She looked around and added: "My, what a lovely house. It's so big!"

"It's a bit large," Cosegrove conceded, "but we enjoy rambling around in it."

"I'll bet." Since Cosegrove was still smiling down at her, anticipating more of a reply, she hesitated a second and continued: "It must be some job, keeping it clean. I spend half the week, cleaning my house. But if I had to clean *this* place..."

As social small talk goes, that was far below the level of bright repartee expected of Midwest executives' wives. Mrs. Cosegrove, though, was broad-minded enough to overlook this first hint of conversational ineptitude.

"You're a very lucky girl," she said, "married to such a clever, handsome man. I hear so many complimentary things about Edmund. If you don't mind my asking — where'd you meet him?"

Jane glanced at Blake. Then she ventured an uncertain smile. "A bar and grill. I — I worked there. As a waitress."

"Don't apologize." Trained to put others at their ease no matter what, Cosegrove's wife gave Jane a motherly wink. "At one time," she lied graciously, "I was a working girl myself. And I always say, you meet the most interesting people at bars. Bars and golf courses. That's where I met Howard, on a golf course. He has a whole cabinet full of trophies. You play, don't you?"

"Frankly," Jane admitted, "I always thought it was a waste of time, knocking that little ball around...." As three startled pairs of eyes bore down on her, Jane turned a little red, apparently becoming aware that she'd said the wrong thing. "But golf's all right, I guess," she added hastily, "if you like it..."

Embarrassed, Blake looked down at the rug. Mrs. Cosegrove glanced briefly at her husband and then smiled at Jane again, a certain coolness in her eyes belying the warmth of her tone. "Care for a cocktail?"

"I would, yes. Very much."

"Martini? Manhattan? Or perhaps..."

A maid approached, carrying a tray of drinks.

"I think I — well, a martini. Yeah, I'll try one of those."

"Fine." Cosegrove's wife handed her one. "Now come along," she steered Jane away. "I'll introduce you to the others. We want to learn all about you...."

The Blakes were the first to leave. That

seemed advisable. Socially speaking, Jane had been a good deal less than a success. During the cocktail hour — a very long one, and deliberately so, since McGill always sought to learn if a potential executive's wife could hold her liquor — Jane was at first timid and hesitant, volunteering nothing and answering questions in monosyllables. As time went on, though, she grew more voluble, laughing too loudly at remarks that weren't really funny, and disclosing facts about herself, her husband, and their respective families that no wise company wife in her right mind would volunteer.

Dinner seemed to sober her somewhat, sending her back behind a fog of sullen insecurity that even J.J. McGill, seated at her left, was mostly unable to penetrate. Brandies came after dinner, however. Jane had three of those, one more than anyone else, and as she left the table, she spilled her ashtray on McGill's lap.

All that followed, including a brief, bitter exchange on politics with McGill's wife that Blake headed off just in time, was anticlimactic.

The Cosegroves escorted the Blakes to the door.

"We so enjoyed having you," Mrs. Cosegrove said.

"Indeed we did," Cosegrove put in, shaking Blake's hand vigorously.

It was a fiction that deceived nobody, but Blake made the best of it. His thin lips twisted in a forced smile, he said:

"Thanks again. And I'll see you in the morning about the inventory."

The Blakes walked to their car, got in and drove off.

Slowly, Cosegrove closed the door. Behind him, McGill stepped from the living room, cigar in hand.

Discreetly, Cosegrove's wife melted away, and the two men strode to the study,

118 where Cosegrove poured out two more bran-dies.

"No need," McGill said, "to even ask our wives about this one. Pathetic, wasn't it?"

"I'm afraid so."

"Not bad looking, but she's wrapped up in her petty little self. Can't discuss anything but her house, her neighbors, her shopping trips, and her relatives. Scared to death of strangers, can't handle liquor but drinks anyhow, and doesn't know a thing about her husband's business. No intellectual curiosity or social grace whatever. Makes you wonder what a man like Blake ever saw in her."

"He's no fool, J.J. He's as aware of what was at stake for him tonight as we are."

"I know. It's a delicate situation. We want to keep him happy, so first thing next week put him in for a raise. A good healthy one. And increase his allotment under the stock-option plan. But as for the promotion and the directorship..." McGill shook his head. "It's too bad, about Blake's wife. But so long as he's saddled with her, he's gone as far in this business as he'll ever go."

Expressionless, Blake drove down the free-way, while Jane slumped on the other end of the front seat, puffing on the stub of still another cigarette. Only the odd brightness in Blake's eyes showed that he was thinking about something – thinking very, very in-tently.

Finally Jane crushed out the cigarette, folded her arms over her chest, looked at Blake and said, "Well?" Her voice was cold and angry. "How was I?"

"What do *you* think?"

"Don't be funny. I know what those peo-ple thought of me. I just hope you're satis-fied."

"There's just one thing. Spilling the ashes on McGill's lap – was that necessary?"

"Sorry, but I lost my temper. As I told you, I didn't like it, pretending to be what I wasn't. Making a fool of myself. Wearing this sleazy dress. Playing the part of a witless, unsophisticated dummy...."

Jane opened her purse. Casually, she began trimming her nails. She was, sud-denly, quite sober and entirely self-possessed. "How much longer?"

"Six months. By then, I'll have siphoned a million into the Swiss bank. The audit's in six months, but we'll skip the country before it starts."

"Unless," Jane pointed out, "you're offered the promotion anyhow."

"True. If I accepted it and a new man took over my department, he'd spot the em-bezzlement immediately. And if I refused the promotion, McGill and Cosegrove would get suspicious and order a special audit, and that would ruin everything."

Blake smiled thinly. "But after your stel-lar performance tonight, I think we can stop worrying about the promotion. You did fine, Jane. So instead, let's think about how we'll furnish the mansion in Rio. And the parties we'll give there once I'm running a Midwest-financed business of my own...."

Robert L. Fish

Hijack

"And
he wants –
two
parachutes...."

Five o'clock on a late-summer afternoon, a warm hazy day with only a faint cloud line at the distant horizon hovering over the low Tennessee mountains sloping toward flatness to the west, and the plane – a 727 tri-jet at 28 000 feet approaching the Tennessee River Valley on a south-southwestern heading from Kennedy in New York to New Orleans, with the sun quartering in on the co-pilot, sinking fast.

The radioman pushed himself into the cockpit through the narrow door from the cabin, adjusting his trousers, nodding comfortably to the captain. He settled himself at his desk again, putting his earphones back in place, reaching to fiddle with knobs. The captain studied him a moment, reading nothing in the even expression, and then glanced over his shoulder, looking below. Sunlight winked from water. The captain reached for his microphone, switching off the soft cabin music to gain priority, pressing the button that transferred the intercom system from tape to voice.

"Ladies and gentlemen, this is your captain speaking. To the right of the plane and almost directly beneath us is Watts Bar Lake, a part of the TVA project. Those passengers on the left can see the Watts Bar Dam and Lake Chickamauga beyond. In the distance to the east, for those with sharp eyesight, there are the Great Smoky Mountains...."

He replaced the microphone neatly and flipped the switch; the music returned. Almost in the same instant a light flashed on his intercom panel. The captain leaned over and pressed a button.

"Yes?"

Originally appeared in *Playboy*. Reprinted by permission of Robert P. Mills, Limited.

"Captain, this is Clarisse. We've got trouble."

"Trouble?"

"A passenger is locked in the washroom with Milly." The stewardess's voice hurried on, anxious to avoid misunderstanding. "It isn't a pass, Captain. It's a hijacking." Her voice, striving for steadiness, echoed metallically in the crowded cockpit.

The radioman stared; the co-pilot started to come to his feet. Captain Littlejohn's restraining hand motioned him to sit down again.

"Where are the air marshals?"

"One of them is here with me now...."

"Before you put him on, what about the passengers?"

"They don't know a thing yet."

"Good. Let's keep it that way. Now, let me talk to the marshal."

There was a brief pause and then a man's low voice was heard in the cockpit.

"Hello, Captain. Apparently what happened was the man walked back to the lavatory, nobody paying any attention to him, and when he got there he pulled a gun on the girl and forced her into the washroom. I've spoken to her through the door. So far she's all right, but she says he's got a gun and a knife, and also a bottle he claims is nitro. She says it looks oily and yellow." The sky marshal cleared his throat. "What do you want us to do?"

"Nothing," the captain said quickly and firmly. "Go back to your seat. He's having Milly talk because he has her between him and the door. Go sit down. Let Clarisse handle any communication. I'll get through to New Orleans for instructions."

The radioman was already at work, calling the New Orleans tower. The captain's face was stiff. He spoke into the microphone.

"Clarisse?"

"Yes, Captain?"

"Put an OUT OF ORDER sign on that washroom door. And keep the curtain drawn. Is Milly still all right?"

"Yes, sir. Wait a second – she's saying something" – there was a pause. "Hello, Captain? She says he wants the plane diverted to Jacksonville. To refuel."

"Where does he want to go? We have more than enough fuel for Cuba. Better have Milly remind him this isn't a 747, however."

"Yes, sir. She didn't say anything else."

"Who is he, do you know?"

"He's on the seat chart as a Charles Wagner from Hartford. He was in seat sixteen C, on the aisle. I served him lunch when we left Kennedy...."

"What did he look like?"

Clarisse sounded unsure of herself. "Like – like anybody, I guess. Middle thirties, hair a little long but getting thin...."

"How much did he have to drink?"

"Just a beer. I'm sure he wasn't drunk. What should I do?"

"Nothing. Try to look busy back there, in case anybody wonders why you're hanging around there. Get that sign up right away. And remember the curtain. And let me know if..."

The radioman swung around. "New Orleans tower. I've already identified."

"Mayday here," the captain said into the microphone. "We've got a hijacker on board."

"What condition?"

"He has one of our stewardesses locked in a washroom. Armed. Several times. Maybe with nitroglycerin, too. It sounds like it."

"Where does he want to go?"

"So far, just to JAX. For refuelling, he says."

"Hold it," said the voice. "I'll contact higher up and be back."

The captain stared ahead, his face a mask. Under his hand the wheel held steady.

The shadows ahead deepened. The wait seemed endless, filled with niggling static. Then the static cleared; a different voice was on the radio. It sounded more assured, more authoritative.

"Captain Littlejohn? This is Security, New Orleans. Permission granted to change course to Jacksonville."

The co-pilot was already digging into his map bag for routing maps. Captain Littlejohn's hand was already swinging the wheel, banking gently. A thought came to him to explain away any of his passengers' doubts.

"Ladies and gentlemen," he said into the cabin intercom, "to give the people on the other side of the plane a chance to see what little can be seen of the TVA project at this late hour...."

He continued on a wide banking circle, coming out of it gently with the nose pointing now to the southeast and the growing darkness there. The voice of Security came on.

"Good work, Captain. Eventually, of course, they're going to have to know. In the meantime, tie into Jacksonville Security. They've been informed. We'll be on, too."

"Roger," Littlejohn said, and he peered over the co-pilot's shoulder at the air map. Clarisse's voice came back.

"Captain?"

The captain straightened up from the folded map almost reluctantly.

"Yes?"

"He wants money. A ransom for the passengers and the plane. He wants it waiting for him when we get there. Otherwise, he says he'll take Milly first and then blow up the plane."

"How much ransom?"

Clarisse swallowed. "A – a quarter of a million dollars."

Captain Littlejohn's expression didn't change in the least. He picked up his microphone.

"New Orleans Security? Do you still read me?"

A different voice answered. "This is JAX. We read you loud and clear."

"The hijacker wants a quarter of a million dollars."

"We heard. Who is he?"

"He's listed as a Charles Wagner, from Hartford, Connecticut."

"What else does he want?"

"One second." The microphone was laid aside temporarily, the intercom button pressed. "Clarisse – anything else?"

"Yes, sir. A whole flock of things. I guess he's had time to think. I scribbled them down." Clarisse referred to her paper; her tone changed abruptly. "I'm sorry, sir, that lavatory is out of order. No, the other one is fine. Yes, sir." Her voice dropped again. "A passenger. I put the sign up, but some people..."

"Never mind. Go on."

"Yes, sir. Here's what he wants. The money in an overnight bag, nothing smaller than fifties, nothing bigger than hundreds, banded in twenty-five-thousand-dollar bundles. He wants the plane to land at the end of runway 725 at Jacksonville, as far from the terminal as possible...."

"Hold it," Captain Littlejohn said and spoke into the mike. "Security, did you get that?"

"We got it. Go on."

"Go ahead, Clarisse."

"Yes, sir. He doesn't want anyone to come near. He says the passengers can get off. After that, he will come out of the washroom. The money will be delivered, but no one can enter the plane. And he wants – two parachutes...."

"Two of them?"

122

"That's what he said. A sports model and an Army standard."

Security could be heard, speaking in an aside to someone. "Get a fast check on a Charles Wagner through the U.S. Parachute Association right away, hear?" It came back full. "What else, Captain?"

"Clarisse?"

"That's all, Captain. So far. He says further instructions will be given when we're on the ground."

"Right." The intercom button was depressed; the captain spoke into his mike. "Security? We'll want to be cleared for landing on 725 regardless of wind direction."

"Roger."

"And what about the money he wants?"

"It'll be there. I don't know how long he'll keep it, but he'll get it. As well as the parachutes."

"Good," Captain Littlejohn said. "I'd hate to lose Milly. Not to mention a plane full of passengers."

There was no reply. The mike was switched off, attention given to flying the plane. The sunset was almost behind them now, the shadows of the Smokies creeping beneath their wings. The Knoxville-Jacksonville beam was intercepted; the plane banked smoothly into the air corridor, its heading now nearly due south. The engines droned in the deepening darkness; the cockpit lights showed the strain on the faces of the men within. At last the lights of Jacksonville could be seen, together with the feathery trail outlining the beach down toward St. Augustine. The plane began losing altitude. With a sigh, Captain Littlejohn turned over the plane to the co-pilot, who immediately began speaking with the tower. Captain Littlejohn took over the task of informing the passengers. He pressed the proper button. His voice was completely impersonal.

"Ladies and gentlemen, this is your captain again. Due to adverse weather conditions, we are forced to make our landing at the Jacksonville, Florida, airport. A company representative on the ground will explain the delay and arrange any necessary transportation. We regret this inconvenience. Now, please fasten your seat belts, bring your seats to the vertical position and observe the NO SMOKING sign...."

The last grumbling passenger had filed from the plane, surprised to find himself forced to take a waiting bus to the distant terminal building, unaware that very shortly he and his fellows would be in the enviable position of being able to tell their friends of their adventure. Gasoline trucks were completing their refuelling operation; a small station wagon took the place of the departing bus and two men got out.

One brought a small parachute in one hand and an overnight bag in the other; the second man carried a more cumbersome parachute. They climbed the aluminum steps, placed their loads on the floor of the plane without entering, nodded to a pale Clarisse, merely glanced in the direction of the washroom door and made their departure. They looked like F.B.I. and were. From the cockpit window, Captain Littlejohn watched them climb into their car and back off. He raised his microphone.

"Clarisse?"

"Yes, Captain?"

"Where do we go from here?"

"Just a second" – there was a long pause. On the ground, the fuel lines were being sucked into the trucks like monsters consuming outsized spaghetti. Clarisse was back. "Captain, he says first to head toward Miami. He wants you to maintain minimum flying speed – he says two hundred knots will do – and to stay at two-thousand-feet altitude. And he wants the rear passenger entrance door left unlatched from the outside...."

Security in the tower had heard. It cut in.

"Captain, is it possible to jump from your plane?"

"It is from this one," Littlejohn said. "He obviously selected a 727 on purpose. He couldn't do it with a 707 or a 747. Either he must know something about flying or he studied up for this caper."

"For a quarter of a million dollars," Security said dryly, "I imagine a man would be willing to study. Or even to make his first parachute jump. There's no record of him in any sky-diving group we've dug up so far."

"If it's his real name."

"As you say, if it's his real name. Any danger of depressurization at that altitude with the door being opened?"

"Not at two thousand feet. And Florida's flat. And if we didn't leave the door unlatched, he could still always use one of the emergency doors." Captain Littlejohn's voice was getting tight; the wait was making him nervous. "Well, what do we do?"

There was a pause. A new voice came on.

"Captain? This is Major Willoughby of the Air Force. Do you have any suggestion?"

"Well," Littlejohn said slowly, "I suppose we could keep over water; he wouldn't jump there. It might give you time to scramble a few planes and meet us somewhere. He won't stand still for that water bit very long, but if you have a few planes follow, it might help."

The co-pilot cut in, a boy with much wartime experience.

"If he free-falls even five hundred feet, they'll never see him at night."

"At least they could try."

"I'll buy that," Major Willoughby said. "I'll get you cleared for following the coast as

long as you can; we'll get other aircraft out of the way, although you'll be flying far below anything commercial until you get near airports. Try to hold over water until Daytona, if you can. We'll be with you by then at the latest. All right?"

"Fine."

"Captain," Clarisse said in a tight voice. "He's getting nervous."

"Tell him we're on our way," Littlejohn said, and he pressed the first of the engine-starting buttons.

The plane swung about; the engine whine built up, and then they seemed to leap free. The large plane raced down the runway, gathering speed, and then seemed to raise itself slightly. They swooped up vertically; the city lights fell away, twisting as they banked. Littlejohn levelled off, following the coast a mile offshore. Security came back on the radio.

"What's our boy doing now?"

"God knows," Littlejohn said. "He'll undoubtedly be coming out of his little washroom soon and he'll see we're over water. Then...," he shrugged; the shrug was reflected in his voice. "Well, then we'll see."

"Keep this radio link open."

"Don't worry."

"Captain..."

"Yes, Clarisse?"

"He's going to come out...."

Littlejohn spoke rapidly:

"Clarisse! That microphone cord should reach to the next seat. I want you to strap yourself in and I want Milly to strap *herself* in as soon as she comes out. That nut can jump or fall, for all I care, but I don't want either of you girls to take any chances near that open door. Do you hear?"

"Yes, sir. Just a second" – there was a short pause. "I'm strapped in, Captain." The timbre of her voice changed. "Captain – they're out...."

124

"How's Milly?"

"Pale as a ghost, and I don't wonder. Milly, sit down. Strap yourself in" — a brief pause, with everyone in the cockpit staring intently at the small cloth-covered speaker. "Captain, he's looking down at the water. He says either you turn overland right now or he'll kill Milly and then me. Captain — I — I think he means it...."

"Turn," Security said at once.

"It's all right, anyway," Major Willoughby's voice said. "We just picked you up."

Littlejohn instantly put the plane into a bank; the lights of Crescent Beach fled beneath them, a cluster with Route A1A etched on either side.

"Captain..."

"Yes, Clarisse?"

"He says..."

"Let me talk to him."

"Just a second." Silence. "Captain, he won't talk into the microphone. But he says fly to Ocala and then turn straight south for Naples, same speed, same altitude as now. He says you can come out of the cockpit by Naples; he'll be gone by then."

Security cut in:

"Do it his way, Captain. Don't take any chances. The major's planes have you in sight and we've also got every town's police notified to be on the lookout for a chute. He won't get far."

"There's a lot of empty space in central Florida, but whatever you say," Littlejohn said. "In that case, why not get us cleared from Naples over to Miami at a reasonable altitude and make us some hotel reservations there for tonight?"

"Will do."

Clarisse came back on, nervous.

"Captain, he wants us to get up into the cockpit before he jumps, doesn't want us to see...."

Littlejohn sighed. "All right, but hang on. I'll bank slightly to keep you away from that door. Come ahead."

The men waited impatiently; at last there was a tap on the door. It opened and two very nervous stewardesses sidled into the cramped space, shutting the door behind them. Milly was pale from her ordeal; Clarisse was partially supporting her. Littlejohn looked at them questioningly.

"She'll be all right," Clarisse said.

Littlejohn set his jaw and stared down. Beneath their steady nose, Dade City came and went, and then the vastness of southwestern Florida, inching past at the maddeningly slow speed of two hundred knots. At long last the lights of the west coast could be seen in the still night. The radio-man looked up.

"Naples coming up," he said.

They stared down, watching the lights pass them, and then they were out over the Gulf. Littlejohn turned to the co-pilot.

"Mike, want to take a look? Be careful."

"Right," said the co-pilot, and he pushed past the stewardesses and into the empty corridor of the plane. He walked to the other end of the plane and back, hanging onto the seats as he passed the cabin door, swinging back and forth, clanking as it struck each time. He came back into the cockpit and closed the door.

"All clear."

"We missed him," Major Willoughby's voice said, disappointed.

"We'll pick him up. Don't worry," Security promised. "We've got the whole state covered under your route. Well, Captain, you're cleared to Miami. Good night and good luck."

"Thanks," Littlejohn said, and he switched off the microphone. His hand pressed the engine throttles forward. "Well, children," he said, "it's been a long day. Let's go get some rest."

The maps from the map bag were piled to one side. Captain Littlejohn was reaching into the bag.

"Fifty thousand each," the captain said softly. "Not bad for a few hours' work, plus a little careful planning. Especially considering that it's tax-free."

"I ought to get more," Milly said sullenly. "Five long damned hours crammed into a tiny washroom with a dead man!"

"You?" Clarisse said. "What about me? I had to push him out of that damn door. Even though I was fastened in with the harness and the rope, I was scared silly that I'd go out of the plane with him."

"I had to kill the poor bastard," the radioman said.

The co-pilot was paying no attention to the complaints. He was neatly putting his share in his attaché case.

"Charles Wagner..." he said to no one in particular. "The hard-luck guy who went to the john at the wrong time. I wonder what he did for a living."

O. Henry

The Ransom of Red Chief

"Ha! cursed paleface,
do you dare to enter the camp of Red Chief,
the terror of the plains?"

It looked like a good thing: but wait till I tell you. We were down South, in Alabama – Bill Driscoll and myself – when this kidnapping idea struck us. It was, as Bill afterward expressed it, "during a moment of temporary mental apparition"; but we didn't find that out till later.

There was a town down there, as flat as a flannel-cake, and called Summit, of course. It contained inhabitants of as undeleterious and self-satisfied a class of peasantry as ever clustered around a Maypole.

Bill and me had a joint capital of about six hundred dollars, and we needed just two thousand dollars more to pull off a fraudulent town-lot scheme in Western Illinois with. We talked it over on the front steps of the hotel. Philoprogenitiveness, says we, is strong in semirural communities; therefore, and for other reasons, a kidnapping project ought to do better there than in the radius of newspapers that send reporters out in plain clothes to stir up talk about such things. We knew that Summit couldn't get after us with anything stronger than constables and, maybe, some lackadaisical bloodhounds and a diatribe or two in the *Weekly Farmers' Budget*. So, it looked good.

We selected for our victim the only child of a prominent citizen named Ebenezer Dorset. The father was respectable and tight, a mortgage fancier and a stern, upright collection-plate passer and forecloser. The kid was a boy of ten, with bas-relief freckles, and hair the color of the cover of the magazine you buy at the newsstand when you want to catch a train. Bill and me figured that Ebenezer would melt down for a ransom of two thousand dollars to a cent. But wait till I tell you.

About two miles from Summit was a little mountain, covered with a dense cedar brake. On the rear elevation of this mountain was a cave. There we stored provisions.

One evening after sundown, we drove in a buggy past old Dorset's house. The kid was in the street, throwing rocks at a kitten on the opposite fence.

"Hey, little boy!" says Bill, "would you like to have a bag of candy and a nice ride?"

The boy catches Bill neatly in the eye with a piece of brick.

"That will cost the old man an extra five hundred dollars," says Bill, climbing over the wheel.

That boy put up a fight like a welterweight cinnamon bear; but, at last, we got him down in the bottom of the buggy and drove away. We took him up to the cave, and I hitched the horse in the cedar brake. After dark I drove the buggy to the little village, three miles away, where we had hired it, and walked back to the mountain.

Bill was pasting court plaster over the scratches and bruises on his features. There was a fire burning behind the big rock at the entrance of the cave, and the boy was watching a pot of boiling coffee, with two buzzard tail-feathers stuck in his red hair. He points a stick at me when I come up, and says:

"Ha! cursed paleface, do you dare to enter the camp of Red Chief, the terror of the plains?"

"He's all right now," says Bill, rolling up his trousers and examining some bruises on his shins. "We're playing Indian. We're making Buffalo Bill's show look like magic-lantern views of Palestine in the town hall. I'm Old Hank, the Trapper, Red Chief's captive, and I'm to be scalped at daybreak. By Geronimo! that kid can kick hard."

Yes, sir, that boy seemed to be having the time of his life. The fun of camping out in a cave had made him forget that he was a captive himself. He immediately christened me Snake-eye, the Spy, and announced that, when his braves returned from the warpath, I was to be broiled at the stake at the rising of the sun.

Then we had supper; and he filled his

128 mouth full of bacon and bread and gravy, and began to talk. He made a during-dinner speech something like this:

"I like this fine. I never camped out before; but I had a pet 'possum once, and I was nine last birthday. I hate to go to school. Rats ate up sixteen of Jimmy Talbot's aunt's speckled hen's eggs. Are there any real Indians in these woods? I want some more gravy. Does the trees moving make the wind blow? We had five puppies. What makes your nose so red, Hank? My father has lots of money. Are the stars hot? I whipped Ed Walker twice, Saturday. I don't like girls. You dassent catch toads unless with a string. Do oxen make any noise? Why are oranges round? Have you got beds to sleep on in this cave? Amos Murray has got six toes. A parrot can talk, but a monkey or a fish can't. How many does it take to make twelve?"

Every few minutes he would remember that he was a pesky redskin, and pick up his stick rifle and tiptoe to the mouth of the cave to rubber for the scouts of the hated paleface. Now and then he would let out a war-whoop that made Old Hank, the Trapper, shiver. That boy had Bill terrorized from the start.

"Red Chief," says I to the kid, "would you like to go home?"

"Aw, what for?" says he. "I don't have any fun at home. I hate to go to school. I like to camp out. You won't take me back home again, Snake-eye, will you?"

"Not right away," says I. "We'll stay here in the cave a while."

"All right!" says he. "That'll be fine. I never had such fun in all my life."

We went to bed about eleven o'clock. We spread down some wide blankets and quilts and put Red Chief between us. We weren't afraid he'd run away. He kept us awake for three hours, jumping up and reaching for his rifle and screeching: "Hist! pard," in mine and Bill's ears, as the fancied crackle of a twig or the rustle of a leaf revealed to his young imagination the stealthy approach of the outlaw band. At last, I fell into a troubled sleep, and dreamed that I had been kidnapped and chained to a tree by a ferocious pirate with red hair.

Just at daybreak, I was awakened by a series of awful screams from Bill. They weren't yells, or howls, or shouts, or whoops, or yawps, such as you'd expect from a manly set of vocal organs – they were simply indecent, terrifying, humiliating screams, such as women emit when they see ghosts or caterpillars. It's an awful thing to hear a strong, desperate, fat man scream incontinently in a cave at daybreak.

I jumped up to see what the matter was. Red Chief was sitting on Bill's chest, with one hand twined in Bill's hair. In the other he had the sharp case knife we used for slicing bacon; and he was industriously and realistically trying to take Bill's scalp, according to the sentence that had been pronounced upon him the evening before.

I got the knife away from the kid and made him lie down again. But, from that moment, Bill's spirit was broken. He laid down on his side of the bed, but he never closed an eye again in sleep as long as that boy was with us. I dozed off for a while, but along toward sun-up I remembered that Red Chief had said I was to be burned at the stake at the rising of the sun. I wasn't nervous or afraid; but I sat up and lit my pipe and leaned against a rock.

"What you getting up so soon for, Sam?" asked Bill.

"Me?" says I. "Oh, I got a kind of pain in my shoulder. I thought sitting up would rest it."

"You're a liar!" says Bill. "You're afraid. You was to be burned at sunrise, and you was afraid he'd do it. And he would, too, if he could find a match. Ain't it awful, Sam? Do you think anybody will pay out money to get a little imp like that back home?"

"Sure," said I. "A rowdy kid like that is just the kind parents dote on. Now, you and the Chief get up and cook breakfast, while I go up on the top of this mountain and reconnoitre."

I went up on the peak of the little mountain and ran my eye over the contiguous vicinity. Over toward Summit I expected to see the sturdy yeomanry of the village armed with scythes and pitchforks beating the countryside for the dastardly kidnappers. But what I saw was a peaceful landscape dotted with one man plowing with a dun mule. Nobody was dragging the creek; no couriers dashed hither and yon, bringing tidings of no news to the distracted parents. There was a sylvan attitude of somnolent sleepiness pervading that section of the external outward surface of Alabama that lay exposed to my view. "Perhaps," says I to myself, "it has not yet been discovered that the wolves have borne away the tender lambkin from the fold. Heaven help the wolves!" says I, and I went down the mountain to breakfast.

When I got to the cave I found Bill backed up against the side of it, breathing hard, and the boy threatening to smash him with a rock half as big as a coconut.

"He put a red-hot boiled potato down my back," explained Bill, "and then mashed it with his foot; and I boxed his ears. Have you got a gun about you, Sam?"

I took the rock away from the boy and kind of patched up the argument. "I'll fix you," says the kid to Bill. "No man ever yet struck the Red Chief but he got paid for it. You better beware!"

After breakfast the kid takes a piece of leather with strings wrapped around it out of his pocket and goes outside the cave unwinding it.

"What's he up to now?" says Bill, anxiously. "You don't think he'll run away, do you, Sam?"

"No fear of it," says I. "He don't seem to be much of a homebody. But we've got to fix up some plan about the ransom. There don't seem to be much excitement around Summit on account of his disappearance; but maybe they haven't realized yet that he's gone. His folks may think he's spending the night with Aunt Jane or one of the neighbors. Anyhow, he'll be missed today. Tonight we must get a message to his father demanding the two thousand dollars for his return."

Just then we heard a kind of war-whoop, such as David might have emitted when he knocked out the champion Goliath. It was a sling that Red Chief had pulled out of his pocket, and he was whirling it around his head.

I dodged, and heard a heavy thud and a kind of a sigh from Bill, like a horse gives out when you take his saddle off. A niggerhead rock the size of an egg had caught Bill just behind his left ear. He loosened himself all over and fell in the fire across the frying pan of hot water for washing the dishes. I dragged him out and poured cold water on his head for half an hour.

By and by, Bill sits up and feels behind his ear and says: "Sam, do you know who my favorite Biblical character is?"

"Take it easy," says I. "You'll come to your senses presently."

"King Herod," says he. "You won't go away and leave me here alone, will you, Sam?"

I went out and caught that boy and shook him until his freckles rattled.

"If you don't behave," says I, "I'll take you straight home. Now, are you going to be good, or not?"

"I was only funning," says he sullenly. "I didn't mean to hurt Old Hank. But what did he hit me for? I'll behave, Snake-eye, if you won't send me home, and if you'll let me play the Black Scout today."

"I don't know the game," says I. "That's for you and Mr. Bill to decide. He's your playmate for the day. I'm going away for a while, on business. Now, you come in and make friends with him and say you are sorry for hurting him, or home you go, at once."

I made him and Bill shake hands, and then I took Bill aside and told him I was going to Poplar Cove, a little village three miles from the cave, and find out what I could about how the kidnapping had been regarded in Summit. Also, I thought it best to send a peremptory letter to old man Dorset that day, demanding the ransom and dictating how it should be paid.

"You know, Sam," says Bill, "I've stood by you without batting an eye in earthquakes, fire and flood – in poker games, dynamite outrages, police raids, train robberies, and cyclones. I never lost my nerve yet till we kidnapped that two-legged skyrocket of a kid. He's got me going. You won't leave me long with him, will you, Sam?"

"I'll be back some time this afternoon," says I. "You must keep the boy amused and quiet till I return. And now we'll write the letter to old Dorset."

Bill and I got paper and pencil and worked on the letter while Red Chief, with a blanket wrapped around him, strutted up and down, guarding the mouth of the cave. Bill begged me tearfully to make the ransom fifteen hundred dollars instead of two thousand. "I ain't attempting," says he, "to decry the celebrated moral aspect of parental affection, but we're dealing with humans, and it ain't human for anybody to give up two thousand dollars for that forty-pound chunk of freckled wildcat. I'm willing to take a chance at fifteen hundred dollars. You can

charge the difference up to me."

So, to relieve Bill, I acceded, and we collaborated on a letter that ran this way:

Ebenezer Dorset, Esq:
We have your boy concealed in a place far from Summit. It is useless for you or the most skillful detective to attempt to find him. Absolutely, the only terms on which you can have him restored to you are these: We demand fifteen hundred dollars in large bills for his return; the money to be left at midnight tonight at the same spot and in the same box as your reply – as hereinafter described. If you agree to these terms, send your answer in writing by a solitary messenger tonight at half-past eight o'clock. After crossing Owl Creek, on the road to Poplar Cove, there are three large trees about a hundred yards apart, close to the fence of the wheat field on the right-hand side. At the bottom of the fence-post, opposite the third tree, will be found a small pasteboard box.

The messenger will place the answer in this box and return immediately to Summit.

If you attempt any treachery or fail to comply with our demand as stated, you will never see your boy again.

If you pay the money as demanded, he will be returned to you safe and well within three hours. These terms are final, and if you do not accede to them no further communication will be attempted.

TWO DESPERATE MEN

I addressed this letter to Dorset, and put it in my pocket. As I was about to start, the kid comes up to me and says:

"Aw, Snake-eye, you said I could play the Black Scout while you was gone."

"Play it, of course," says I. "Mr. Bill will play with you. What kind of game is it?"

"I'm the Black Scout," says Red Chief, "and I have to ride to the stockade to warn the settlers that the Indians are coming. I'm tired of playing Indian myself. I want to be the Black Scout."

"All right," says I. "It sounds harmless to me. I guess Mr. Bill will help you foil the pesky savages."

"What am I to do?" asks Bill, looking at the kid, suspicious.

"You are the hoss," says the Black Scout. "Get down on your hands and knees. How can I ride to the stockade without a hoss?"

"You'd better keep him interested," said I, "till we get the scheme going. Loosen up."

Bill gets down on his all fours, and a look comes in his eye like a rabbit's when you catch it in a trap.

"How far is it to the stockade, kid?" he asks, in a husky manner of voice.

"Ninety miles," says the Black Scout. "And you have to hump yourself to get there on time. Whoa, now!"

The Black Scout jumps on Bill's back and digs his heels in his side.

"For Heaven's sake," says Bill, "hurry back, Sam, as soon as you can. I wish we hadn't made the ransom more than a thousand. Say, you quit kicking me or I'll get up and warm you good."

I walked over to Poplar Cove and sat around the post office and store, talking with the chawbacons that came in to trade. One whiskerando says that he hears Summit is all upset on account of Elder Ebenezer Dorset's boy having been lost or stolen. That was all I wanted to know. I bought some smoking tobacco, referred casually to the price of black-eyed peas, posted my letter surreptitiously, and came away. The postmaster said the mail carrier would come by in an hour to take the mail on to Summit.

When I got back to the cave Bill and the boy were not to be found. I explored the vicinity of the cave, and risked a yodel or two, but there was no response.

So I lighted my pipe and sat down on a mossy bank to await developments.

In about half an hour I heard the bushes rustle, and Bill wabbled out into the little glade in front of the cave. Behind him was the kid, stepping softly like a scout, with a broad grin on his face. Bill stopped, took off his hat, and wiped his face with a red handkerchief. The kid stopped about eight feet behind him.

"Sam," says Bill, "I suppose you'll think I'm a renegade, but I couldn't help it. I'm a grown person with masculine proclivities and habits of self-defence, but there is a time when all systems of egotism and predominance fail. The boy is gone. I have sent him home. All is off. There was martyrs in old times," goes on Bill, "that suffered death rather than give up the particular graft they enjoyed. None of 'em ever was subjugated to such supernatural tortures as I have been. I tried to be faithful to our articles of depredation; but there came a limit."

"I was rode," says Bill, "the ninety miles to the stockade, not barring an inch. Then, when the settlers was rescued, I was given oats. Sand ain't a palatable substitute. And then, for an hour I had to try to explain to him why there was nothin' in holes, how a road can run both ways, and what makes the grass green. I tell you, Sam, a human can only stand so much. I takes him by the neck of his clothes and drags him down the mountain. On the way he kicks my legs black-and-blue from the knees down; and I've got to have two or three bites on my thumb and hand cauterized.

"But he's gone" – continues Bill – "gone home. I showed him the road to Summit and kicked him about eight feet nearer there at one kick. I'm sorry we lose the ransom; but it

132

was either that or Bill Driscoll to the madhouse."

Bill is puffing and blowing, but there is a look of ineffable peace and growing content on his rose-pink features.

"Bill," says I, "there isn't any heart disease in your family, is there?"

"No," says Bill, "nothing chronic except malaria and accidents. Why?"

"Then you might turn around," says I, "and have a look behind you."

Bill turns and sees the boy, and loses his complexion and sits down plump on the ground and begins to pluck aimlessly at grass and little sticks. For an hour I was afraid for his mind. And then I told him that my scheme was to put the whole job through immediately and that we would get the ransom and be off with it by midnight if old Dorset fell in with our proposition. So Bill braced up enough to give the kid a weak sort of a smile and a promise to play the Russian in a Japanese war with him as soon as he felt a little better.

I had a scheme for collecting that ransom without danger of being caught by counterplots that ought to commend itself to professional kidnappers. The tree under which the answer was to be left – and the money later on – was close to the road fence with big, bare fields on all sides. If a gang of constables should be watching for anyone to come for the note they could see him a long way off crossing the fields or in the road. But, no sirree! At half-past eight I was up in that tree, as well hidden as a tree toad, waiting for the messenger to arrive.

Exactly on time, a half-grown boy rides up the road on a bicycle, locates the pasteboard box at the foot of the fence-post, slips a folded piece of paper into it and pedals away again back toward Summit.

I waited an hour and then concluded the thing was square. I slid down the tree, got the note, slipped along the fence till I struck the woods, and was back at the cave in another half an hour. I opened the note, got near the lantern, and read it to Bill. It was written with a pen in a crabbed hand, and the sum and substance of it was this:

Two Desperate Men.
Gentlemen: I received your letter today by post, in regard to the ransom you ask for the return of my son. I think you are a little high in your demands, and I hereby make you a counter-proposition, which I am inclined to believe you will accept. You bring Johnny home and pay me two hundred and fifty dollars in cash, and I agree to take him off your hands. You had better come at night, for the neighbors believe he is lost, and I couldn't be responsible for what they would do to anybody they saw bringing him back. Very respectfully,

EBENEZER DORSET

"Great pirates of Penzance!" says I; "of all the impudent –– "

But I glanced at Bill, and hesitated. He had the most appealing look in his eyes I ever saw on the face of a dumb or a talking brute.

"Sam," says he, "what's two hundred and fifty dollars, after all? We've got the money. One more night of this kid will send me to a bed in Bedlam. Besides being a thorough gentleman, I think Mr. Dorset is a spendthrift for making us such a liberal offer. You ain't going to let the chance go, are you?"

"Tell you the truth, Bill," says I, "this little he ewe lamb has somewhat got on my nerves, too. We'll take him home, pay the ransom and make our getaway."

We took him home that night. We got him to go by telling him that his father had bought a silver-mounted rifle and a pair of moccasins for him, and we were going to hunt bears the next day.

It was just twelve o'clock when we knocked at Ebenezer's front door. Just at the moment when I should have been abstracting the fifteen hundred dollars from the box under the tree, according to the original proposition, Bill was counting out two hundred and fifty dollars into Dorset's hand.

When the kid found out we were going to leave him at home he started up a howl like a calliope and fastened himself as tight as a leech to Bill's leg. His father peeled him away gradually, like a porous plaster.

"How long can you hold him?" asks Bill.

"I am not as strong as I used to be," says old Dorset, "but I think I can promise you ten minutes."

"Enough," says Bill. "In ten minutes I shall cross the Central, Southern, and Middle Western States, and be legging it trippingly for the Canadian border."

And, as dark as it was, and as fat as Bill was, and as good a runner as I am, he was a good mile and a half out of Summit before I could catch up with him.

Tom Hirsh

Are You a Highway Killer?

*"A driver is not an island unto himself.
He shares the road,
as responsible to others as to himself."*

Are you a potential murderer? Could your careless, unthinking behavior at the wheel of a car leave death in your wake, just as surely as if you had pulled the trigger of a gun?

That's a repugnant thought, isn't it? Yet it happens too often. Here are some of the ways:

1. You're driving along a two-lane country highway 55 m.p.h. Suddenly you see a farm sign offering fresh eggs for sale. Without signalling, you hit the brakes and make a fast left turn into the farm, cutting in front of an approaching car. The driver brakes hard and you squeak through, but he isn't so lucky. A truck camper coming up behind him can't stop in time and plows into his rear, killing him and his passenger.

2. You're starting out on vacation. Your station wagon is loaded with assorted gear, which you've covered with an improvised tarp (actually a discarded plastic shower curtain tied down with wrapping twine). Everything seems snug and secure, but you haven't thought about the tearing, whipping power of the wind stream over a fast-moving car.

Unknown to you, a tie-down snaps – and then another. Suddenly the plastic rips loose and plasters itself across the windshield of a car behind. The driver following, instantly blinded, hits the brakes, spins out and smashes into a concrete abutment. The father, mother, and three kids are killed. A five-year-old boy is the only survivor.

3. It's a beautiful autumn Sunday. You and your spouse are admiring the fall colors as you drive along one of those winding two-lane highways. The speed limit is fifty-five, but beauty should be savored, so you're doing about twenty. Before you know it, a line of cars is queued up behind you. Finally a teenager in a souped-up, aging sedan pulls out of line and floors the gas pedal. He just makes it, but only because an auto approaching from around the next bend has to take to the ditch to avoid a head-on collision and rolls over. The toll is three dead and two seriously injured.

4. You're returning home from a party late at night. The road is dark and rain is cascading against your windshield, so you have your brights on. You round a curve and meet another car. The other driver quickly dims his lights, but with bleary eyes and a fogged mind you're afraid of losing sight of the road, so you don't dim yours. Too bad. The combination of darkness, rain on the windshield and the bright glare of your headlights causes the other driver to drop a wheel off the edge of the pavement. He skids, loses control and hits a utility pole broadside. An eight-year-old girl sitting in the front seat is thrown from the car and killed.

5. Circling the block in busy downtown traffic, you finally spot a parking place at the curb. You park, then open your door to get out. An 18-year-old girl on a bike has to swerve suddenly to avoid crashing into your door. She loses control and slides into the left lane, where a passing repairman's van, unable to stop or veer in time, runs over her. She dies two hours later in hospital.

6. You try to beat a stale green light at an intersection but it changes before you get there. You brake hard and stop, but not soon enough to avoid blocking the crosswalk. Another car pulls up right behind you – so close that a group of fourth graders coming home from school is forced to cross in front of your car. One of the kids playfully pushes another, who stumbles into the path of an on-coming car. The child suffers a concussion and dies twelve hours later in the hospital.

Have you committed one of the misdeeds recounted here? Or come close? Maybe you drove blithely on your way, never realizing the havoc left in your wake, or the shaken motorists you placed in heart-stopping jeopardy.

A driver is not an island unto himself. He shares the road, as responsible to others as to himself. He accepts responsibilities that include:

Driving smoothly. Weaving in and out, cutting in on other drivers, spurting through narrow gaps in traffic, abrupt changes in direction – all are accident makers. Driving too fast or too slow can cause trouble, too. Both result in unnecessary passing – by you or by other drivers. If someone is itching to get around you, don't compete. Help him on his way.

Signalling your intention. Whether slowing down, turning, or changing lanes, use your brake lights and turn signals early enough to let other drivers know well in advance what you are going to do. Use your horn sparingly, but use it if necessary – not as a snarling expletive but to communicate and attract attention.

Allowing plenty of room. Tailgating is a foolhardy tactic that accounts for innumerable mishaps. Learn the two-second rule, a simple method devised by traffic experts to help you estimate a safe following distance at any speed. Follow at least two seconds behind the car in front of you. (Under bad driving conditions, stretch the margin to three seconds.) As soon as the driver ahead reaches a mark – a sign standard, a tar strip on the road – start counting: "one thousand and one, one thousand and two." If you reach the marker before you finish counting, you are following too closely. And give plenty of room to motorcyclists and bicyclists, too.

Anchoring your cargo. Cargo stowed on a roof carrier can pose a fatal hazard for another driver. If you're carrying cargo, tie it down securely. You know how dangerous it is when you have to swerve to avoid some obstacle in the road. Remember, too, that some trailers can get loose. Bumper hitches are unreliable for high-speed, open-road trailering.

Keeping cool. Be patient and tolerant at the wheel. Psychologists affirm that you're more likely to have an accident when you're angry or tense. The same is true of the other driver.

Anything you do to upset him will increase the chances of an accident.

Courtesy is contagious. Such a small gesture as letting a motorist get out of his driveway into a solid line of traffic will put at least two drivers in a safer frame of mind.

Leaving a margin for error. Mistakes are made by the best of drivers. Make allowances for that. Leave extra room to permit evasive action if the other driver makes a misjudgment or has reflexes dulled by sleepiness or alcohol. Anticipate errors; note erratic behavior by a driver ahead, pay attention to the approach signs for exits.

Murder on the highway is not a nice thing to contemplate. But if you drive with skill, anticipation, and consideration for others, you need be neither its victim nor its perpetrator.

Paul Simon

Everything Put Together Falls Apart

Paraphernalia never hides your broken bones,
And I don't know why you want to try,
It's plain to see you're on your own.
I ain't blind, no,
Some folks are crazy,
Others walk that border line.
Watch what you're doing,
Taking downs to get off to sleep,
And ups to start you on your way;
After a while they'll change your style,
I see it happening every day.
Spare your heart.
Everything put together
Sooner or later falls apart,
There's nothing to it, nothing to it.
You can cry and you can lie,
For all the good it'll do you, you can die,
Oh, but when it's done and the police come,
And they lay you down for dead,
Just remember what I said!

Al Purdy

The Drunk Tank

A man keeps hammering at the door
(he is so noisy it makes my ears ache),
yelling monotonously, "Let me outa here!"
A caged light bulb floats on the ceiling,
where a dung fly circles round and round,
and there is a greasy brown mattress,
too small for the bolted-down steel bunk,
and a high barred window permitting
fungus darkness to creep in the room's
      corners.
The man keeps hammering at the door
until a guard comes:
"I just happen to know the mayor in this
      town,"
he tells the guard,
"and it's gonna be too bad for you
if you keep me locked up here."
The guard laughs and turns away.
"It's no use," I tell my cell mate.
"Just wait until morning.
Then we'll be up in magistrate's court,
and being drunk isn't a very serious – "
"Who are you?" the man asks me.
"I don't know you – "
"I'm your friend," I say to him,
"and I've been your friend a long time.
Don't you remember?"
"I don't know you at all!" he screams.
"Stay away from me!"
"If that's the way you feel about it," I say,

and suddenly I'm not so sure as I was
 – memory is a funny thing isn't it?
"Please sit down and wait until morning,"
I say to him reasonably –
Don't you think that was the right thing
      to say?
But he turns his back and hammers on
      the door:
"Guard! Guard! I want a cell by myself!
You've put a crazy man in here with me!"
He is so noisy.
And I watch him pounding on the black
      steel door,
a patch of sweat spreading on his back,
and his bald spot glistening –
He looks at me over his shoulder,
terrified:
And I spread my hands flat to show him
I have nothing but good intentions.
"Stay away from me! Stay away!"
He backs off into a corner shaking,
while I sit down on the bunk
to wait for morning.
And I think:
this is my friend,
I know it is my friend,
and I say to him,
"Aren't you my friend?"
But there he is at the door again,
he is so noisy....

"The Drunk Tank" from *Being Alive* by Al Purdy.
Reprinted by permission of The Canadian Publishers,
McClelland and Stewart Limited, Toronto.

Understanding
Differences

Langston Hughes

As I Grew Older

It was a long time ago.
I have almost forgotten my dream.
But it was there then,
In front of me,
Bright like a sun –
My dream.

And then the wall rose,
Rose slowly,
Slowly,
Between me and my dream.
Rose slowly, slowly,
Dimming,
Hiding,
The light of my dream.
Rose until it touched the sky –
The wall.

Shadow.
I am black.

I lie down in the shadow.
No longer the light of my dream before me,
Above me.
Only the thick wall.
Only the shadow.

My hands!
My dark hands!
Break through the wall!
Find my dream!
Help me to shatter this darkness,
To smash this night,
To break this shadow
Into a thousand lights of sun,
Into a thousand whirling dreams
Of sun!

Chief Dan George

My
Very Good Dear Friends...

I must find myself. I must find my treasure.
I must wait until you want something of me...
until you need something that is me.

142

Was it only yesterday that men sailed around the moon...and can they now stand up on its barren surface? You and I marvel that man should travel so far and so fast....Yet, if they have travelled far then I have travelled farther... and if they have travelled fast, then I faster...for I was born a thousand years ago...born in a culture of bows and arrows. But within the span of half a lifetime I was flung across the ages to the culture of the atom bomb....And from bows and arrows to atom bombs is a distance far beyond a flight to the moon.

I was born in an age that loved the things of nature and gave them beautiful names like Tes-wall-u-wit instead of dried-up names like Stanley Park.

I was born when people loved all nature and spoke to it as though it had a soul....I can remember going up Indian River with my father when I was very young....I can remember him watching the sun light fires on Mount Pay-nay-nay as it rose above its peak. I can remember him singing his thanks to it as he often did...singing the Indian word "thanks..." so very, very softly.

And then the people came...more and more people came...like a crushing rushing wave they came...hurling the years aside!!...and suddenly I found myself a young man in the midst of the twentieth century.

I found myself and my people adrift in this new age...but not a part of it.

Engulfed by its rushing tide, but only as a captive eddy...going round and round...on little reserves, on plots of land we floated in a kind of grey unreality...ashamed of our cul-

ture which you ridiculed...unsure of who we were or where we were going...uncertain of our grip on the present...weak in our hope of the future....And that is pretty well where we stand today.

I had a glimpse of something better than this. For a few brief years I knew my people when we lived the old life....I knew them when there was still a dignity in our lives and a feeling of worth in our outlook. I knew them when there was unspoken confidence in the home and a certain knowledge of the path we walked upon. But we were living on the dying energy of a dying culture...a culture that was slowly losing its forward thrust.

I think it was the suddenness of it all that hurt us so. We did not have time to adjust to the startling upheaval around us. We seemed to have lost what we had without a replacement for it. We did not have time to take our twentieth-century progress and eat it little by little and digest it. It was forced feeding from the start and our stomachs turned sick and we vomited.

Do you know what it is like to be without moorings? Do you know what it is like to live in surroundings that are ugly and everywhere you look you see ugly things... strange things...strange and ugly things? It depresses man, for man must be surrounded by the beautiful if his soul is to grow.

What did we see in the new surroundings you brought us? Laughing faces, pitying faces, sneering faces, conniving faces. Faces that ridiculed, faces that stole from us. It is no wonder we turned to the only people who did not steal and who did not sneer, who came with love. They were the missionaries and they came with love and I for one will ever return that love.

Do you know what it is like to feel you are of no value to society and those around you? To know that people came to help you but

"My Very Good Dear Friends" by Chief Dan George from *The Only Good Indian* edited by Waubageshig. Reprinted by permission of New Press, Don Mills, Ontario.

not to work with you for you knew that they knew you had nothing to offer... ?

Do you know what it is like to have your race belittled and to come to learn that you are only a burden to the country? Maybe we did not have the skills to make a meaningful contribution, but no one would wait for us to catch up. We were shoved aside because they thought we were dumb and could never learn.

What is it like to be without pride in your race, pride in your family, pride and confidence in yourself? What is it like? You don't know for you never tasted its bitterness.

I shall tell you what it is like. It is like not caring about tomorrow for what does tomorrow matter. It is like having a reserve that looks like a junk yard because the beauty in the soul is dead and why should the soul express an external beauty that does not match it? It is like getting drunk for a few brief moments, an escape from ugly reality, and feeling a sense of importance. It is most of all like awaking next morning to the guilt of betrayal. For the alcohol did not fill the emptiness but only dug it deeper.

And now you hold out your hand and you beckon to me to come across the street... come and integrate you say....But how can I come? I am naked and ashamed. How can I come in dignity? I have no presents...I have no gifts. What is there in my culture you value?...My poor treasure you can only scorn. Am I then to come as a beggar and receive all from your omnipotent hand? Somehow I must wait...I must delay. I must find myself. I must find my treasure. I must wait until you want something of me...until you need something that is me. Then I can raise my head and say to my wife and family...listen...they are calling...they need me...I must go....

Then I can walk across the street and I will hold my head high for I will meet you as an equal. I will not scorn you for your demeaning gifts and you will not receive me in pity. Pity I can do without; my manhood I cannot.

I can only come as Chief Capilano came to Captain Vancouver...as one sure of his authority...certain of his worth...master of his house and leader of his people. I shall not come as a cringing object of your pity. I shall come in dignity or I shall not come at all.

You talk big words of integration in the schools. Does it really exist? Can we talk of integration until there is social integration? Unless there is integration of hearts and minds you have only a physical presence... and the walls are as high as the mountain range.

Come with me to the playgrounds of an integrated high school...see how level and flat and ugly the black top is....But look... now it is recess time...the students pour through the doors...soon over here is a group of white students...and see...over there near a fence...a group of native students...and look again...the black is no longer level...mountain ranges rising... valleys falling...and a great chasm seems to be opening up between the two groups... yours and mine...and no one seems capable of crossing over. But wait....Soon the bell will ring and the students will leave the play yard. Integration has moved indoors. There isn't much room in a classroom to dig chasms so there are only little ones there... only little ones...for we won't allow big ones...at least, not right under our noses... so we will cover it all over with black top... cold...black...flat...and full of ugliness in its sameness.

I know you must be saying...tell us what *do* you want. What do we want? We want first of all to be respected and to feel we are people of worth. We want an equal opportunity to succeed in life...but we cannot suc-

144 ceed on your terms...we cannot raise our-selves on your norms. We need specialized help in education...specialized help in the formative years...special courses in English. We need guidance counselling...we need equal job opportunities for graduates, otherwise our students will lose courage and ask what is the use of it all.

Let no one forget it...we are a people with special rights guaranteed to us by promises and treaties. We do not beg for these rights, nor do we thank you...we do not thank you for them because we paid for them...and, God help us, the price we paid was exorbitant. We paid for them with our culture, our dignity, and self-respect. We paid and paid and paid until we became a beaten race, poverty-stricken and conquered.

But you have been kind to listen to me and I know that in your heart you wished you could help. I wonder if there is much you can do and yet I believe there is a lot you can do...when you meet my children in your classroom, respect each one for what he is... a child of our Father in heaven, and your brother. Maybe it all boils down to that.

And now it is the end. May I say thanks to you for the warmth of your understanding.

William Paluk

Back Door

Characters

PETER KRITIUK, the baker   ANNA NOVAK, the mother   HALIA (HELEN), the daughter

HENRY SMITH, the suitor   HENRIETTA SMITH, Henry's mother

SCENE 1

Scene:

A kitchen, stage left, and a living room, stage right, of a Ukrainian-Canadian home. Door out of living room goes into bedroom. Door out of kitchen − that is, the back door − is the entry and exit of the play.

Reprinted by permission of the author.

PETER: (*knocks on door − shave-and-a -haircut, two bits*) Baker!

ANNA: Come in, Peter.

PETER: (*enters, humming "Yes, My Darling Daughter"*) Hello, Mama Novak. Here's something for you on a beautiful spring day. (*Kisses her on nape of neck.*) Mmmm − ahhh.

ANNA: (*taken aback*) Hey! What kiss for? And from a baker! If I was young, I would slap.

PETER: That's to my future mother-in-law. One kiss on account.

146

ANNA: Oh? On what kind account?

PETER: On account I'm in love with your daughter. And – know something? She's in love with me. Yeh, yeh. No foolin'.

ANNA: (*Goes back to ironing. She's hard to excite*.) So? She in love. You in love. So I seen lots people in love. So leave extra rye bread today. Vladimir coming to dinner.

PETER: Is that all you can say? Look, Mama. All the world is upside down, and all you can say is "Vladimir coming to dinner." Ain't you got poetry in your soul?

ANNA: I got lots of work on my hands. (*mildly curious*) You say Halia love you. How you know this?

PETER: Aha! You stopped ironing! Ha Ha! (*mysteriously*) I know. I just know, that's all. Last night – oh, it was a beautiful night. Halia had a – a special kind of look in her eyes. I know, Mama, I know. (*seriously*) Tell me something. What did she say to you this morning? Tell me, what?

ANNA: I tell you. She get up as usual, and she say, "Hurry breakfast, Mama. No egg this morning. Just toast and coffee."

PETER: (*sighs*) That's Halia all right. Hiding her feelings. I can tell.

ANNA: (*back to her ironing*) Tell me one thing. You gonna leave me extra rye?

PETER: But she must have said or done something. Think, Mama Novak. Didn't you notice something – different – about her?

ANNA: Ech . . . !

PETER: Think. Think!

ANNA: Wait a minute. Maybe . . . but no, no . . .

PETER: (*excited*) What was it? What was it? C'mon, c'mon. What?

ANNA: Oh, just – she didn't eat her toast.

PETER: Aha! Didn't eat her toast. That's unusual, isn't it? Tell me the truth, Mama.

ANNA: Mmmm . . . yeah. For Halia, unusual.

PETER: There! I told you. And you wouldn't believe me.

ANNA: But, last night, did you ask her – anything?

PETER: We-e-ell, n-not exactly.

ANNA: Did *she* say anything?

PETER: Er . . . n-no. Not really.

ANNA: (*sighs, resumes ironing vigorously*) Don't forget leave extra rye.

PETER: But you don't understand Halia like I do, Mama. I know how she feels, inside. I can tell by her face, her eyes. We ain't been goin' steady for a year and a half for nothin', Mama. But we got another date Saturday night. You wait. It'll all come out Saturday. Well, g'bye, Mama Novak.

ANNA: G'bye, g'bye. Hey! You forgot extra rye bread.

PETER: (*coming back*) Oh. You want an extra rye. Why didn't you say so, Mama? One extra rye comin' up. (*leaves bread, whistles "Wedding Invitatory Polka" as he departs*)

SCENE 2

Scene:

The same, a little later. Halia enters as her mother irons. It is obvious from her first words that she is indeed in love.

HALIA: Hello, Mama.

ANNA: Halia! Home already? Are you sick, *donyu*?

HALIA: (*leans against back door*) You might call it that.

ANNA: (*relieved*) Mus' be. Standin' there, lookin' at ceiling. Take coat off and stay.

HALIA: Oh. I forgot. Been forgetting things all day. That's why I'm home. I kept putting chocolate creams in the wrong boxes, so the boss told me to do him a favor and go home and get some sleep. But who wants to sleep?

ANNA: What time you come home last night? Must be two – t'ree o'clock.

HALIA: Oh, Peter and I got home early. Or-r,

maybe it was late. In any case, I didn't get a wink of sleep last night.

ANNA: *hums "Wedding Polka."*

HALIA: (*recognizing it, focuses her look on her mother*) What're you ironing, Mama? Hey! Those aren't our clothes. You're taking in Mrs. Macdonald's washing again. You clean her house – that should be enough.

ANNA: (*embarrassed*) You not supposed to see clothes.

HALIA: But why do you do that? You don't have to take in anybody's washing! You have enough to live on, Mama.

ANNA: You gonna need weddin' dress, maybe. And other clothes. I have pay for all my daughter weddings. I will pay for yours.

HALIA: (*runs to her, embraces her*) Mama, you're the greatest! But – I haven't said anything about a wedding. How did you know?

ANNA: I marry off eight children. I know.

HALIA: (*takes off coat, drops it absent-mindedly on floor and sits dreamily on edge of kitchen chair*) But you're right, Mama. Oh, it's so grand to be alive, and – and to be wanted. Such a heavenly feeling.

ANNA: Everybody have heavenly feelin' today. Don't nobody feel...er...earthly?

HALIA: Mama, you must have been in love once. I mean when you and Daddy met. What did it feel like? Tell me.

ANNA: Well, let me see. Oh, I was young, and so pretty. Your father...well, we were immigrants. We had nothin'. We borrow money for licence. On weddin' night, your father got drun...got feelin' good, like you say. Then we have nine children in thirteen years. Yes – our marriage was earthly.

HALIA: (*laughs, rises and hugs Anna*) You know, Mama, I've read about boys asking girls to marry them. You see it on television. But when he asked me, sort of suddenly, well, I – I can't describe it.

ANNA: (*surprised*) He asked you? Already?

HALIA: You could have knocked me over with a feather.

ANNA: (*shrugs shoulders*) Ech! People in love!

HALIA: When you love somebody very, very much – is that all you need? To get married, I mean.

ANNA: Well, er...ech! How should I know? Go ask your sisters.

HALIA: But I'm asking you! How would you size up a boy who wanted to marry me? Tell me. It's important to me what you think.

ANNA: (*pleased and flattered*) Oh. Important, huh? Well, he should have steady job. That important. And good heart. Good Ukrainian heart. Nice, but not too friendly. When he working, tell him no kissin' women. Kissin' not nice when he have wife at home.

HALIA: I don't know what you mean. But I'm sure you'll like Henry.

ANNA: I mean like today – I...like...*who*?

HALIA: Henry. Henry Smith.

ANNA: What...what dis...Henry Smit'?

HALIA: Henry's the most wonderful man in the whole, whole world. We were having lunch yesterday. All of a sudden, right out of the blue, he asks me to marry him. Just like that! And he's serious, Mama. Dead serious.

ANNA: (*her temper is beginning to rise*) Henry Smit', huh? And what's about Peter Kritiuk, the baker?

HALIA: Peter? Oh, he'll be okay for some other girl. He's still a little immature, though.

ANNA: O-o-oh? So you mature, huh? Well, come wit' me, mature daughter. (*grasps Halia by the hand and pulls her to the living room*)

HALIA: Mother! You're hurting my hand, Mama! You're hurting me.

ANNA: I should hurt you in another place. Come here to bureau.

148

HALIA: I'll come. Let go!

ANNA: (*drops Halia's hand when they face the old oak buffet*) Now! Tell me, mature daughter, how many weddin' pictures on dis bureau?

HALIA: I could have told you in the kitchen. There are eight. Eight wedding pictures.

ANNA: (*proudly*) Yes. Eight. Eight nice Ukrainian, some Polish, daughter-in-law and son-in-law. Today I have twenty-two grandchildren. In two months twenty-four.

HALIA: Mama! Why all the statistics? I know them all.

ANNA: Why? I tell why. Because you don't have brain in head. What's trouble wit' Peter?

HALIA: Peter's not for me, that's all.

ANNA: Henry Smit' not for you! What you t'ink, you English or somet'ing? Maybe you t'ink *I'm* English?

HALIA: Henry's a Canadian, and so am I.

ANNA: Aya! Can-a-dian! You see Canadian on – on boxcars, so you t'ink you Canadian. You...Ukrainian and he...English.

HALIA: I...hadn't thought...about that part of it. (*decisively*) Mama! You've got to do one thing for me. Promise. Please promise!

ANNA: Forget dis Henry Smit' and I promise.

HALIA: Mama! You've got to be fair. You haven't even met him. How can you say such a thing?

ANNA: I can say. I mother.

HALIA: And I love you very much. But you've got to meet him.

ANNA: I don't got to not'ing.

HALIA: Mother, I have a plan. Henry's coming to take me out tonight. You can meet him then.

ANNA: How come he never be here before?

HALIA: I told him I couldn't go out with him because I had a steady boyfriend. So we just had coffee breaks together and we had lunch every day for the last two weeks.

ANNA: And from dis you want he should marry you?

HALIA: It's hard to explain. It just happened. I can't explain it.

ANNA: I can. You crazy. He crazy.

HALIA: Mama, you must meet him and speak to him. I'll tell him to be here early. Then I'll pretend I'm getting ready upstairs, and you can talk to him and get to know him. Will you do that, Mama? Please promise.

ANNA: (*most unwillingly*) Yeh, yeh. Promise. I promise.

SCENE 3

Scene:

The same, but there are crocheted antimacassars on sofa, ceremonial towels on pictures and buffet, the result of much preparation. It is evening. There is a knock on the front door.

ANNA: Why he knock on front door?

HALIA: (*from upstairs*) I forgot to tell him. You tell him, please?

ANNA: (*shouting through front door*) Go to back door!

HENRY: *knocks on back door.*

ANNA: Come in, come in.

HENRY: (*enters, somewhat sheepishly*) Good evening, Mrs. Novak. I'm...I'm Henry Smith.

ANNA: (*feigning surprise*) Oh. It's pleasure. We...we never use front door. (*ushers him into living room*) You sit here on sofa and wait, please, for Halia to...er...finish dressing.

HALIA: (*from upstairs*) Hi, down there. Is that you, Henry?

HENRY: Right the first time.

HALIA: I'll be a little while yet. Mind waiting?

HENRY: Take your time, hon.

ANNA: (*Sits on other end of sofa, and turns so she can face him squarely. Methodically she*

examines him, head to toe.) My! You are...
handsome boy. Thin, but handsome.

HENRY: (*still nervous*) Thank you...er...
thank you, Mrs. Novak, for that...that
statement.

ANNA: You have dark hair – almost like
Ukrainian boy.

HENRY: Er...all our family is dark.

ANNA: (*suddenly serious*) You have steady
job?

HENRY: No. I go to school – that is,
university. But...I'll be finished this year.

ANNA: No steady job.

HENRY: I...I'm majoring in business
administration. But my favorite subject is
psychology.

ANNA: You major...you...subject...but no
job.

HENRY: Nope. Maybe university *is* a kind of
waste of time. But Dad insisted.

ANNA: (*glad to get off unpleasant subject*) You
Dad and Mother – they both English?

HENRY: Mom and Dad are both third-
generation Canadians. I've heard them
say that.

ANNA: Mmm hmmm. You know we all
Ukrainian in this house. *Many* generations
Ukrainian.

HENRY: Ukrainian. That's sort of Russian, or
Polish, isn't it? Or...what *is* Ukrainian?

ANNA: (*pleased for the first time*) Oh, you want
to know where is Ukraine. I show you. I
bring from bedroom map. Excuse, please.
(*vanishes into bedroom, calls from there*) I
have nice big map here. (*enters*) Here is
map of Ukraine. (*It is a big one, and he has
to move over*.) And here is Znyva, village
where husband and I born.

HENRY: Sure is a big country. I suppose your
country has lots of famous men. I've
never...

ANNA: (*breaking in*) Famous men! You have
heard of poet Shevchenko?

HENRY: Shev-chen-ko. I do believe...

ANNA: I show you. Wait! I go find something
in trunk in bedroom. (*vanishes, then
returns with books*) Here. One. Two. Three.
Four. Four volumes poetry work by one
man – famous poet Shevchenko. And you
ask if we have famous men!

HENRY: Well, while you were gone, I found
the capital of your country. It's Kiev, isn't
it?

ANNA: Capital – Kiev. Now I get you book –
beautiful color book showing pictures of
our capital. (*vanishes again*)

HENRY: You haven't got the *Encyclopaedia
Britannica* stashed away there somewhere,
have you? Er...I'm just joking.

ANNA: (*enters, carrying volume*) Here. Picture
history of Kiev. Old capital. Beautiful. We
have many songs about Kiev. Also about
many other things. You have heard of
Koshetz Choir?

HENRY: I'm afraid to say it.

ANNA: Some day, maybe, I will play you
records. (*Henry is busily poring over map.
Anna is pleased with the interest he has
shown.*) But you *are* nice boy. I know many
our boys who grow up in Canada not
interested in our songs or history or poets.
But *you*...

HENRY: I'm not *really* interested in history.

ANNA: No?

HENRY: Well, that is, *this* is interesting. But I
find Canadian history a little beyond me
most of the time. It's so boring.

ANNA: But you ask questions. That is interest.
Yes, you *are* interested. And I t'ink I like
you. Only, if you are Ukrainian, it would
be so nice.

HENRY: Does Helen mind?

ANNA: N-no. Halia not mind now. But
later...You name Smit'. I know our boy
name Pitkowsky, call himself Pitt. So you
could be Smitkowsky. But no, no...

HENRY: (*Picks up Kiev book. A letter falls out.*)
Look! A letter just fell out of this book.

150

ANNA: (*takes the letter, unfolds it*) It very old letter. My father – he dead now – he write me letter and I get it on my wedding day. Then I lose it. Now letter found again. (*She begins to sniff.*)

HENRY: Sentimental value, eh, Mrs. Novak?

ANNA: Oh, yes! Excuse me now, please. (*hurries into kitchen, hand to eyes*)

HALIA: (*enters*) Well, here I am at last. Hope you weren't bored.

HENRY: Hi, gorgeous. Your Mom and I had a nice long talk.

HALIA: What's all this – books, map...?

HENRY: I asked your mother about her native country.

HALIA: And you got your answer complete with map and illustrations.

HENRY: Your mother said she likes me. (*They stand close together, looking into each other's eyes.*)

ANNA: (*enters, carrying bowl*) Here some Ukrainian baking – *khroosty*. Sit down, sit down. Why you not sit down?

HALIA: Mama, there isn't any room left on the chesterfield.

Blackout

SCENE 4

Scene:

The same. It is the next day. Anna picks up telephone and dials.

ANNA: Hello? Hello, Maria? This is you sister Anna. How rheumatism today? Oh, thank you, my side still bad, but at my age, what you expect – I don't go dancing no more... Well, this boy – this Henry Smit', come like I expect. We had talk. Nice boy, but not Ukrainian. No job. Dumb Dora, why she not fall in love wit' Peter Kritiuk? Oh. You think I should not try stop affair, eh? Don't make it out to be forbidden fruit, eh?

Act like it okay, eh? But why? Oh. Halia may tire of boy. Yeah. That good idea. No, I not meet Mrs. Smit'. Hmmmm...drop in for coffee to Henry mother. Ech! I drink coffee when I have dinner. No time for coffee in between...what you mean I have old-country ideas? I see lots lady drop in to my Mrs. Macdonald for coffee. Maybe I will. Yes. Maybe tomorrow...I go shopping in morning, buy new hat, and drop in to Mrs. Smit' for coffee.

Curtain

SCENE 5

Scene:

A telephone table and chair at stage right, in front of curtain. Henrietta Smith is on phone.

HENRIETTA: Hello, Agnes? This is Henrietta Smith. Sorry you couldn't make it for bridge last night. Your substitute was a Kay Wiggins from Grant Bay...I never could get onto her bidding...(*Back door gong sounds.*) Oh, hang on, Agnes. Someone's at the back door. Be right back – don't hang up, now. (*walks across stage to door on stage left, opens it, and Anna enters*) Oh, hello.

ANNA: Hello. You Meesus Smit'?

HENRIETTA: Yes, I am.

ANNA: I Anna – Anna Novak.

HENRIETTA: Oh, you must be the new cleaning-woman. Thank heaven for that. It's a month since Katrina left, and the place is a mess. She told me she would try to find someone else.

ANNA: You don't un'erstan'. My name Anna Novak, and my daughter...

HENRIETTA: Anna. That's enough. I never can get my tongue around your long surnames. Although I must say Novak is an easy one.

ANNA: I drop in for coffee.

HENRIETTA: Of course you can have coffee. You go ahead and make yourself a cup. I'm on the phone, so I can't join you right now.

ANNA: My daughter and you...

HENRIETTA: Take your time, and when you're ready you can start in the basement. Vacuum's in the hall closet. But it'll need tidying before you vacuum. (*pause*) You understand me, don't you?

ANNA: (*defeated*) Yes. I un'erstan'.

HENRIETTA: Excuse me now, won't you, Anna? You go ahead and have your coffee now. The kitchen is right over there. (*walks over to stage right and picks up phone*) Hello, Agnes? That was the new cleaning-woman. Name of Anna Novak. Clean-looking. (*in undertone*) But you should see the hat! Looks like a wet towel with purple plums all over it. Now, this hand I held last night...(*Anna exits.*) I held nine spades, and as it turned out, Kay had three. So my opener was three spades. But how could we know the ace was out against us? (*looks out through window*) Agnes, I can't understand it. The new cleaning-woman has just left. Told me she wanted coffee, then ups and leaves. Ah, I know. She took one look at my basement and quit. And I can't really blame her. But about this hand I was holding...

Blackout

SCENE 6

Scene:

Same as Scene 3. It is evening of the same day. Anna is stacking clothes in a wicker basket. Halia enters.

HALIA: Hi, Mama.

ANNA: Hello, *donyu*.

HALIA: (*Takes off coat, hangs it in closet, and sees hat box. Mystified, she takes the hat out of the box.*) A new hat, Mama! (*Anna reacts. She had forgotten to hide it.*) What is the occasion?

ANNA: (*confused*) Oh...I just buy it. But I do not like. Will take back.

HALIA: (*fits hat onto Anna's head*) You bought it for some reason, Mama. Tell me.

ANNA: (*Sits down and removes hat. She is now resigned to telling truth.*) I bought it to go have coffee with Henry mother.

HALIA: With Mrs. Smith? You didn't say anything.

ANNA: It was to be surprise to you.

HALIA: And what happened?

ANNA: She thought I was new cleaning-woman. Said I should clean house.

HALIA: I don't believe it. How did it happen? Tell me.

ANNA: I went to the back door and rang bell and she came to door and said...

HALIA: Back door? Why the back door, Mama?

ANNA: What is matter with back door? I always go in back door.

HALIA: (*leans against chair for support*) Yes. Yes, of course. You – always go in the back door. (*She goes to Anna, puts her arms around her, kisses her.*) And I love you, Mama. I love you very, very much, and I'll never leave you, never!

ANNA: You will. You will. You want marry dis Henry Smit', no?

HALIA: (*in tears now*) Henry? O – I barely knew him. It was just one of those things. A girl is allowed to have *some* silly ideas, isn't she?

ANNA: I pay seven dollars and half for new hat.

HALIA: It's a gorgeous hat. It makes you look smart and young. Wait...(*with decision*) just wait till Peter Kritiuk sees it!

Curtain

SCENE 7

Scene:

As in Scene 5. Henrietta is on phone.

HENRIETTA: Hello, Helen Novak? This is Henrietta Smith. May I speak with your mother? Oh, she's not feeling well. Henry told me about what happened this morning. I'm phoning to apologize for being so stupid. Will you tell her that I am truly, deeply sorry? Your mother came to the back door and I...never for a moment...thought of her being your mother. Would you tell her that Mr. Smith and I would be pleased and honored to drop in and see you both at your home some time soon? Do please tell her.

Blackout

SCENE 8

Scene:

Curtain rises on same set as Scene 6. Later that evening. There is a knock on the door. Halia opens it and Henry enters. Halia turns face away as Henry tries to kiss her.

HENRY: I don't get it, hon.

HALIA: I tried to make it clear on the phone, Henry. Let's face it. It's all over with us. It's not as bad as all that – people break up every day.

HENRY: I won't listen to any more of this. What you're saying is nonsense. What about the things we talked about – a home, a family?

HALIA: They were just dreams. Some dreams don't come true.

HENRY: You've been reading the wrong paperbacks. Look. We love each other. We're free, white, and twenty-one. So what's the natural thing to do?

HALIA: For my mother – to enter a house by way of the back door.

HENRY: But I don't want to marry your mother!

HALIA: She comes in the same package. You order one, you get the other free.

HENRY: So you get a mother from my side. So we're even. Now, let's start where we left off...

HALIA: Uh-uh. It's got to be a clean break. No sentimental slush.

HENRY: (*unbelievingly*) You're serious!

HALIA: Marriage is serious.

HENRY: Look, honey. What's most important? It would have been nice if our mothers had been compatible. Okay. So they're not. So let's look at us.

HALIA: You lost me away back. I'm still looking at our mothers. Mine is very important to me.

HENRY: What about me? Remember me?

HALIA: Oh, yes, I do.

HENRY: Then what's the problem?

HALIA: Mama's happiness matters to me. You can't build your own happiness on someone else's misery. Especially if that someone else is your mother.

HENRY: I'll make you forget your worries, everything. Give me a chance.

HALIA: How long would that last? Till our honeymoon was over. Then we'd have to come back and face facts. I couldn't stand my mother's rejecting me...or you... (*cries*)

HENRY: I'm sorry you have to cry. I haven't seen you cry before.

HALIA: It's nothing. I'm especially good when I peel onions.

HENRY: (*Doesn't know which way to turn. He reaches for his hat and turns to the door, then turns back and holds out his hand uncertainly.*) Then it's goodbye. (*She comes to him and takes his hand, but the next moment they are crushed in each other's arms. She pulls herself free and turns away. Henry's voice seems suddenly mature.*) One thing. This clean break business – that's your idea. I still think we could work it out. And if you change your mind about our date tonight, I'll be waiting at the drugstore. (*exits*)

ANNA: (*Appears in bedroom doorway. Halia rushes into her arms, sobbing.*) I know, I know ...

HALIA: I'll get over it, Mama.

ANNA: Come over to sofa, *donyu*. I want speak with you.

HALIA: I don't want to talk about – him.

ANNA: Not about him, *donyu*. About my own father. You know he dead a long time. But many year ago, when I young girl like you back in Carpathian Ukraine, he love me like I love you today. He want me to stay wit' him in old country, but I want go away, see new world. We had quarrel. But I stubborn. I sail away to Canada. He never write.

HALIA: Never?

ANNA: Not for very long time. Then one day I write I am getting married in Canada. On my wedding day, I get dis letter from my father. Henry found letter in Kiev book. It lost t'irty year.

HALIA: Thirty years!

ANNA: I will read you little bit. (*Reads*) "At home in mountains are bighorn sheep. Young mountain sheep go fast to very top of mountain, see green pasture far away, and leave flock for new grazing ground. But old sheep cannot climb high. Must stay in lower pasture, and graze there. So I am old. I cannot go high up any more. But you, Anna, you young. You climb higher and higher till you young feet carry you to top of mountain. And only you can see new distant pasture land, green and beautiful. So," my father writes, "go, Anna, climb high as you can. I old and must stay below. I can no more help you, my child, but I can wish you Godspeed."

HALIA: He *did* forgive you, Mama – and on your wedding day.

ANNA: Yes, but when letter found, it come like a message from God to me.

HALIA: Message?

ANNA: Yes. For you, Halia. Now it is I who am too old to see new future. But you are young, and future belong to young.

HALIA: Mama, I won't listen any more.

ANNA: Yes, you will listen. And you will go to you Henry Smit'.

HALIA: But ...

ANNA: And not tomorrow or next week – tonight.

HALIA: I don't know what to say ...

ANNA: You say not'ing. Just go.

HALIA:(*looks searchingly at her mother, then speaks with decision and joy*) I will, Mama. I'll go to him.

ANNA: And Godspeed, my child.

Curtain

Joy Kogawa

What Do I Remember of the Evacuation?

From "What Do I Remember of the Evacuation?" by Joy Kogawa. Reprinted by permission of The Canadian Publishers, McClelland and Stewart Limited, Toronto.

What do I remember of the evacuation?
I remember my father telling Tim and me
About the mountains and the train
And the excitement of going on a trip.
What do I remember of the evacuation?
I remember my mother weeping
A blanket around me and my
Pretending to fall asleep so she would be
    happy
Though I was so excited I couldn't sleep
(I hear there were people herded
Into the Hastings Park like cattle.
Families were made to move in two hours
Abandoning everything, leaving pets
And possessions at gun point.
I hear families were broken up
Men were forced to work. I heard
It whispered late at night
That there was suffering) and
I missed my dolls.
What do I remember of the evacuation?
I remember Miss Foster and Miss Tucker
Who still live in Vancouver
And who did what they could
And loved the children and who gave me
A puzzle to play with on the train.
And I remember the mountains and I was
Six years old and I swear I saw a giant
Gulliver of Gulliver's Travels scanning
    the horizon
And when I told my mother she believed
    it too
And I remember how careful my parents
    were
Not to bruise us with bitterness
And I remember the puzzle of Lorraine Life
Who said "Don't insult me" when I
Proudly wrote my name in Japanese
And Tim flew the Union Jack
When the war was over but Lorraine
And her friends spat on us anyway
And I prayed to the God who loves
All the children in his sight
That I might be white.

Robert Finch

Select Samaritan

We think we might adopt two children and
The problem is to know which kind we want.
Not Canadians.   Refugees.   But they can't
Be Jewish.   A couple of Spaniards would be grand
If they were fair.   My husband hates dark hair.
Afraid they are mostly dark in any case.
Germans would do, we don't care about race,
Except Chinese, must draw the line somewhere.

So would you let us know soon as you could
What sort's available?   We have a car
And would be glad to come and look them over
Whatever time you say.   Poles might be good,
Of the right type.   Fussy?   Perhaps we are
But any kids we take will be in clover.

From *Poems* by Robert Finch. Reprinted by permission of Oxford University Press.

Walter Stewart

O-Oh Say, What They See

*"I got nothing against the place,
but what has Canada
ever done?"*

There is no American attitude to Canada. Some Americans love us, some despise us, most view us with indifference. Sometimes, the indifference is tinged with contempt; more often, with warmth. Sometimes it contains neither heat nor cold, it is indifference pure and simple.

Americans are not constantly confronted, as we are, with the actions and neglects, comings and goings, virtues and failures, of their next-door neighbor. We, perforce, hold strong views about them because they loom across our horizon, dominate our trade, bestride our culture; we love them or we hate them, but we are not indifferent. They can afford a wider range of responses. For most, we are merely a background noise; it is easy to tune us out.

I wanted to find out what Americans really think about us, and I began collecting material for a book in October, 1974. The surveying technique was not scientific, nor even consistent. By not scientific, I mean that no attempt was made to balance the sample for race, economic level, religion, urban-versus-rural background, or even sex. I simply lighted on whomever happened to

be handy and blurted out my question: What do you think of when you think of Canada or Canadians? By not consistent, I mean that the question wasn't always put that way. It depended on how the conversation got started.

At first, I always carried my tape-recorder at the ready; sometimes I even had it on as I strolled along. But a tape-recorder can be inhibiting, even to a people as accustomed to being badgered, surveyed, and poked at with hidden cameras as the Americans. In a small town in Alabama I braced the local police force in a dry goods store, hoisted up my tape-recorder, and asked him what he thought of Canada. He began to make abrupt gestures with his hand, but didn't say anything. Finally, he made a cutting motion, and it dawned on me that he wanted me to turn the tape-recorder off. I did that, and he said, "Try to tape me, boy, and ah'll break your arm." I said, "Oh." After that, I was more circumspect; sometimes I used the recorder, sometimes not. I always carried a notebook, and turned to that if the subject seemed likely to balk.

I also dropped my earlier resolve to use everybody's name, age and address, the way I was taught as a boy journalist many years ago. People who thought they might be held to account some day, might be criticized, or

From *As They See Us* by Walter Stewart. Reprinted by permission of The Canadian Publishers, McClelland and Stewart Limited, Toronto.

even singled out, either clammed up or retreated into banalities. Knowing they were free to fire away, my subjects began to put a little more muscle into their remarks. I was astonished to find that – once the discussion is opened to uninhibited comment – there are pockets of entrenched ill-feeling toward Canada.

I accept no responsibility for the views propounded; the ignorance often appalled me, the occasional hostility astonished me, and some of the offbeat comments – that Canadians sleep a lot, for example, or that we can't cook – struck me as simply daffy. I do accept responsibility for trying to depict, fairly and accurately, the complex range of American views about Canada.

Canadians sleep all the time. They sleep more than any other people in the whole, wide world. Every time you turn around, they're going off somewhere to have a nap.
Printer, Huntington, N.Y.

They're nice folks, not in a hurry all the time. They're like Southerners in that, though, of course, they live up north.
Farm wife, near Evergreen, Alabama

A God-fearing people, instilled and inspired of the true love of Jesus, an example to others, as the Book says.
Lay preacher, Racine, Wisconsin

Canada? I don't know nothing about it. This bus just goes to Farragut Square.
Bus driver, Washington, D.C.

Canadian drivers are crazy. I'm sorry, but there's no other word for it. They put their foot on the gas and their hand on the horn and look out, here I come. I wonder if it's got anything to do with their religion.
Tour guide, Williamsburg, Virginia

That's a very fine place, with very fine people, but they've still got a Queen up there tells them what to do. I wouldn't like that if I was them.
Warehouse clerk, Providence, Rhode Island

Canada is absolutely vital to this country. There is no nation in the world that can compare with Canada as a safe, reliable supply of needed resources. Political stability is there, the resources are there, the friendship is there, and the need for American dollars is there. It's all there.
Research assistant, oil company, New York, N.Y.

I think if we need it and they won't give it to us, we should just take it.
National Guardsman, Fremont, Ohio

I used to be all in favor of Canada. Some of my best friends, and all that. But that was up until they elected that Commie Prime Minister. Trudeau is his name. A Commie, everybody knows it. A fellow from out west, he got up in the Congress and said it right out, that the Prime Minister of Canada was a Commie. Well, I naturally expected that to be the end of Mr. Trudeau. No such thing. If they didn't go and put him right back in the next time. All I can say is that was the end of Canada, as far as I'm concerned, and I don't care who knows it.
Farmer, near Rutland, Vermont

Canada, that's up north, near New York State, isn't it? Only it's not a state, it's a whole country. Is that right? Do I win a prize?
Liquor store clerk, Albuquerque, New Mexico

A lot of the people speak French and a lot of the other people don't. And those that don't don't like those that do. I read that in the paper.
Security guard, Banning, California

Mountains, I think of mountains, and people singing.
Housewife, Austin, Texas

158 | Canada – just to say the name gives me goose bumps. It's so romantic. Vancouver, Canada, or Montreal, Canada – when I see that in the paper it's like reading Paris, France. It has a faraway, exciting ring to it.
Typist, Albuquerque, New Mexico

"Pardon me, but can you tell me anything about Canada, or Canadians?"
  "Short hair."
  "Anything else?"
  "Nope."
In a barber shop, East Holden, Maine

My boy got his draft notice and said to hell with it and went up to Canada. He got a job up there, he's an English major, but he got a job working with crippled kids, for the government, not much money but he liked it. He couldn't come back here, of course; he's still on the indictment list as a deserter. He wasn't good enough for the U.S., but he was good enough for Canada, so now he's becoming a Canadian citizen. Good for him, and good for Canada, treating him right.
Pensioner, Washington, D.C.

We went up to the border once, but they wouldn't let my Dad through with his rifle and pistol, so we had to come back, 'cause he wouldn't go anywhere without a gun, he needs it for protection. Why would they do that to him?
Mechanic, Napa, California

They don't have any heroes, and not much history.
History student, University of Rochester, N.Y.

Canadian whisky is good, Canadian weather is bad and the Canada goose is a bird. That's the sum total of my knowledge.
History student, University of Arizona, Tucson

Canada produced Anne Murray, what more can I say? Fantastic!
Insurance salesman, Richmond, Virginia

My mother always told me Canadians made beautiful blankets. You should get a Canadian blanket, she used to say. They really know how to make blankets up there. Well, I've seen Canadian blankets, and they look just like American blankets to me.
Waitress, Minot, North Dakota

My daughter lived with a Canadian doctor in San Francisco. He seemed real nice, he was very generous and kind, kind of a tubby fella, but friendly. He didn't marry her, though.
Saleslady, Minot, North Dakota

They took in draft dodgers, yellerbellies, and that weren't right.
Pensioner, Kearney, Nebraska

"I don't know what to think of a country where I've never heard of a single writer from there. I've heard of British writers and German writers and Russian writers and French writers and I even know of a Swiss writer, but I have never heard of a Canadian writer."
  "How about Morley Callaghan?"
  "Who?"
  "You've never heard of Pierre Berton, or Farley Mowat, or Margaret Laurence?"
  "Margaret Laurence is a South African. I've heard of her. She's a South African."
  "She's a Canadian."
  "Well, it shows. I thought she was a South African. It shows what I mean about Canada."
Literary conversation with an English Lit. Major, University of California at Los Angeles

I got nothing against the place, but what has Canada ever done? You never hear "Canadian Astronaut Lands On Moon," do you? No, really, do you? Or Canadian-Russian troops clash, or Canada invents new medical miracle, no, really, do you? So, what kind of place is it?
National Guardsman, Cleveland, Ohio

All I can think of is a railroad going through beautiful mountains. That's Canada.
Student, Boston College, Boston, Massachusetts

Nice people, very nice. Not bright, but nice.
Tractor salesman, Fargo, North Dakota

You never hear anything bad about Canada, that's one thing. In fact, I guess it's the only thing.
English major, University of Indiana, Bloomington

They're very polite, come in, sign the register – a lot of people don't sign the register – and we answer any questions, and they're really friendly. Maybe you get a better class of people when they travel, maybe all Canadians aren't like that, I'm not saying, but they seem real interested in the history of San Francisco. And they always say "thank you."
Tourist guide, San Francisco, California

"Yew cain't hardly unnerstan' what Canadians say, the way they tawk."

"What do you mean?"

"They tawk funny, sorta mumbly an' ah donno whatall. Yew cain't harly make 'em aout."

"Am I doing it now?"

"Yessir, yew surely ahr."
In a restaurant, Tucker, Georgia

Canadians do some things very well, know what I mean, and other things not so hot and some things not at all. You take hockey, Canadians can really play hockey. When the Rangers were up on top, it was all Canadians, whether it was your Andy Bathgate or whoever, they wasn't hardly any Americans in the game and they still ain't. But you take your baseball, Canada isn't even in it. You got Montreal Expos, yeah, but a Canadian couldn't get on the team without he showed his passport, know what I mean? Your football, same thing, who the hell ever heard of a Canadian football player?

I don't know why it is they should be so good at hockey and not them other things. Only thing I figure is, it's so cold up there, they gotta play hockey all the time to keep warm.
Cab driver, New York, N.Y.

Look around here, you want to see some Canadians. Doctors. You see a lot of Canadian doctors come down here to get away from that godawful socialized medicine they've got up there. That and the weather.
Physician, Phoenix, Arizona

I think every American dreams of having a tract of land in Canada where he could retire and retreat from the world. A mythology of the frontier. Around the table in a saloon, you'll hear people talking about having a hunting lodge in Canada or a farm up in the Canadian hills. There's a mysticism, the cleanness, the wide expanses.
Store manager, Hays, Kansas

They got a game up there, you ever hear of it, called curling? You have this big stone and you throw it down the ice, like bowling, really more like lawn bowling, and these other people standing around have brooms and they brush the living hell out of the ice and that's the way it's played. I saw it on the television one time. It's practically a national sport the way the guy explained it, and he said they used to play it with jam pots. What the hell? They say you can tell a lot about people by the sport, you know, they reflect what they feel in the sports they pick. Well, all I got to say is every time I think of Canada I think of these poor, dumb nuts flailing away with a broom while a rock goes whizzing by.
Hardware clerk, Cape Charles, Virginia

159

Canada has always stood for peace in my mind until they went and gave India the bomb. That was a very crappy thing to do and I couldn't understand it. Canada took a very major role as peacemaker in the Middle East and that in the Suez thing and here they are giving away the bomb to the Indians. Screwy thing to do. I can only assume that something's going on up there that we don't know about down here that would make them swing around like that.

Psychology major, Harvard University, Cambridge, Massachusetts

They's good fishermen, that's for sure. They know what to do with a net and a boat. Sometimes they's pushy, that's okay, we pushes back.

Fisherman, Ocean Point, Maine

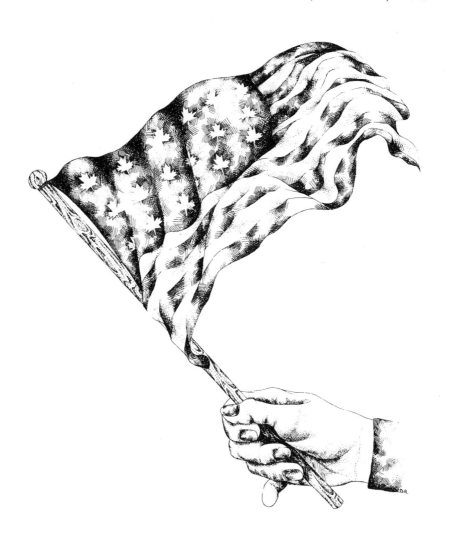

Elizabeth Brewster

Jamie

When Jamie was sixteen,
Suddenly he was deaf. There were no songs,
No voices any more.
He walked about stunned by the terrible silence.
Kicking a stick, rapping his knuckles on doors,
He felt a spell of silence all about him,
So loud it made a whirring in his ears.
People moved mouths without a sound escaping:
He shuddered at the straining of their throats.
And suddenly he watched them with suspicion,
Wondering if they were talking of his faults,
Were pitying him or seeing him with scorn.
He dived into their eyes and dragged up sneers,
And sauntering the streets, imagined laughter behind him.
Working at odd jobs, ploughing, picking potatoes,
Chopping trees in the lumber woods in winter,
He became accustomed to an aimless and lonely labor.
He was solitary and unloquacious as a stone,
And silence grew over him like moss on an old stump.
But sometimes, going to town,
He was sore with the hunger for company among the people,
And, getting drunk, would shout at them for friendship,
Laughing aloud in the streets.
He returned to the woods,
And dreaming at night of a shining cowboy heaven
Where guns crashed through his deafness, woke morose,
And chopped the necks of pine trees in his anger.

Reprinted by permission of the author.

Russell Freedman

Light for the Blind

Braille never knew that his system
would someday win universal acceptance.

The dormitory was dark and still. Only one boy was still awake. He sat on the edge of his bed at a far corner of the room, holding a sheet of thick paper on his lap. Slowly and deliberately, he punched tiny holes across the page with the point of a sharp stylus.

A husky whisper coming from the next bed finally interrupted him. "Louis? That you? Still punching dots?"

"Shh! Be quiet, Gauthier. It's late. You'll wake up everyone."

"You'd better quit and get some rest, Louis. The director will be furious if you doze off in class again."

"I know. I know. I'm almost finished now. Please, go back to sleep."

Louise Braille placed his paper and stylus on a shelf behind his bed. Extending his arm before him, he walked across the dormitory and stood before an open window. He was a gaunt boy, but handsome, with sharp, intelligent features which made him seem somewhat older than his thirteen years. His appearance was marred only by his eyes. Tinged with purple, they stared blankly from above prominent cheekbones.

Louis was a student at the National Institute for Blind Youth in Paris. For months now he had been absorbed in a project which had fired his imagination and dominated his entire life. He was trying to work out a special system of reading and writing for the blind, a system based on combinations of dots punched into paper....

From the street below, Louis heard the rumble of wheels and the clicking of horses' hoofs as a carriage moved rapidly past along the cobblestone pavement. Suddenly he felt lonely and homesick. A warm April breeze swept through the room, reminding him of spring in his own village. Louis tried to remember what the village square looked like. But he knew it was useless. He could remember nothing he had ever seen. He had been blind much too long.

As a child, Louis used to sit on the stone floor of the harness shop, hugging his knees as he watched his father, Simon, at work. Simon Braille was the saddle and harness maker in Coupvray, a small farming village about twenty miles east of Paris.

Sometimes the boy tried to imitate his father. One morning shortly before his fourth birthday, Louis watched carefully as Simon punched holes down a long strip of leather. Then the youngster went to the workbench and picked out an awl which looked like the one his father was using. He began hacking away at a stray piece of leather he found on the floor.

Pretending to measure with one eye, as he had often seen his father do, Louis bent his head close to the leather scrap and stabbed hard with the awl. The sharp instrument

Reprinted by permission of the author.

glanced off the smooth surface of the leather, and Louis shrieked.

Simon whirled around from his bench; blood was streaming down the boy's face. The frightened harness maker stooped over to pick his son up and saw to his horror that the blood was coming from Louis' eye. Clutching the hysterical child in his arms, he ran out into the courtyard, shouting for his wife. Louis' mother flung open the door of their stone house. "Merciful God!" she screamed "What is it! The child's face!" She pulled Louis from his father's arms and rushed back into the house.

Simon ran back across the courtyard, leaped on his horse, and galloped off to find the local doctor. By the time he returned, Louis lay on his straw pallet beneath a dormer window on the second floor of the house.

The boy had punctured his eye. There was little the doctor could do but shake his head and apply cold compresses to the wound. Later, when infection set in, he was helpless. Within a few days, the infection had spread to Louis' other eye. Louis lay in a darkened room for nearly two weeks, a bandage wrapped tightly about his head. Each day when the doctor came, Louis' parents asked, "For the love of God, what can we do?" And each day, the doctor answered, "You can do nothing but pray."

Simon and his wife waited nervously as the bandage was finally removed from their son's eyes. Watching the boy carefully, the doctor threw back the window shutters, flooding the room with sunlight. Louis did not blink. "What do you see?" the doctor asked. He took Louis in his arms and carried him to the window. "Come, come now. What do you see?"

"Nothing, monsieur," Louis murmured, in a barely audible voice. "I see nothing."

When Louis was old enough, he entered the village school. Since he was a bright boy, he outshone many of his classmates in subjects requiring only a good memory. But most subjects depended on reading and writing, and Louis, being blind, could not hope to learn to read or write. The schoolmaster took great pride in the youngster's accomplishments, completely overlooking his failings. After all the poor little one was blind. What could be expected? Any accomplishments at all seemed miraculous.

Louis' mother and father, however, could not overlook his failings. They knew that no matter how bright or adaptable their son might be, he could never take his place in the life of the village. What would happen to him when his parents were gone? At the time, the vast majority of the blind were forced to earn their livelihood as professional beggars. The Brailles prayed that this would not be the fate of their son.

They found an answer to their prayers shortly before Louis' tenth birthday. One day the village priest returned from a trip to Paris and went immediately to the Braille house. He had visited a remarkable school, he said, a school where blind youngsters were taught useful trades. But the greatest miracle was this: the poor sightless ones could learn to read and write by a special method.

On the morning of February 15, 1819, six weeks after Louis' tenth birthday, he was bundled up for the trip to Paris. It had been decided that he would enter the school, live there for a few weeks, and then return home if he wished.

Shortly after daybreak every morning, a loud gong reverberated through the corridors of the ramshackle old building which housed the National Institute for Blind Youth. Soon afterward, a rapid tapping of canes advanced down the hallways and converged on the school's dining room, where the students bent hurriedly over breakfasts of thick porridge and steaming coffee mixed with scalded milk. At the end of the meal, an instructor called for silence, waited for the talk to subside, and made any necessary announcements. Then there was a rattling of dishes, the rumble of chairs being pushed back, and again, the tapping of canes as the students crowded out of the dining room to start the day's activities.

Gradually, Louis grew accustomed to his new surroundings. He made his first friend, a young student named Gauthier, and began to feel like a welcome member of a group, not an isolated object of pity as he had been in Coupvray. More important, he realized that his blindness was not an insurmountable obstacle. The accomplishments of his classmates proved that. Before long, Louis felt at home at the institute and became a surprisingly alert and eager pupil.

As a new student, his first lessons were in embossing, the best system of reading and writing then available to the blind. Embossing meant printing large letters of the alphabet into thick, heavy paper. The result was similar to an embossed calling card; the impressions left on the other side of the paper could be "read" by tracing their outlines with the finger.

To begin with, Louis practised the alphabet until he could print each individual letter and recognize its shape with his finger tips. Then he was able to write his first sentence: *My name is Louis Braille*. Finally, he was ready to enter the reading classes where students slowly ran their fingers across huge pages of embossed print, bound in heavy, cumbersome volumes which had to be propped up on wooden platforms in the middle of the room.

Embossed books were necessarily large.

The printed letters had to be widely spaced and tall enough to be clearly legible to the touch. One page of embossed print contained only a few sentences at most. The thick embossing paper could be printed on one side only, and individual pages were pasted back-to-back before being bound. Several weighty volumes were required to contain the text of a small schoolbook. As a result, embossed books were not only ponderous, but extremely expensive as well. Not many were printed. Once a student left the institute, it was almost as if he had never learned to read at all, for in the outside world, embossed books were practically nonexistent.

Like all students before him, Louis was bitterly disappointed in the system. The blind, he discovered, had to read slowly and hesitantly, just as they had to walk slowly and hesitantly. In theory, embossing was a fine idea. But in practice, it was more a classroom exercise than an adequate means of communication.

Even so, Louis was far too busy during his early months at the institute to brood much about the shortcomings of embossing. The institute's program was balanced between practical crafts, academic subjects, and music. His classes included history, grammar, arithmetic, and geography. In his geography classroom, there was a large relief map of France. The first time Louis placed his fingers on this map, he could actually feel the outlines of Paris. He could trace the winding course of the river Seine into the countryside, touch the sharp pinnacles of the Alps. It was as though the world had suddenly unfolded before him.

But nothing that Louis learned or experienced during his first months at school captured his imagination more than his classes in music. Here, blindness was no obstacle. For this reason, music was heavily emphasized at the institute. Many graduates became professional musicians. In Louis' day, more than fifty graduates played as organists in Paris churches.

Louis took lessons in piano and organ, and soon demonstrated that he was richly talented. In the world of music, there was no stumbling, no hestitation, no fear. Here, he was master, and when the music flowed forth he could scale soaring mountain peaks, lead conquering armies, sail off on voyages of discovery to the far corners of the earth.

By the end of his second year at the institute, Louis was considered one of the most promising youngsters who had ever entered the school. When he returned home for summer vacations, he astonished his family and fellow townspeople with his learning and self-confidence. Louis was even allowed to play the organ at the village church one Sunday, and he spoke hopefully of becoming a professional musician.

Then a dramatic event changed the course of Louis' life. In April 1821, at the beginning of his third year at school, a retired army captain named Charles Barbier called on the director of the institute. Barbier claimed to have invented an improved method of teaching the blind to read and write, a method based on clusters of dots punched into paper.

Barbier called his system "night-writing." Originally, he had devised it as a military code designed to transmit secret messages at night. With the code, sentries at frontline outposts could read simple messages in the dark with their finger tips. Later, it occurred to Barbier that his system of raised dots might be useful to the blind. He made some improvements in the system and then presented it to the Institute for Blind Youth.

The school officials took an interest in

night-writing and began experimenting with it in the classroom. But it soon became apparent that Barbier's system was not suitable. The dot clusters, or symbols, were extremely complex and difficult to read. There was no provision for accurate spelling, punctuation, or numerals. The basic fault, however, lay in the size of the symbols. Like embossed letters, Barbier's symbols were much too large to be read with a single touch of the finger.

Despite these faults, young Braille was fascinated with night-writing. He recognized immediately that the system had one great advantage over embossing. Clusters of dots punched into paper were far more responsive to the touch than the raised impressions of embossed letters.

Before long, Barbier's code held no secrets for Louis. He and his friend Gauthier practised with the system by writing sentences and giving them to each other to read. But their enthusiasm was not shared by the teachers at the institute. After a few months, the teachers decided that night-writing was hopelessly impractical as an effective means of reading and writing for the blind.

Louis could not believe that night-writing offered no hope of improvement over embossing. He began to experiment with night-writing on his own, and managed to improvise a few simple changes. He hoped to work out new dotted symbols representing the letters of the alphabet, numerals, and punctuation marks. At first, he had no luck at all.

He began working in the dormitory late at night, after his fellow students had gone to bed. Sometimes he dozed off from exhaustion, the stylus grasped tightly in his hand as though he wanted to continue working in his sleep. Occasionally, he lost all track of time and was still punching dots when the jolting sounds of the first wagons moving along the street suddenly made him conscious of day-break.

Louis had never been robust, and this demanding schedule began to have a telling effect. He fell asleep in class. He lost weight and developed a persistent cough. Often he wondered if he were merely wasting his time.

At home and at school, Louis worked on his system for nearly three years before finally evolving a practical alphabet of dotted symbols. The alphabet was finally ready to be demonstrated at the opening of the fall term in 1824. Louis was only fifteen years old, yet he had succeeded in devising the basis of the system which was destined to open the doors of learning to millions of blind people in future generations. His system seems simple enough at first glance, but that is a true indication of its genius. A simple system is exactly what he had spent hundreds of hours trying to develop.

To begin with, Louis had reduced Barbier's dot clusters to a basic unit small enough to be encompassed by the tip of the finger. This unit, now called the Braille cell, has space for six dots – two across and three down:

1	• •	4
2	• •	5
3	• •	6

Within this cell, Louis worked out different combinations of dots, each combination representing a letter of the alphabet. As used today, the first ten symbols of the system represent the first ten letters of the alphabet and the ten Arabic numerals.

	A	B	C	D	E
	1	2	3	4	5

	F	G	H	I	J
	6	7	8	9	0

Additional letters and numerals are formed by placing dot combinations under these ten symbols. Eventually, Louis devised sixty-three different symbols, including the entire alphabet, numerals, punctuation signs, contractions, some commonly used words, and later, musical notation and mathematical signs. For use in writing his system, he adapted the same device Barbier had used to write his military code – a perforated metal slate. A thick sheet of paper was placed beneath this slate, and a stylus used to punch through the perforations.

With this system, young Braille swept away all the faults of embossing. His dotted symbols were simple and complete. They could be read rapidly and easily with a light touch of the finger, and they took up little more space than conventional printed letters. For the first time in the history of mankind, all the world's literature could be placed at the finger tips of the blind.

Louis unveiled his system in a classroom after dinner one evening. He asked one of the sighted teachers to select a passage from any book. "Read from it slowly and distinctly," he said, "as though you were reading to a sighted friend who was going to copy down all your words."

The teacher chose Milton and began to recite the sonorous lines of the blind poet. Seated in the centre of the room, Louis worked over his slate and stylus, transcribing Milton's words as rapidly as they were read to him. The sighted teachers leaned forward in their seats and watched him. The blind teachers listened intently to the sound of the metal point punching through the paper.

After the passage had been read, Louis ran his finger over his transcript for a moment, as if to reassure himself. Then he stood up. In a tense voice, he repeated Milton's lines at about the same speed at which the sighted teacher had read them, without missing a word or making an error. When he finished, an excited murmur filled the room, and the teachers crowded around him.

The institute's director, Dr. Pignier, was convinced. "This is a remarkable thing you have done," he said. "I am going to instruct the teachers to begin using your system in the classroom. But you must understand, Louis, that your method has not yet been proved. Before it can be officially adopted, we must give it a thorough trial."

Louis' alphabet of dots was mastered quickly by his fellow students. For the first time, they were able to take notes in class. They could now write letters, keep diaries, and engage in correspondence with comparative ease. Louis personally began the task of transcribing the first textbook into his system, a small volume called *Grammar of Grammars*.

Yet he was still not satisfied. During his remaining years as a student, he continued to improve and simplify his system. Meanwhile, he did not neglect his studies. In 1826, when Louis was seventeen, he became an assistant teacher. When he graduated the following year, Dr. Pignier regarded him as indispensable, and asked him to stay on at the institute as a professor of algebra, grammar, and geography. Louis accepted gladly. By now, the institute had become home to him.

In 1828, Louis began to apply his system to musical notation. By 1829, when he reached his twentieth birthday, his dotted alphabet had been perfected to the point where it was substantially the same as the Braille system used today by the blind. That year Louis published a small pamphlet called *Method of Writing Words, Music and Plain Songs by Means of Dots, for Use by the Blind and Arranged for Them*. In the preface to this pamphlet, he carefully gave credit to everyone who had helped him evolve his system, particularly to Charles Barbier, inventor of night-writing. "We must say in his honor," wrote Louis, "that his method gave us the first idea of our own."

Braille's invention has opened a new age for the blind. His system could be applied to any language, to longhand or shorthand, to mathematics or music. For the first time, it offered the blind the promise of convenient, inexpensive books. It gave them the opportunity to read those books with a facility approaching that of the sighted. Yet outside the Institute for Blind Youth, the system had been ignored. Dr. Pignier's repeated requests for government approval of the dotted alphabet had been lost in a limbo of red tape and official inertia.

Louis Braille spent the rest of his life at the National Institute for Blind Youth, struggling to gain official acceptance for his dotted alphabet, and training a growing corps of students in its use. The blind immediately recognized the superiority of his system. As students graduated, they went out into the world like fervent missionaries, carrying word of the system with them. Yet government authorities continued to ignore Braille's work. Embossing remained the official method of teaching the blind at the Paris institute, and at other schools all over Europe.

These were disappointing years, but

168 Braille found some consolation in his teaching and music. He was exceptionally popular as a teacher. As one of his students wrote, "Attending his classes was a pleasure to enjoy rather than a duty to fulfill."

During these years, Braille's health declined steadily. The cough which had started during his student days had developed into a severe case of tuberculosis. Still in his twenties, he was forced to give up many of his outside activities and make several prolonged trips home to Coupvray to recuperate.

Then in 1840, he nearly lost all hope for eventual recognition of his dotted alphabet. Dr. Pignier, who had encouraged his efforts from the beginning, retired as director of the institute. The new director, a man named Dufau, immediately declared his opposition to Braille's system. After ten years of official indifference, Braille was now confronted with outright hostility. The faith shown by his fellow blind was the one thing which sustained him during this dismal period of discouragement and ill-health. Before long, a silent war had broken out between the school administration and the blind students and teachers. "We had to use the Braille system in secret," one of the students later wrote, "and when we were caught using it, we were punished."

It was the insistence of the blind themselves which finally enabled Braille's system to prevail. Eventually, Dufau realized that enthusiasm for the dotted alphabet could never be stifled. He decided to reconsider before the blind teachers forced a showdown, and in 1844 he announced publicly that the Braille system would be adopted as the standard means of instruction at the National Institute for Blind Youth. Thus, after twenty years of unceasing work and struggle, Louis Braille enjoyed his first official success.

By this time, he was seriously ill. He continued to teach a bit longer, but with his constant cough, his voice began to fail and he could not be heard as he lectured. He no longer had the energy to work more than two or three hours a day. Finally, he could not work at all. Not yet forty, he was forced to abandon both his teaching duties and his own projects. He spend the final years of his life as a semi-invalid at the institute.

Braille never knew that his system would someday win universal acceptance. When he died just after his forty-third birthday, his alphabet had not yet spread to other parts of Europe and he was still virtually unknown outside his own school. There was no mention of official awards. The Paris newspapers did not devote a single line to his passing. Few people realized that in his brief lifetime he had done more than anyone else in history to make the blind part of the world around them.

Today, the saddler's son from Coupvray has received the highest honor his country can bestow. He rests in the Pantheon among France's immortals. His system is in use throughout the world, in nearly every country and in every language. It has been adapted to African dialects and to the complexities of the Chinese ideogram. Networks of Braille libraries offer the blind a vast range of reading material. Other than sight itself, no gift could be more precious to the blind.

Braille's stone house in Coupvray has been preserved as a shrine. A plaque on the front of the house reads:

In this house
on January 4, 1809
was born
LOUIS BRAILLE
the inventor of the system of
writing in raised dots for use
by the blind
He opened the doors of
knowledge to all those
who cannot see

The public square in Coupvray, where the boy Louis once sat in the sun with his cane over his knees, is now called Braille Square and is the site of a national monument. On one side of the monument, a relief statue shows Louis teaching a blind child to read. The other side is inscribed with the alphabet invented by the fifteen-year-old boy who refused to accept the limitations of his own blindness.

Al Capp

My Well-Balanced Life on a Wooden Leg

With two legs I had been a nobody.
With one leg I was somebody.

I became a candidate for a wooden leg on August 21, 1919, when I was nine years old. That day my father, a vague and unworldly man, gave me fifty cents to get a haircut: thirty-five cents for the haircut, five cents for a tip, ten cents for trolley fare. At least that was the way he figured it. I, a calculating and worldly kid, figured it a little differently. I had seen a tantalizing offer on a sign in a downtown New Haven window: "Prof. Amoroso, Barber Academy – Haircuts fifteen cents – No Tipping." By hitching a ride on the back of an ice wagon I could step into Professor Amoroso's with fifty cents and, with luck, step out again with most of the money (and possibly some of my scalp) intact. Clutching that fifty-cent piece, blinded with dreams of riches and power, I hopped off the ice cart in front of the barber academy – and directly in the path of a huge old-fashioned trolley car. I was caught under the wheels and before the car could be stopped my left leg was severed at the thigh.

©Julie (Manning) Cairol 1981.

During the ride to the hospital and later while I was under anaesthetic, I never once unclutched that half dollar. My mother finally took it from me. For years afterward she kept that coin, the kind of melancholy memento that only mothers understand, in the drawer of her sewing machine. I used to find her now and then, staring into the open drawer and quietly weeping. (A dozen years later, during the Depression and a particularly severe family financial crisis, she opened the drawer again, stared at the coin for the last time, and marched to the grocery store with it.)

Losing a leg at nine is not all loss. For one thing it made me a celebrity among the other kids, to whom I had previously been merely another vague and grubby menace. True, I was not much good at baseball, wrestling, or apple-orchard raiding, but then I never had been much good at them, and now I was spared the embarrassment of displaying my awkwardness. As for grownups, suddenly they noticed spiritual qualities in me as a slow-moving, one-legged boy which had been totally hidden from them when I was a hooting, howling, fast-moving two-legger. Gifts poured in from formerly unenchanted, unprofitable, and unheard-of relatives. Yes, at nine I revelled in the drama and distinction of that shocking pinned-up pants leg and those swagger crutches. With two legs I had been a nobody. With one leg I was somebody.

Then came the day that had been hailed so glowingly by my doctor, my parents, and the local wooden-leg salesman – the day when I could strap on my new leg and walk around again like everyone else. It was one of the most shattering letdowns of my life. I damn well did *not* walk around like everyone else. I went through weeks of stumbling, of toppling, of aching, cursing, and weeping before I mastered the gadget. And still I did not walk around like everyone else. I walked like everyone else who had a wooden leg. I swayed and I dragged.

For a while the other kids were even more fascinated by the wooden leg than they had been by the absence of the real one, and that made a satisfyingly unique figure of me for as long as it lasted. But the novelty wore off and the years wore on. I became a teenager with all the routine problems of teenagers – and one special problem: namely, how to get myself treated by girls in their teens as though I did not have a special problem.

A teenager wants more than anything else in life to look, act, and be treated like all other teenagers. On the first two counts I did fine. I am sure that I looked and behaved as oddly as all the other teenagers at Central High School in Bridgeport, Connecticut, where I then lived. But I got different and special treatment, especially from the girls, and that made life hell for me. My rooster roughness and rowdiness was forgiven with sweet understanding, when what I wanted was the same thrilled contempt that was accorded two-legged rowdies for the same behavior.

So I took to hanging out on street corners. Every afternoon I would leave the high school world, limp a half-dozen blocks along Main Street, and prop myself against the corner of D. M. Read's store at the city's busiest intersection. I was then in a different world, and I was then a different guy. As long as I stayed in one place, the girls I stared at and whistled at treated me like any other street-corner wise guy – with the exaggerated disdain that a nicely behaved girl uses to tell a boy on a street corner who is not behaving very nicely that she would not dream of acknowledging him because she is terribly interested in him. If a girl did look back invitingly, I would look away, pleased but immobile. On a good afternoon there might be as many as a dozen look-backs and look-aways before the streets thinned out. I would go home delighted, having had a remarkable few hours of being treated ordinarily.

Then one day three teen-age girls stopped for traffic in what was then called a roadster, and I aimed a brassy leer their way. Two of them turned up their noses. But the third and prettiest smiled at me – and then, to my joy and dismay, dropped her school pad over the side and motioned me with an inviting smile to pick up the pad and, possibly, her too. My triumph filled me with panic. If I moved she'd find out. So I stared stonily in the other direction until at last they were forced to move on. When I turned back the pad still lay in the street. I limped over and snatched it up. Inside was a girl's name and address. The address was in Brooklawn, then the best residential section of Bridgeport, an area of great houses, all with verandas – and all with steps.

Now to a man who has lost his leg above the knee, steps are an endless horror. On level ground he can make reasonable progress, striding forward with his good leg and

172

rhythmically swinging the wooden one up behind. On steps, however, he must rise on the good leg, stop, pull up the wooden one, rise again with the good leg – pull and stop, pull and stop. It is a slow and unappealing process, the only experience with my wooden leg that irritates me to this day. When I was a boy, it was a humiliation I'd go to any length to avoid.

But I wanted to meet that girl. I phoned her. She had driven off before I could return the pad, I explained gravely, but I would be glad to deliver it to her tonight. She said that was awfully nice of me and maybe if I had no other plans I could have lemonade with her – say at seven o'clock? She would be waiting on the porch.

At a quarter to seven I hurried up the walk to her house. I was deliberately early: if I reached the veranda before her, she would find me seated and would not see me climbing the stairs, or even walking. My plan worked fine, and when she opened the door a few minutes before seven, I was waiting. There was a long pause.

"I'm sorry," she said at last from the doorway. "But I can't see you tonight. I have to go away. Thank you for returning the pad. Please leave it on the chair." She turned back in, and the door closed behind her.

I dropped the pad and hurried down the stairs and away as fast as I could. I never saw her again. It would have been too much for both of us to bear, for we had both been playing the same game. I had arrived early so she would not see me walk. She had planned to be waiting on the porch so I would not see her walk. For in the instant of her turning away at the door, I had seen the stiffening of her shoulder, the outthrust movement of her hip – the sure signs that she, too, of all the sad, shy girls on earth, had an artificial leg.

In time much of my embarrassment about the leg passed. I discovered that there are three types of wooden-leg wearers: one large group, one small group – and me. The great majority of people with artificial limbs are reasonable people who treat these appendages with common civility and understanding and give them routine care. They do not deliberately abuse their wooden legs, but they do not go out of their way to pamper them.

Then there is a small, fanatically dedicated group of people who regard themselves as appendages to their wooden legs. They devote their lives to coddling these hunks of wood and tin. They study body balance and coordination. They twist their bodies – and their minds – all out of shape to serve it. I once knew a quiet, bookish, tolerably interesting young man who lost his leg. Suddenly he changed. Formerly unathletic, he now devoted his life to proving that he was as good a man as anyone with two legs. He challenged his friends to foot races. He danced like a maniac. He charged and snorted around like a crazed Arabian steed. He became a crashing bore.

Then there is the third group: me. I buy, use and enjoy all the marvellous gadgets of the twentieth century, but I believe their purpose is to serve and understand me, not that mine is to serve and understand them. So when any gadget which I have bought, used and enjoyed but do not understand breaks down, from tie clasp to Cadillac, I abandon it. In the case of my wooden leg, which I cannot abandon, I ignore it. The most I will do is pick up any important parts that drop off and, if I have time, take them around to the nearest garage for a quick repair job. Otherwise I leave my wooden leg to shift for itself. If it wants to come where I am going, all it has to do is follow me.

One result of this sort of stern handling is that I am a free man instead of a slave to a gadget. Another is that now and then I become the central figure of bloodcurdling spectacles, when my leg suddenly and totally disintegrates. Sometimes the result is pure slapstick, such as the time when the collapse of my leg kept me, an eager eighteen-year-old, from making a pass at another eighteen-year-old of the opposite sex. Sometimes the result is merely pleasant, such as the time in Washington a few years ago when the leg broke down just in time to keep me from hearing a speech by Allen Dulles.

The romantic fiasco occurred while I was living in Boston as a pure but impatient art student at the Museum School. One day I was tipped off by a fellow student, a cad and *bon vivant* who had learned much about life in his travels (mainly after dark, from the girls' dormitory to Reservoir Park in his Marmon roadster), that a quiet, hitherto-unnoticed female art student named Norma necked. Now it was not clear to me what this meant exactly, or where exactly it ended, but I was pretty sure it did not end with a wholesome handshake, the way all of my dates had panned out up to then. So I made a date with Norma. I discovered that she lived in Lynn, a suburb of Boston which was reached by a series of trolley routes and finally by a bus. On the way out I discovered that the last bus going in the other direction came by at twelve sharp. After that there was nothing. I had to make hay by midnight if I was going to catch that bus.

Norma's parents, well mannered but totally out of touch with the dreams of youth, stayed around, fed me lemonade and cookies, and jabbered until after eleven, and then, with a reminder that tomorrow was a school day for both of us now frantic children, went upstairs to bed.

It was eleven fifteen. I put my arm around Norma. She said, "Let's go out to the porch." We both rose. Then I sat down. Norma looked at me, puzzled. Then she explained, "It's darker on the porch."

I remained sitting. I had to. My wooden leg was jammed – immovably locked at the knee. I looked all right sitting. Standing, I looked like a crane.

Both Norma and I, frenzied by the inexorable approach of that bus, tugged at that leg, pounded it, yanked it. Aroused by the commotion, Norma's father came down and went at it with a screwdriver and hammer with such vigor that in no time at all the knee joint was separated from the thigh joint, the ankle joint was separated from the knee joint, and the whole mass, including me, was spread in lunatic disorder on the parlor floor.

The bus had long since gone, and so had our golden chance. Norma flounced off to bed and her parents bedded me down on the parlor sofa. The next morning her father gathered my ankle and my knee, my nuts and my bolts, drove them and me in to Boston, and deposited the lot at a wooden leggery.

I called Norma again about three years later, when I had a car and could be sure of getting myself home, intact or in sections, come what may. I could tell that Norma's father, who answered the phone, remembered me, because he said, "Oh, yes, you're the boy who came apart – uh – just a minute, I'll call her to the phone." I then heard Norma being called, my name spoken, and her voice: "Oh, no! Not *him*! Say I've just gone out. We can't go through that again!"

It was thirty years later when my good old unreliable leg rescued me from Allen Dulles. A man who said he was in the State Department called me from Washington. "Mr. Capp," he said, "the President has noticed the increasing hostility toward America all over the world. To counter it he has decided to launch a People-to-People campaign – our people talking plain American sense to the plain people of the rest of the world. He has decided to appoint forty-one leaders of American industry and thought as chairmen of committees to carry out this program. The President want to know if you will accept the chairmanship of the Cartoonists' Committee."

Well, first we had to be checked for security, and then we forty-one certified leaders of American industry and thought were invited to Washington to attend a top-secret, high-level briefing on the world situation, beginning with the President at the White House, running through a luncheon with Vice President Nixon, and winding up with a speech at four o'clock by Mr. Dulles.

By four o'clock we were forty-one mighty disturbed leaders of American industry and thought. We had been given the inside dope. We had been told the appalling news that the Communist Conspiracy and the Free World were locked in a mighty struggle for men's minds and, what was even more appalling, we had been told in exactly those words.

As we entered the meeting room to hear the director of our Central Intelligence Agency, I was walking with a large leader of either American industry or thought, I forget which, named Gene Tunney. Suddenly I know I had better not take another step – I had better grab something solid. So I grabbed Gene Tunney. He looked at me, astonished. I looked astonished at my left pants leg. It was empty, flapping in the breeze, and dripping nuts and bolts. A yard behind, teetering crazily on the carpet, was the naked lower half of my wooden leg, still, of course, gruesomely garbed in shoe and sock.

Forty horrified patriots rushed to my rescue. "Capp has broken his leg," went the cry. "Send for an ambulance!"

"The hell with that," I said. "All I need is a broom to sweep up all this loose stuff, a bag to put it in, and a ride to the nearest garage."

The man at the garage said he could screw me together in a few minutes. "Take your time," I said. And so this story has a happy ending. When I sauntered back into the meeting room, the speech was over. I was, however, provided with a copy of it. Allen Dulles had not minced words. He had stated that the Communist Conspiracy and the Free World were locked in a mighty struggle for men's minds.

As you sway through life on a wooden leg, an odd and blessed thing happens. The rest of the world becomes accustomed, and then forgets that you have one, just as it becomes accustomed to, and then forgets, the color of your eyes or whether you wear a vest. And you become accustomed to the limitations of one-legged life, such as not being able to pole-vault or drive a shift car, or being limited to half as much athlete's foot as other people have. But to children a wooden leg is eternally a surprise and a delight. Strange children gape unabashed, ask questions, and fool with it to see how it works. And when the wooden leg is actually in their own family, it is a sparkling source of entertainment.

When my own children were small they used to come into my bedroom while I dressed and fight for the privilege of pulling Poppa's "broken leg" out from under the bed and handing it to him, just as my grandchildren do now. And I have been asked the same questions by two generations of wide-eyed, fascinated little girls.

"Does it hurt, Poppa (or Grandpa)?"

"No, it feels good. See, no matter how hard I hit it with this shoehorn, it doesn't hurt a bit."

Or, in mock terror: "Poppa! You're not going to stick that tack into your leg!"

"I certainly am. It's the best way to keep a sock up on a leg like this one. Garters slip."

For twenty-five years tiny daughters and granddaughters of mine have been trying to walk like me and have carefully followed me around with one little leg held stiff. My son's reaction was more matter of fact. As a very little boy, he was interested in the mechanics of my leg. When I explained how it worked he instantly lost interest. And small wonder, since the most modern wooden leg is more primitive than a child's simple mechanical toy.

Strange children, like my own children, have always been perfectly straightforward and unembarrassed about my leg. I have responded in kind. "What's the matter with your darn old leg?" they ask.

"It's a wooden leg," I explain.

"Kin I see it?"

I raise my trouser leg a bit and then I go on. It's the best way to handle it, I explain to my startled friends.

But sometimes it is not the best way. One day, walking through Harvard Square in Cambridge, I approached a small boy sitting on the sidewalk, tinkering with a bicycle. He looked up at me without interest and then down with sudden fascination at my left leg.

He rose, staring, to get a better view. It was a creepy sensation, but I just kept walking. As I came up to him he said without lifting his eyes, "Why do you walk so funny?"

I explained why.

"Kin I see it?" said the boy.

I lifted my pants legs and showed it to him. He then went back to his bicycle and I went on with my walk.

The next morning there was the boy again, this time without the bicycle but with another boy. They were waiting for me.

"Show it to him," said my friend. I showed it to both of them.

"Let's see you walk on it some more," they said.

"Sure," I said. They followed me for a while, then vanished.

The next morning there were four of them. I tried to turn down a side street, but they spotted me.

"There he is!" yelled my little nemesis. They all dashed after me. Quite a few people glanced our way.

"Show it to them!" screeched the leading little monster, dancing around me.

"Scat!" I said.

"Lift up your pants," he shouted, "and show us all your wooden leg!"

"Some other time," I managed a smile. "I'm in kind of a hurry, fellas."

"LIFT UP YOUR PANTS," they all roared, "AND SHOW US ALL YOUR WOODEN LAAAIG!"

"YOU ALL GET THE HELL OUT OF HERE," I bellowed, "OR I'LL KICK YOU WITH IT."

Nobody talks to Cambridge kids like that and ever sees them again.

Adults, on the other hand, are embarrassed if they are caught looking at my wooden leg. If they are strangers, they look guiltily away. If they are not, they hastily talk about something else. But nobody ever handled the situation with greater aplomb than the waiter to whom I gave my breakfast order as I lay in bed one morning in the Savoy Hotel in London. As he was taking my order, he caught sight of the shoed and stockinged leg that peeped out from under the bed. He stared. Suddenly he realized that I was watching him. He finished writing down the order, then looked me straight in the eye and said, "Very good, sir. And what will the other gentleman have?"

Anonymous

Of Men and Women

from the 1800-1810 edition of the Encyclopaedia Britannica

The man, bold and vigorous,
is qualified for being a protector;
the woman, delicate and timid,
requires protection.

The man, more robust, is fitted for severe labor, and for field exercise; the woman, more delicate, is fitted for sedentary occupations, and particularly for nursing children. The man, bold and vigorous, is qualified for being a protector; the woman, delicate and timid, requires protection. Hence it is that a man never admires a woman for possessing bodily strength or personal courage; and women always despise men who are totally destitute of these qualities. The man, as a protector, is directed by nature to govern; the woman, conscious of inferiority, is disposed to obey. Their intellectual powers correspond to the destination of nature. Men have penetration and solid judgment to fit them for governing; women have sufficient understanding to make a decent figure under a good government. A greater portion would excite dangerous rivalry between the sexes, which nature has avoided by giving them different talents. Women have more imagination and sensibility than men, which make all their enjoyments more exquisite; at the same time that they are better qualified to communicate enjoyment. Add another capital difference of disposition: the gentle and insinuating manners of the female sex tend to soften the roughness of the other sex; and wherever women are indulged with any freedom, they polish sooner than men.

Alden Nowlan

A Call in December

"Ain't nobody gonna take my baby,"
she crooned.

We stopped at the DeLaGarde shack. Not even tar papered, this one: naked boards the color of a Canadian winter, the long sills set on an island of yellowish ice.

"See that ice?" the old man asked disgustedly. "They built that shack right smack in the middle of a bog hole. Could have built it anywhere. But they built it in a bog hole. What you gonna do for that kind of people?"

At that time we were taking them Christmas gifts: twenty-four pounds of flour, a roast of beef, two packages of margarine.

The old man didn't knock. He walked into the shack and I followed him. I coughed, meeting the fumes of coal oil and the acrid smoke of green maple. Coal oil has to be poured on such wood frequently or the fire will succumb to the moisture and fizzle out.

The girl slumped on the open oven door, clutching a bundle shrouded in a dirty flannel blanket. Greasy black hair like a tangle of snarled shoe laces fell to her sloping shoulders.

She looked up at us, grinning. Her eyes narrowed suddenly, became fox-like and suspicious. The grin vanished. She bent down quickly, the hair flopping over her face, and kissed the hidden baby.

"Mummy loves you," she crooned. "Mummy won't let nobody take her baby."

The old man laid the margarine on the bed. There were neither pillows, quilts nor blankets on the bed: a pile of limp, nauseating rags, crumpled undershirts, socks, scarves, slips, shirts, sweaters, an army tunic, gathered together like a nest so that one knew without being told that something alive had slept there.

"Brought you a little somethin' from the Christmas tree in town," the old man said,

shuffling in embarrassment, but also proud of what he had done and desirous of thanks.

She looked up again.

"Gee. Thanks," she giggled, her eyes soft and remote as a heifer's.

I put the flour and meat on the table, shoving aside plates which had gone unwashed so long that the scraps of food cemented to them had become unrecognizable, ceasing to be bits of bean or shreds of sardine or flecks of mustard and becoming simply dirt, obscene and anonymous.

"Billy's gone to work," she explained, "Ain't nobody here but me and the baby."

She drew the blankets back from the child's face and kissed his forehead fervently. He lay motionless, his eyes flat and unfocussed, only his dull white face protruding from the stained pink flannel.

"Mummy loves you, baby. Oh yes, Mummy loves you. Yes. Mummy loves you. Mummy won't let nobody take her baby away. Mummy's gonna keep her little baby forever and ever. Yes. Mummy's gonna keep her little baby...ain't nobody gonna take my baby."

Her voice trailed away in a wordless chant. She kissed him again and again, the moisture of her spittle glistening on his cheeks, neck, and forehead, his eyes unreachable.

"Glad to hear Billy's workin'," the old man said.

He glanced down at the baby.

"Little feller looks kinda peaked," he said.

Her head jerked up, tossing the hair back.

"What you mean?" she shrilled, her voice pregnant with terror and warning, like a cornered animal's.

"Didn't mean nothin'," the old man soothed her. "Just said he looks a little peaked, that's all."

"Ain't nobody gonna take my baby."

She turned back to the child and repeated the ritual of kisses, smothering him, moaning.

"Ain't nobody gonna take my baby," she whispered. "Ain't nobody gonna take my little baby away from me."

The old man looked at me and winked and shook his head as if he were listening to a story and was not yet sure whether it was supposed to be sad or funny.

"Ain't nobody gonna take my baby," she whispered.

I looked around the room. The bed. The stove. The table. A chair without a back. Corrugated cardboard nailed to the walls to keep out the wind and prevent the snow from sifting in through the cracks. Three pictures: Jesus Christ, Queen Elizabeth II, Elizabeth Taylor. I winked back at the old man, wanting to laugh and wanting to cry and strangely ashamed that I could not choose between tears and laughter.

"Ain't nobody gonna take my baby," she reiterated with the single-mindedness found in birds, children, and the insane.

"We ain't from the welfare, Rita," the old man said.

She looked up again.

"You ain't?"

"No. We just come to bring you this stuff...just a few little things from the Christmas tree in town. Just some stuff to help you out a little bit at Christmas time."

She giggled and hid her head.

"Ain't nobody gonna take my baby."

"Hope not, Rita," the old man said. "Hope not."

I looked down at the floor. Rough boards laid on the ground, the ice visible through the cracks. Pieces of bark. Bits of something that may once have been intended for food. A crust of stale bread. A broken shoe lace. Two empty sardine cans, their tops drawn back like the open mouths of crocodiles. Beer bottle caps. Bits of tinfoil and cellophane.

"Well. Merry Christmas, Rita," the old man said, turning to the door.

"Merry Christmas," I echoed.

"Same to yourself," Rita replied, her voice muffled in the baby's blanket. Once again she was drowning the baby in kisses.

We went outside and shut the door behind us. Rita's voice rose, making certain we could hear.

"Ain't nobody gonna take my baby," she crooned.

We edged gingerly across the yellowish ice and climbed back into the stationwagon.

The old man settled back in his seat and lit his pipe.

"Why in hell does a man have to build his house in a bog hole?" he demanded angrily.

James Mulligan

"Look, Granddad, a have-not."

Gordon Lightfoot

Home from the Forest

Oh, the neon lights were flashing and the ice wind did blow.
The water seeped into his shoes and the drizzle turned to snow.
His eyes were red, his hopes were dead, and the wine was runnin' low,
And the old man came home from the forest.

His tears fell on the sidewalk as he stumbled in the street.
A dozen faces stopped to stare, but no one stopped to speak.
For his castle was a hallway and the bottle was his friend,
And the old man stumbled in from the forest.

Up a dark and dingy staircase, the old man made his way,
His ragged coat around him as upon his cot he lay.
And he wondered how it happened that he'd ended up this way,
Getting lost like a fool in the forest.

And as he lay there sleeping, a vision did appear
Upon his mantle shining the face of one so dear,
Who'd loved him in the springtime of the long-forgotten year,
When the wildflowers did bloom in the forest.

She touched his grizzled fingers and she called him by his name.
And then he heard the joyful sound of children at their games
In an old house on a hillside, in some forgotten town
Where the river runs down from the forest.

With a mighty roar, the big jet soars above the canyon streets.
And the con men con, but life goes on for the city never sleeps.
And to an old forgotten soldier, the dawn will come no more
For the old man has come home from the forest.

Sharon Curtin

Aging in the Land of the Young

A kind of cultural attitude
makes me bigoted against old people;
it makes me think young is best;
it makes me treat old people like outcasts."

Old men, old women, almost twenty million of them. They constitute ten percent of the total population, and the percentage is steadily growing. Some of them, like conspirators, walk all bent over, as if hiding some precious secret, filled with self-protection. The body seems to gather itself around those vital parts, folding shoulders, arms, pelvis like a fading rose. Watch and you see how fragile old people come to think they are.

Aging paints every action grey, lies heavy on every movement, imprisons every thought. It governs each decision with a ruthless and single-minded perversity. To age is to learn the feeling of no longer growing, of struggling to do old tasks, to remember familiar actions. The cells of the brain are destroyed with thousands of unfelt tiny strokes, little pockets of clotted blood wiping out memories and abilities without warning. The body seems slowly to give up, randomly stopping, sometimes starting again as if to torture and tease with the memory of lost strength. Hands become clumsy, frail transparencies, held together with knotted blue veins.

From *Nobody Ever Died of Old Age* by Sharon Curtin. Copyright © 1972 by Sharon R. Curtin.

Sometimes it seems as if the distance between your feet and the floor were constantly changing, as if you were walking on shifting and not quite solid ground. One foot down, slowly, carefully force the other foot forward. Sometimes you are a shuffler, not daring to lift your feet from the uncertain earth but forced to slide hesitantly forward in little whispering movements. Sometimes you are able to "step out," but this effort – in fact the pure exhilaration of easy movement – soon exhausts you.

The world becomes narrower as friends and family die or move away. To climb stairs, to ride in a car, to walk to the corner, to talk on the telephone; each action seems to take away from the energy needed to stay alive. Everything is limited by the strength you hoard greedily. Your needs decrease, you require less food, less sleep, and finally less human contact; yet this little bit becomes more and more difficult. You fear that one day you will be reduced to the simple acts of breathing, and taking nourishment. This is the ultimate stage you dread, the period of helplessness and hopelessness, when independence will be over.

There is nothing to prepare you for the experience of growing old. Living is a process, an irreversible progression toward old age and eventual death. You see men of eighty still vital and straight as oaks; you see men of fifty reduced to grey shadows in the human landscape. The cellular clock differs for each one of us, and is profoundly affected by our own life experiences, our heredity, and perhaps most important, by the concepts of aging encountered in society and in oneself.

The aged live with enforced leisure, on fixed incomes, subject to many chronic illnesses, and most of their money goes to keep a roof over their heads. They also live in a culture that worships youth.

A kind of cultural attitude makes me bigoted against old people; it makes me think young is best; it makes me treat old people like outcasts.

Hate that grey? Wash it away!
Wrinkle cream.
Monkey glands.
Face-lifting.
Look like a bride again.
Don't trust anyone over thirty.
I fear growing old.
Feel Young Again!

I am afraid to grow old – we're all afraid. In fact, the fear of growing old is so great that every aged person is an insult and a threat to the society. They remind us of our own death, that our body won't always remain smooth and responsive, but will someday betray us by aging, wrinkling, faltering, failing. The ideal way to age would be to grow slowly invisible, gradually disappearing, without causing worry or discomfort to the young. In some ways that does happen. Sitting in a small park across from a nursing home one day, I noticed that the young mothers and their children gathered on one side, and the old people from the home on the other. Whenever a youngster would run over to the "wrong" side, chasing a ball or just trying to cover all the available space, the old people would lean forward and smile. But before any communication could be established, the mother would come over, murmuring embarrassed apologies, and take her child back to the "young" side.

Now, it seemed to me that the children didn't feel any particular fear and the old people didn't seem to be threatened by the children. The division of space was drawn by the mothers. And the mothers never looked at the old people who lined the other side of the park like so many pigeons perched on the benches. These well-dressed young matrons had a way of sliding their eyes over, around, through the old people; they never looked at them directly. The old people may as well have been invisible; they had no reality for the youngsters, who were not permitted to speak to them, and they offended the aesthetic eye of the mothers.

My early experiences were somewhat different; since I grew up in a small town, my childhood had more of a nineteenth-century flavor. I knew a lot of old people, and considered some of them friends. There was no culturally defined way for me to "relate" to old people, except the rules of courtesy which applied to all adults. My grandparents were an integral and important part of the family and of the community. I sometimes have a dreadful fear that mine will be the last generation to know old people as friends, to have a sense of what growing old means, to respect and understand man's mortality and his courage in the face of death. Mine may be the last generation to have a sense of living history, of stories passed from generation to generation, of identity established by family history.

John Donne

No Man
Is an Island

No man is an island, entire of itself:
Every man is a piece of the continent,
A part of the main.
If a clod be washed away by the sea,
Europe is the less,
As well as if a promontory were,
As well as if a manor of thy friend
Or of thine own, were.
Any man's death diminishes me,
Because I am involved in mankind;
And, therefore, never send to know
For whom the bell tolls:
It tolls for thee.

Youth:
The Awakening
Years

Brian Patten

Where Are You Now, Batman?

Where are you now, Batman? Now that Aunt Heriot has
    reported Robin missing
And Superman's fallen asleep in the sixpenny childhood
    seats?
Where are you now that Captain Marvel's SHAZAM!
    echoes round the auditorium,
The magicians don't hear it.
Must all be deaf...or dead...
The Purple Monster who came down from the Purple
    Planet disguised as a man
Is wandering aimlessly about the streets
With no way of getting back.
Sir Galahad's been strangled by the Incredible Living
    Trees,
Zorro killed by his own sword.
Blackhawk has buried the last of his companions
And has now gone off to commit suicide in the disused
    Hangars of Innocence.
The Monster and the Ape still fight it out in a room
Where the walls are continually closing in;
Rocketman's fuel tanks gave out over London.
Even Flash Gordon's lost, he wanders among the stars
Weeping over the woman he loved
7 Universes ago.
       My celluloid companions, it's only a few
          years
Since I knew you. Something in us has faded.
       Has the Terrible Fiend, That Ghastly
          Adversary,
Mr. Old Age, Caught you in his deadly trap,
And come finally to polish you off,
His machinegun dripping with years...?

From *Little Johnny's Confession* by Brian Patten.
Reprinted by permission of George Allen & Unwin
(Publishers) Limited.

Alice Munro

Boys and Girls

I had never seen
them shoot a horse,
but I knew where
it was done.

My father was a fox farmer. That is, he raised silver foxes, in pens; and in the fall and early winter, when their fur was prime, he killed them and skinned them and sold their pelts to the Hudson's Bay Company or the Montreal Fur Traders. These companies supplied us with heroic calendars to hang, one on each side of the kitchen door. Against a background of cold blue sky and black pine forests and treacherous northern rivers, plumed adventurers planted the flags of England or of France; magnificent savages bent their backs to the portage.

For several weeks before Christmas, my father worked after supper in the cellar of our house. The cellar was white-washed, and lit by a hundred-watt bulb over the work-table. My brother Laird and I sat on the top step and watched. My father removed the pelt inside-out from the body of the fox, which looked surprisingly small, mean and rat-like, deprived of its arrogant weight of fur. The naked, slippery bodies were collected in a sack and buried at the dump. One time the hired man, Henry Bailey, had taken a swipe at me with this sack, saying, "Christmas present!" My mother thought that was not funny. In fact she disliked the whole pelting operation – that was what the killing, skinning, and preparation of the furs was called – and wished it did not have to take place in the house. There was the smell. After the pelt had been stretched inside-out on a long board my father scraped away delicately, removing the little clotted webs of blood vessels, the bubbles of fat; the smell of blood and animal fat, with the strong primitive odor of the fox itself, penetrated all parts of the house. I found it reassuringly seasonal, like the smell of oranges and pine needles.

Henry Bailey suffered from bronchial troubles. He would cough and cough until his narrow face turned scarlet, and his light blue, derisive eyes filled up with tears; then he took the lid off the stove, and, standing well back, shot out a great clot of phlegm – hsss – straight into the heart of the flames. We admired him for this performance and for his ability to make his stomach growl at will, and for his laughter, which was full of high whistlings and gurglings and involved the whole faulty machinery of his chest. It was sometimes hard to tell what he was laughing at, and always possible that it might be us.

After we had been sent to bed we could still smell fox and still hear Henry's laugh, but these things, reminders of the warm, safe, brightly lit downstairs world, seemed lost and diminished, floating on the stale cold air upstairs. We were afraid at night in the winter. We were not afraid of *outside* though this was the time of year when snowdrifts curled around our house like sleeping whales and the wind harassed us all night, coming up from the buried fields, the frozen swamp, with its old bugbear chorus of threats and misery. We were afraid of *inside*, the room where we slept. At this time the upstairs of our house was not finished. A brick chimney went up one wall. In the middle of the floor was a square hole, with a wooden railing around it; that was where the stairs came up. On the other side of the stairwell were the things that nobody had any use for any more – a soldiery roll of linoleum, standing on end, a wicker baby carriage, a fern basket, china jugs and basins with cracks in them, a picture of the Battle of Balaclava, very sad to look at. I had told Laird, as soon as he was old enough to understand such things, that bats and skeletons lived over there; whenever a man escaped from the county jail, twenty miles away, I

imagined that he had somehow let himself in the window and was hiding behind the linoleum. But we had rules to keep us safe. When the light was on, we were safe as long as we did not step off the square of worn carpet which defined our bedroom space; when the light was off no place was safe but the beds themselves. I had to turn out the light kneeling on the end of my bed, and stretching as far as I could to reach the cord.

In the dark we lay on our beds, our narrow life rafts, and fixed our eyes on the faint light coming up the stairwell, and sang songs. Laird sang "Jingle Bells," which he would sing any time, whether it was Christmas or not, and I sang "Danny Boy." I loved the sound of my own voice, frail and supplicating, rising in the dark. We could make out the tall frosted shapes of the windows now, gloomy and white. When I came to the part, *When I am dead, as dead I well may be* – a fit of shivering caused not by the cold sheets but by pleasurable emotion almost silenced me. *You'll kneel and say, an Ave there above me* – What was an Ave? Every day I forgot to find out.

Laird went straight from singing to sleep. I could hear his long, satisfied, bubbly breaths. Now for the time that remained to me, the most perfectly private and perhaps the best time of the whole day, I arranged myself tightly under the covers and went on with one of the stories I was telling myself from night to night. These stories were about myself, when I had grown a little older; they took place in a world that was recognizably mine, yet one that presented opportunities for courage, boldness and self-sacrifice, as mine never did. I rescued people from a bombed building (it discouraged me that the real war had gone on so far away from Jubilee). I shot two rabid wolves who were menacing the schoolyard (the teachers cowered terrified at my back). I rode a fine horse

190

spiritedly down the main street of Jubilee, acknowledging the townspeople's gratitude for some yet-to-be-worked-out piece of heroism (nobody ever rode a horse there, except King Billy in the Orangemen's Day parade). There was always riding and shooting in these stories, though I had only been on a horse twice – bareback because we did not own a saddle – and the second time I had slid right around and dropped under the horse's feet; it had stepped placidly over me. I really was learning to shoot, but I could not hit anything yet, not even tin cans on fence posts.

Alive, the foxes inhabited a world my father made for them. It was surrounded by a high guard fence, like a medieval town, with a gate that was padlocked at night. Along the streets of this town were ranged large, sturdy pens. Each of them had a real door that a man could go through, a wooden ramp along the wire, for the foxes to run up and down on, and a kennel – something like a clothes chest with airholes – where they slept and stayed in winter and had their young. There were feeding and watering dishes attached to the wire in such a way that they could be emptied and cleaned from the outside. The dishes were made of old tin cans, and the ramps and kennels of odds and ends of old lumber. Everything was tidy and ingenious; my father was tirelessly inventive and his favorite book in the world was *Robinson Crusoe*. He had fitted a tin drum on a wheelbarrow, for bringing water down to the pens. This was my job in summer, when the foxes had to have water twice a day. Between nine and ten o'clock in the morning, and again after supper, I filled the drum at the pump and trundled it down through the barnyard to the pens, where I parked it, and filled my watering can and went along the streets.

Laird came too, with his little cream and green gardening can, filled too full and knocking against his legs and slopping water on his canvas shoes. I had the real watering can, my father's, though I could only carry it three-quarters full.

The foxes all had names, which were printed on a tin plate and hung beside their doors. They were not named when they were born, but when they survived the first year's pelting and were added to the breeding stock. Those my father had named were called names like Prince, Bob, Wally, and Betty. Those I had named were called Star or Turk, or Maureen or Diana. Laird named one Maud after a hired girl we had when he was little, one Harold after a boy at school, and one Mexico, he did not say why.

Naming them did not make pets out of them, or anything like it. Nobody but my father ever went into the pens, and he had twice had blood-poisoning from bites. When I was bringing them their water they prowled up and down on the paths they had made inside their pens, barking seldom – they saved that for nighttime, when they might get up a chorus of community frenzy – but always watching me, their eyes burning, clear gold, in their pointed, malevolent faces. They were beautiful for their delicate legs and heavy, aristocratic tails and the bright fur sprinkled on dark down their backs – which gave them their name – but especially for their faces, drawn exquisitely sharp in pure hostility, and their golden eyes.

Besides carrying water I helped my father when he cut the long grass, and the lamb's quarter and flowering money-musk, that grew between the pens. He cut with the scythe and I raked into piles. Then he took a pitchfork and threw fresh-cut grass all over the top of the pens, to keep the foxes cooler and shade their coats, which were browned by too much sun. My father did not talk to me unless it was about the job we were doing. In this he was quite different from my mother, who, if she was feeling cheerful, would tell me all sorts of things – the name of a dog she had had when she was a little girl, the names of boys she had gone out with later on when she was grown up, and what certain dresses of hers had looked like – she could not imagine now what had become of them. Whatever thoughts and stories my father had were private, and I was shy of him and would never ask him questions. Nevertheless I worked willingly under his eyes, and with a feeling of pride. One time a feed salesman came down into the pens to talk to him and my father said, "Like to have you meet my new hired man." I turned away and raked furiously, red in the face with pleasure.

"Could of fooled me," said the salesman. "I thought it was only a girl."

After the grass was cut, it seemed suddenly much later in the year. I walked on stubble in the earlier evening, aware of the reddening skies, the entering silences, of fall. When I wheeled the tank out of the gate and put the padlock on, it was almost dark. One night at this time I saw my mother and father standing talking on the little rise of ground we called the gangway, in front of the barn. My father had just come from the meathouse; he had his stiff bloody apron on, and a pail of cut-up meat in his hand.

It was an odd thing to see my mother down at the barn. She did not often come out of the house unless it was to do something – hang out the wash or dig potatoes in the garden. She looked out of place, with her bare lumpy legs, not touched by the sun, her apron still on and damp across the stomach from the supper dishes. Her hair was tied up in a kerchief, wisps of it falling out. She would tie her hair up like this in the morning, saying she did not have time to do it

properly, and it would stay tied up all day. It was true, too; she really did not have time. These days our back porch was piled with baskets of peaches and grapes and pears, bought in town, and onions and tomatoes and cucumbers grown at home, all waiting to be made into jelly and jam and preserves, pickles and chili sauce. In the kitchen there was a fire in the stove all day, jars clinked in boiling water, sometimes a cheesecloth bag was strung on a pole between two chairs, straining blue-black grape pulp for jelly. I was given jobs to do and I would sit at the table peeling peaches that had been soaked in the hot water, or cutting up onions, my eyes smarting and streaming. As soon as I was done I ran out of the house, trying to get out of earshot before my mother thought of what she wanted me to do next. I hated the hot dark kitchen in summer, the green blinds and the flypapers, the same old oilcloth table and wavy mirror and bumpy linoleum. My mother was too tired and preoccupied to talk to me, she had no heart to tell about the Normal School Graduation Dance; sweat trickled over her face and she was always counting under her breath, pointing at jars, dumping cups of sugar. It seemed to me that work in the house was endless, dreary, and peculiarly depressing; work done out of doors, and in my father's service, was ritualistically important.

I wheeled the tank up to the barn, where it was kept, and I heard my mother saying, "Wait till Laird gets a little bigger, then you'll have a real help."

What my father said I did not hear. I was pleased by the way he stood listening, politely as he would to a salesman or a stranger, but with an air of wanting to get on with his real work. I felt my mother had no business down here and I wanted him to feel the same way. What did she mean about Laird? He was no help to anybody. Where was he now? Swinging himself sick on the swing, going around in circles, or trying to catch caterpillars. He never once stayed with me till I was finished.

"And then I can use her more in the house," I heard my mother say. She had a dead-quiet, regretful way of talking about me that always made me uneasy. "I just get my back turned and she runs off. It's not like I had a girl in the family at all."

I went and sat on a feed bag in the corner of the barn, not wanting to appear when this conversation was going on. My mother, I felt, was not to be trusted. She was kinder than my father and more easily fooled, but you could not depend on her, and the real reasons for the things she said and did were not to be known. She loved me, and she sat up late at night making a dress of the difficult style I wanted, for me to wear when school started, but she was also my enemy. She was always plotting. She was plotting now to get me to stay in the house more, although she knew I hated it (*because* she knew I hated it) and keep me from working for my father. It seemed to me she would do this simply out of perversity, and to try her power. It did not occur to me that she could be lonely, or jealous. No grown-up could be; they were too fortunate. I sat and kicked my heels monotonously against a feedbag, raising dust, and did not come out till she had gone.

At any rate, I did not expect my father to pay any attention to what she said. Who could imagine Laird doing my work – Laird remembering the padlock and cleaning out the watering-dishes with a leaf on the end of a stick, or even wheeling the tank without it tumbling over? It showed how little my mother knew about the way things really were.

I have forgotten to say what the foxes were fed. My father's bloody apron reminded me.

They were fed horsemeat. At this time most farmers still kept horses, and when a horse got too old to work, or broke a leg or got down and would not get up, as they sometimes did, the owner would call my father, and he and Henry went out to the farm in the truck. Usually they shot and butchered the horse there, paying the farmer from five to twelve dollars. If they had already too much meat on hand, they would bring the horse back alive, and keep it for a few days or weeks in our stable, until the meat was needed. After the war the farmers were buying tractors and gradually getting rid of horses altogether, so it sometimes happened that we got a good healthy horse, that there was just no use for any more. If this happened in the winter we might keep the horse in our stable till spring, for we had plenty of hay and if there was a lot of snow – and the plow did not always get our road cleared – it was convenient to be able to go to town with a horse and cutter.

The winter I was eleven years old we had two horses in the stable. We did not know what names they had had before, so we called them Mack and Flora. Mack was an old black workhorse, sooty and indifferent. Flora was a sorrel mare, a driver. We took them both out in the cutter. Mack was slow and easy to handle. Flora was given to fits of violent alarm, veering at cars and even at other horses, but we loved her speed and high-stepping, her general air of gallantry and abandon. On Saturdays we went down to the stable and as soon as we opened the door on its cosy, animal-smelling darkness Flora threw up her head, rolled her eyes, whinnied despairingly and pulled herself through a crisis of nerves on the spot. It was not safe to go into her stall; she would kick.

This winter also I began to hear a great deal more on the theme my mother had sounded when she had been talking in front of the barn. I no longer felt safe. It seemed that in the minds of the people around me there was a steady undercurrent of thought, not to be deflected, on this one subject. The word *girl* had formerly seemed to me innocent and unburdened, like the word *child*; now it appeared that it was no such thing. A girl was not, as I had supposed, simply what I was; it was what I had become. It was a definition, always touched with emphasis, with reproach and disappointment. Also it was a joke on me. Once Laird and I were fighting, and for the first time ever I had to use all my strength against him; even so, he caught and pinned my arm for a moment, really hurting me. Henry saw this, and laughed, saying, "Oh, that there Laird's gonna show you, one of these days!" Laird was getting a lot bigger. But I was getting bigger too.

My grandmother came to stay with us for a few weeks and I heard other things. "Girls don't slam doors like that." "Girls keep their knees together when they sit down." And worse still, when I asked some questions, "That's none of girls' business." I continued to slam the doors and sit as awkwardly as possible, thinking that by such measures I kept myself free.

When spring came, the horses were let out in the barnyard. Mack stood against the barn wall trying to scratch his neck and haunches, but Flora trotted up and down and reared at the fences, clattering her hooves against the rails. Snow drifts dwindled quickly, revealing the hard grey and brown earth, the familiar rise and fall of the ground, plain and bare after the fantastic landscape of winter. There was a great feeling of opening-out, of release. We just wore rubbers now, over our shoes; our feet felt ridiculously light. One Saturday we went out to the stable and found all the doors open, letting in the unaccustomed sunlight

and fresh air. Henry was there, just idling around looking at his collection of calendars which were tacked up behind the stalls in a part of the stable my mother had probably never seen.

"Come to say goodbye to your old friend Mack?" Henry said. "Here, you give him a taste of oats." He poured some oats into Laird's cupped hands and Laird went to feed Mack. Mack's teeth were in bad shape. He ate very slowly, patiently shifting the oats around in his mouth, trying to find a stump of a molar to grind it on. "Poor old Mack." said Henry mournfully. "When a horse's teeth's gone, he's gone. That's about the way."

"Are you going to shoot him today?" I said. Mack and Flora had been in the stable so long I had almost forgotten they were going to be shot.

Henry didn't answer me. Instead he started to sing in a high, trembly, mocking-sorrowful voice, *Oh, there's no more work, for poor Uncle Ned, he's gone where the good darkies go.* Mack's thick, blackish tongue worked diligently at Laird's hand. I went out before the song was ended and sat down on the gangway.

I had never seen them shoot a horse, but I knew where it was done. Last summer Laird and I had come upon a horse's entrails before they were buried. We had thought it was a big black snake, coiled up in the sun. That was around in the field that ran up beside the barn. I thought that if we went inside the barn, and found a wide crack or a knothole to look through, we would be able to see them do it. It was not something I wanted to see; just the same, if a thing really happened, it was better to see it, and know.

My father came down from the house, carrying the gun.

"What are you doing here?" he said.

"Nothing."

"Go on up and play around the house."

He sent Laird out of the stable. I said to Laird, "Do you want to see them shoot Mack?" and without waiting for an answer led him around to the front door of the barn, opened it carefully, and went in. "Be quiet or they'll hear us," I said. We could hear Henry and my father talking in the stable, then the heavy, shuffling steps of Mack being backed out of his stall.

In the loft it was cold and dark. Thin, crisscrossed beams of sunlight fell through the cracks. The hay was low. It was a rolling country, hills and hollows, slipping under our feet. About four feet up was a beam going around the walls. We piled hay up in one corner and I boosted Laird up and hoisted myself. The beam was not very wide; we crept along it with our hands flat on the barn walls. There were plenty of knotholes, and I found one that gave me the view I wanted – a corner of the barnyard, the gate, part of the field. Laird did not have a knothole and began to complain.

I showed him a widened crack between two boards. "Be quiet and wait. If they hear you you'll get us in trouble."

My father came in sight carrying the gun. Henry was leading Mack by the halter. He dropped it and took out his cigarette papers and tobacco; he rolled cigarettes for my father and himself. While this was going on Mack nosed around in the old, dead grass along the fence. Then my father opened the gate and they took Mack through. Henry led Mack away from the path to a patch of ground and they talked together, not loud enough for us to hear. Mack again began searching for a mouthful of fresh grass, which was not to be found. My father walked away in a straight line, and stopped short at a distance which seemed to suit him. Henry was walking away from Mack too, but sideways, still negligently holding on to the hal-

ter. My father raised the gun and Mack looked up as if he had noticed something and my father shot him.

Mack did not collapse at once but swayed, lurched sideways and fell, first on his side; then he rolled over on his back and, amazingly, kicked his legs for a few seconds in the air. At this Henry laughed, as if Mack had done a trick for him. Laird, who had drawn a long, groaning breath of surprise when the shot was fired, said out loud, "He's not dead." And it seemed to me it might be true. But his legs stopped, he rolled on his side again, his muscles quivered and sank. The two men walked over and looked at him in a businesslike way; they bent down and examined his forehead where the bullet had gone in, and now I saw his blood on the brown grass.

"Now they just skin him and cut him up," I said. "Let's go." My legs were a little shaky and I jumped gratefully down into the hay. "Now you've seen how they shoot a horse," I said in a congratulatory way, as if I had seen it many times before. "Let's see if any barn cat's had kittens in the hay." Laird jumped. He seemed young and obedient again. Suddenly I remembered how, when he was little, I had brought him into the barn and told him to climb the ladder to the top beam. That was in the spring, too, when the hay was low. I had done it out of a need for excitement, a desire for something to happen so that I could tell about it. He was wearing a little bulky brown and white checked coat, made down from one of mine. He went all the way up, just as I had told him, and sat down on the top beam with the hay far below him on one side, and the barn floor and some old machinery on the other. Then I ran screaming to my father, "Laird's up on the top beam!" My father came, my mother came, my father went up the ladder talking very quietly and brought Laird down under his arm, at which my mother leaned against the ladder and began to cry. They said to me, "Why weren't you watching him?" but nobody ever knew the truth. Laird did not know enough to tell. But whenever I saw the brown and white checked coat hanging in the closet, or at the bottom of the rag bag, which was where it ended up, I felt a weight in my stomach, the sadness of unexorcised guilt.

I looked at Laird who did not even remember this, and I did not like the look on his thin, winter-pale face. His expression was not frightened or upset, but remote, concentrating. "Listen," I said, in an unusually bright and friendly voice, "you aren't going to tell, are you?"

"No," he said absently.

"Promise."

"Promise," he said. I grabbed the hand behind his back to make sure he was not crossing his fingers. Even so, he might have a nightmare; it might come out that way. I decided I had better work hard to get all thoughts of what he had seen out of his mind – which, it seemed to me, could not hold very many things at a time. I got some money I had saved and that afternoon we went into Jubilee and saw a show, with Judy Canova, at which we both laughed a great deal. After that I thought it would be all right.

Two weeks later I knew they were going to shoot Flora. I knew from the night before, when I heard my mother ask if the hay was holding out all right, and my father said, "Well, after tomorrow there'll just be the cow, and we should be able to put her out to grass in another week." So I knew it was Flora's turn in the morning.

This time I didn't think of watching it. That was something to see just one time. I had not thought about it very often since, but sometimes when I was busy, working at

school, or standing in front of the mirror combing my hair and wondering if I would be pretty when I grew up, the whole scene would flash into my mind: I would see the easy, practised way my father raised the gun, and hear Henry laughing when Mack kicked his legs in the air. I did not have any great feeling of horror and opposition, such as a city child might have had; I was too used to seeing the death of animals as a necessity by which we lived. Yet I felt a little ashamed, and there was a new wariness, a sense of holding-off, in my attitude to my father and his work.

It was a fine day, and we were going around the yard picking up tree branches that had been torn off in winter storms. This was something we had been told to do, and also we wanted to use them to make a teepee. We heard Flora whinny, and then my father's voice and Henry's shouting, and we ran down to the barnyard to see what was going on.

The stable door was open. Henry had just brought Flora out, and she had broken away from him. She was running free in the barnyard, from one end to the other. We climbed up on the fence. It was exciting to see her running, whinnying, going up on her hind legs, prancing and threatening like a horse in a Western movie, an unbroken ranch horse, though she was just an old driver, an old sorrel mare. My father and Henry ran after her and tried to grab the dangling halter. They tried to work her into a corner, and they had almost succeeded when she made a run between them, wild-eyed, and disappeared around the corner of the barn. We heard the rails clatter down as she got over the fence, and Henry yelled, "She's into the field now!"

That meant she was in the long L-shaped field that ran up by the house. If she got around the centre, heading toward the lane, the gate was open; the truck had been driven into the field this morning. My father shouted to me, because I was on the other side of the fence, nearest the lane, "Go shut the gate!"

I could run very fast. I ran across the garden, past the tree where our swing was hung, and jumped across a ditch into the lane. There was the open gate. She had not got out, I could not see her up on the road; she must have run to the other end of the field. The gate was heavy. I lifted it out of the gravel and carried it across the roadway. I had it half-way across when she came in sight, galloping straight towards me. There was just time to get the chain on. Laird came scrambling through the ditch to help me.

Instead of shutting the gate, I opened it as wide as I could. I did not make any decision to do this, it was just what I did. Flora never slowed down; she galloped straight past me, and Laird jumped up and down, yelling, "Shut it, shut it!" even after it was too late. My father and Henry appeared in the field a moment too late to see what I had done. They only saw Flora heading for the township road. They would think I had not got there in time.

They did not waste any time asking about it. They went back to the barn and got the gun and the knives they used, and put these in the truck; then they turned the truck around and came bouncing up the field toward us. Laird called to them, "Let me go too, let me go too!" and Henry stopped the truck and they took him in. I shut the gate after they were all gone.

I supposed Laird would tell. I wondered what would happen to me. I had never disobeyed my father before, and I could not understand why I had done it. Flora would not really get away. They would catch up with her in the truck. Or if they did not catch her this morning somebody would see her

and telephone us this afternoon or tomorrow. There was no wild country here for her to run to, only farms. What was more, my father had paid for her, we needed the meat to feed the foxes, we needed the foxes to make our living. All I had done was make more work for my father who worked hard enough already. And when my father found out about it he was not going to trust me any more; he would know that I was not entirely on his side. I was on Flora's side, and that made me no use to anybody, not even to her. Just the same, I did not regret it; when she came running at me and I held the gate open, that was the only thing I could do.

I went back to the house, and my mother said, "What's all the commotion?" I told her that Flora had kicked down the fence and got away. "Your poor father," she said, "now he'll have to go chasing over the countryside. Well, there isn't any use planning dinner before one." She put up the ironing board. I wanted to tell her, but thought better of it and went upstairs and sat on my bed.

Lately I had been trying to make my part of the room fancy, spreading the bed with old lace curtains, and fixing myself a dressing table with some leftovers of cretonne for a skirt. I planned to put up some kind of barricade between my bed and Laird's, to keep my section separate from his. In the sunlight, the lace curtains were just dusty rags. We did not sing at night any more. One night when I was singing Laird said, "You sound silly," and I went right on but the next night I did not start. There was not so much need to anyway, we were no longer afraid. We knew it was just old furniture over there, old jumble and confusion. We did not keep to the rules. I still stayed awake after Laird was asleep and told myself stories, but even in these stories something different was happening, mysterious alterations took place. A story might start off in the old way, with a spectacular danger, a fire or wild animals, and for a while I might rescue people; then things would change around, and instead, somebody would be rescuing me. It might be a boy from our class at school, or even Mr. Campbell, our teacher, who tickled girls under the arms. And at this point the story concerned itself at great length with what I looked like – how long my hair was, and what kind of dress I had on; by the time I had these details worked out the real excitement of the story was lost.

It was later than one o'clock when the truck came back. The tarpaulin was over the back, which meant there was meat in it. My mother had to heat dinner up all over again. Henry and my father had changed from their bloody overalls into ordinary working over-alls in the barn, and they washed their arms and necks and faces at the sink, and splashed water on their hair and combed it. Laird lifted his arm to show off a streak of blood. "We shot old Flora," he said, "and cut her up in fifty pieces."

"Well I don't want to hear about it," my mother said. "And don't come to my table like that."

My father made him go and wash the blood off.

We sat down and my father said grace and Henry pasted his chewing gum on the end of his fork, the way he always did; when he took it off he would have us admire the pattern. We began to pass the bowls of steaming, overcooked vegetables. Laird looked across the table at me and said proudly, distinctly, "Anyway it was her fault Flora got away."

"What?" my father said.

"She could of shut the gate and she didn't She just open' it up and Flora ran out."

"Is that right?" my father said.

Everybody at the table was looking at me. I nodded, swallowing food with great difficulty. To my shame, tears flooded my eyes.

My father made a curt sound of disgust. "What did you do that for?"

I did not answer. I put down my fork and waited to be sent from the table, still not looking up.

But this did not happen. For some time nobody said anything, then Laird said matter-of-factly, "She's crying."

"Never mind," my father said. He spoke with resignation, even good humour, the words which absolved and dismissed me for good. "She's only a girl," he said.

I didn't protest that, even in my heart. Maybe it was true.

James Stokely

The Mate

I was only sixteen
And sat trying not to cry in the woods.
I had had no luck
And the October sun was nearly gone.
Uncle Rance, over to my right,
Already had a dozen partridges,
And Lute McSween, a quarter of a mile to the left,
A brace of ducks.
I stood up, wiped my eyes,
And tiptoed into a little clearing
With only the sound of hidden insects
To accompany my ritual stalk and breath.
Suddenly my heart leaped into my hand
As I saw a movement not fifty feet away
The sunlight filtering through the leaves
To envelop the gorgeous creature
In a golden-brown haze,
Strange, proud scion of sky and earth,
Its neck firm and erect,
Its tuft of wing flecked with a lost-world tint
Of rainbow trout in a pool of ferns.
There was no sound
But the beating of two wild hearts.
With the ancient thirst ripe within me
My finger squeezed the lock of my 20-gauge
And the long-tailed ring-necked pheasant
Surprised in its solitary foraging
Collapsed like a rag doll.
The prize was mine!
Why did I not move?
I saw something greenish-blue and red
Come running from the brush
In a frenzy of clucking
Speaking to the lump of bone, flesh, and feathers,
Seeking to lead it to safety.
Rance called from the farther hill
But I did not answer.
I looked at my gun.
The woods and the bird and I
Were equally still.

Reprinted by permission of Wilma Dykeman Stokely.

Philip Aponte

The Wise and the Weak

I hated moving from the place I was brought up in, the place where all my friends lived.

I was new in the neighborhood. I had just moved from the Lower West to the Lower East Side. Not much of a change! They were both dumps. I hated moving from the place I was brought up in, the place where all my friends lived. I had to start all over again making new friends. Days passed and still I had no friends. Sure there were boys, but none would talk to me, and when I tried talking to them, they would just turn and walk away.

After about ten days of doing absolutely nothing, I decided to do something lest I go crazy. One evening after supper I went downstairs and ran across a guy sitting on the stoop. I walked up to him and said, "Hello."

"Hiya," was his reply. He started walking away. I grabbed him by his arm and asked, "Why are you walking away?"

He looked at me, then at my hand on his arm. With a wise grin on his face, he said, "You're wrinkling the skin."

I released my grip. He looked at me sarcastically and said, "Better watch that, son, or next time I might get rough with you."

I returned his sarcasm, answering, "Would you care to try?"

Flying fists, scratching fingernails, feet dancing on a human floor. I was getting the better of it. He went down. He got up. Down, up, down, up, like the continuous beat of a drum. I pushed him on his way and he staggered down the street. A smile ran across my lips. I walked down to the candy store to celebrate by buying a soda.

It was getting dark. Since I had had enough excitement for one day, I decided to go home. I walked slowly at first. Then, realizing it was rapidly getting dark, I increased my speed. I wasn't taking any

200

chances. I opened the door to the hallway and started climbing the stairs.

"Hey you, sonny." I turned around. It was him again, the big would-be tough guy.

"What the heck do you want?" I asked.

"Nothing. I just wanted to meet you and make friends."

Friends. The word seemed to scare me. Yet I had to have some friends. I walked down. He extended his hand. It missed my hand but not my stomach. Another hand, not to mine but to my face. This time I went down. I got up determined to teach this "big wheel" a lesson. But now, instead of one, there were six. This time I was the one who was going up and down, and I didn't like it. It wasn't long before it was over – for me, any- way. My lips were swollen, my eye was shut, my nose was bleeding. I hesitated, feeling for other injuries, fearing they had relieved me of some of my valuables. A hand came down to help me. I was still away from it all. I got up and was about to say thanks. Yeah, it was him again, the "big tough guy." But this time I was in no mood – or rather, no condition – to fight.

"Come on, let's you and me go down to Vito's," he said.

"Vito's?"

"Yeah, the candy store."

"Oh, yeah, sure. Let's go."

We walked down and sat in one of the booths and started talking. I told him my life history and he told me his. His name was Ron. Nice name for a not-so-nice guy. He came to the point.

"Phil, how would you like to join our club?"

"Yeah, sure," I answered. "Why not?"

"First, you'll have to prove you're an able member. You'll have to prove that you're efficient, useful."

"Efficient? Useful? I landed you, didn't I?"

"Yes, but you'll have to do much more than that. Well?"

"Yeah. Okay, what's my assignment?"

"Meet me tomorrow, here at Vito's, at, let's say about seven."

I went back home, entered through the back door, fixed my battered profile, and went to sleep. Nobody was home when I woke up the next morning. The day went slowly. I hadn't seen Ron all day. I hoped he wasn't joking. At six I went up and got my supper. At seven I was at Vito's. Ron hadn't arrived yet. I kept wondering what I was to do. I ordered a small Coke and waited for Ron. Five after seven. Then ten after, fifteen, twenty after. He'll never come, I thought.

I finished drinking the Coke and was ready to leave when the door to Vito's opened. Ron came walking in, looked around, saw me. He walked over, sat down opposite me, lit a cigarette, inhaled, and let the smoke come slowly out his nose and mouth. He was mysterious, and I was jumpy. Maybe I've made a mistake, letting him think I'm bad and bold, I thought. I've never gotten in trouble before, and I wouldn't want to. I'd better go home before something really happens.

I stood up, and then Ron spoke, "Well, Phil, ready? Ready to prove yourself?"

"Well, I, I – "

"Don't worry, Phil. It has nothing to do with defying the law." I was about to say "No," when I spotted Ron's ever-loving friends outside.

"Okay, Ron, let's be on our way," I said.

"Good boy, Phil, you're a real trooper." He laughed. I shook with fright. I had gone beyond my own reach. We walked until we got to the building across the street from where I lived. "Let's go up, Phil," he said.

"Yeah, sure," I answered. That was all I could say, "Yeah, sure." Up the stairs, first, second, third, and then the final floor. I stopped.

"Where are we going, Ron?"

"To the roof. You're not afraid, are you, Phil?" I didn't answer but just kept climbing. We walked out to the roof.

"Well, what now, Ron?"

"Wait a minute, just a minute." The building next to this was about five feet away. In between the two buildings was a four-floor drop. I walked to the ledge, looked over, and quickly jumped back. This I didn't like. The ledge was two feet high. Ron saw that I was jittery.

"No, let's just get on with...the game."

Ron smiled. "Yeah, game." The door on the roof opened. Ron's friends emerged carrying a thick iron pipe a little over five feet long. They laid it from roof to roof. I turned to Ron.

"What's that for?"

"We're going to play Tarzan." Just then more of Ron's friends appeared on our roof.

"Tarzan. What do you mean?"

"Just what I said. You know how Tarzan swings on a rope. Well, this time it isn't going to be a rope but a bar."

"Who's going to be Tarzan?"

"I'll give you one guess."

"You're crazy, Ron. That's a four-floor drop."

"Nervous, Phil? Did I say it was going to be you?"

"No, I guess you didn't, but I have to admit you had me scared there for a minute."

"You should be, Phil, because it is going to be you."

I stood there, stunned, even though I had suspected it from the very beginning. If only someone would call me or come upstairs to the roof, I thought to myself. It suddenly became silent. It was the first time I had really noticed how quiet a city slum can be.

All of Ron's friends bowed politely, saying, "After you, Phil, after you." I took a few steps toward the iron bar, then stopped and turned, looking for a possible opening in their defence. The door to the roof was still open. My last chance, I thought. But Ron's thinking was faster than mine.

"You'll never make it, Phil. If you try and we catch you, we might – ah – accidentally on purpose throw you over." He smiled and bowed politely, saying, "After you, Phil." I walked over to the ledge.

"Look, Ron – "

"Get going, Phil." I grabbed the end of the bar. The other end was being held by a couple of other guys. One foot went over the side – I looked down – my hand grabbed on for dear life, and this time the expression really meant something. My other foot went over. I started on my way toward the other roof, hand over hand in agony, my feet dangling in the air. My muscles ached. My hands started sweating. A little more to go. I made it. Now to put my foot on the ledge. My foot reached the ledge. Then, suddenly, without warning, one of the boys pushed it off. "Sorry," he said, "but you're not welcome on this side."

I tried again to put my foot on the ledge, but again he pushed it off. My strength, or what was left of it, was going. I pleaded with Ron to let me get over. The answer I received was a loud burst of laughter. I started back to where I had originally started. Halfway there, I felt myself slipping. I gripped tighter to the bar; I couldn't go on. Looking down, I could see nothing but darkness. I tried desperately to sit on the bar. Up I would go, then down I would slip.

I couldn't feel my hands any more. My neck muscles hurt me terribly. I tried once more, this time putting my foot on the bar, then swinging up on it. Slowly but surely I started my agonizing journey to the top. My foot was on the bar, my teeth grinding

202

together. Up, up, up a little more. A long sigh of relief. I was sitting on the bar, drenched with sweat. It was silent again. A few seconds, minutes. A plane passed overhead, but I didn't dare look up. Why? I didn't know, nor did I care to think about it.

"Look Ron, what now, please? Please let me go." A few tears slid down my face. I wasn't one of them. I guess I had known it from the beginning.

"Well, Ron, well?"

"Hey, Phil, you want a glass of water or something? You want to play cards? Come on." He laughed. They all laughed. But when you're in death's grasp, you don't laugh.

"Well, Phil, we're going."

"Wait, Ron. If you go, I'll never get out of here."

"Look, Phil, if you get out of this, you're one of the boys. If you don't, well – well, you can bet we'll be at the funeral." He smiled and left, his boys following.

If I swung to one end, the other end would become unbalanced and would be likely to slide off. Another puzzle to figure out. I thought of one solution, then another, and another. No good, no good. None of them were any good. I thought of every possible angle. The only thing to do was to hope the bar wouldn't slide off the roof.

Again I hung from the centre of the bar and inched up toward the ledge.

The bar started slipping. I reached for the ledge, grabbed it as the bar fell clanging below. The little pebbles of the ledge were cutting into my finger tips, but I was close. My arms extended high over my head. My body was close against the building. I lifted myself, scraping my knees and my face. Home was so near, so near. My foot reached for the ledge. One last burst of energy, and over I went, flat on my back on the roof. I lay there, my eyes closed, my lips murmuring a prayer, my legs and arms dead to the world.

I stayed there for what seemed hours. Then slowly I went back home, making sure I wasn't seen. Next day I told my mother the story. At first she didn't believe it, but after I showed her the bruises and cuts, she stood there amazed. The only thought that entered her mind was to call the police. I quickly talked her out of it, telling her it was better to have a living son than a dead one. We moved back to the West Side. Not much of a change. Both dumps, but it was a change for me – plenty.

Borden Deal

The Taste of Melon

At last the melon loomed up before me,
deep green in the moonlight,
and I gasped at the size of it.

When I think of the summer I was sixteen, a lot of things come crowding in to be thought about. We had moved just the year before, and sixteen is still young enough that the bunch makes a difference. I had a bunch, all right, but they weren't sure

From *What Do You Think?* by Borden Deal. Reprinted by permission of Scholar's Choice Limited.

of me yet. I didn't know why. Maybe because I'd lived in town, and my father still worked there instead of farming, like the other fathers did. The boys I knew, even Freddy Gray and J.D., still kept a small distance between us.

Then there was Willadean Wills. I hadn't been much interested in girls before. But I had to admit to myself that I was interested in Willadean. She was my age, nearly as tall as I, and up till the year before, Freddy Gray told me, she had been good at playing Gully Keeper and Ante-Over. But she didn't play such games this year. She was tall and slender, and Freddy Gray and J.D. and I had several discussions about the way she walked. I maintained she was putting it on, but J.D. claimed she couldn't help it. Freddy Gray remarked that she hadn't walked that way last year. He said she'd walked like any other human being. So then I said, put on or not, I liked the way she walked, and then there was a large silence.

It wasn't a comfortable silence, because of Mr. Wills, Willadean's father. We were all afraid of Mr. Wills.

Mr. Wills was a big man. He had bright, fierce eyes under heavy brows and, when he looked down at you, you just withered. The idea of having him directly and immediately angry at one of us was enough to shrivel the soul. All that summer Willadean walked up and down the high road or sat on their front porch in a rocking chair, her dress flared out around her, and not one of us dared do more than say good morning to her.

Mr. Wills was the best farmer in the community. My father said he could drive a stick into the ground and grow a tree out of it. But it wasn't an easy thing with him; Mr. Wills fought the earth when he worked it. When he plowed his fields, you could hear him yelling for a mile. It was as though he dared the earth not to yield him its sustenance.

Above all, Mr. Wills could raise watermelons. Now, watermelons are curious things. Some men can send off for the best watermelon seed, they can plant it in the best ground they own, they can hoe it and tend it with the greatest of care, and they can't raise a melon bigger than your two fists. Other men, like Mr. Wills, can throw seed on the ground, scuff dirt over it, walk off and leave it and have a crop of the prettiest, biggest melons you ever saw.

Mr. Wills always planted the little field directly behind his barn to watermelons. It ran from the barn to the creek, a good piece of land with just the right sandy soil for melon raising. And it seemed as though the melons just bulged up out of the ground for him.

But they were Mr. Wills's melons; he didn't have any idea of sharing them with the boys of the neighborhood. He was fiercer about his melons than anything else; if you just happened to walk close to his melon patch, you'd see Mr. Wills standing and watching you with a glower on his face. And likely as not he'd have his gun under his arm.

Everybody expected to lose a certain quantity of their watermelons to terrapins and a certain quantity to boys. It wasn't considered stealing to sneak into a man's melon patch and judiciously borrow a sample of his raising. You might get a load of salt in the seat of your pants if you were seen, but that was part of the game. You'd be looked down on only if you got malicious and stamped a lot of melons into the ground while you were about it. But Mr. Wills didn't think that way.

That summer I was sixteen Mr. Wills raised the greatest watermelon ever seen in that country. It grew in the very middle of his patch, three times as big as any melon anybody had ever seen. Men came from miles around to look at it. Mr. Wills wouldn't let them go into the melon patch. They had to stand around the edge.

Just like all other daredevil boys in that country, I guess, Freddy Gray and J.D. and I had talked idly about stealing that giant watermelon. But we all knew that it was just talk. Not only were we afraid of Mr. Wills and his rages but we knew that Mr. Wills sat in the hayloft window of his barn every night with his shotgun, guarding the melon. It was his seed melon. He meant to plant next year's crop out of that great one and maybe raise a whole field of them. Mr. Wills was in a frenzy of fear that somebody would steal it. Why, he would rather you stole Willadean than his melon. At least, he didn't guard Willadean with his shotgun.

Every night I could sit on our front porch and see Mr. Wills sitting up there in the window of his hayloft, looking fiercely out over his melon patch. I'd sit there by the hour and watch him, the shotgun cradled in his arm, and feel the tremors of fear and excitement chasing up and down my spine.

"Look at him," my father would say. "Scared to death somebody will steal his seed melon. Wouldn't anybody steal a man's seed melon."

"He ought to be in the house taking care of that wife of his," my mother would say tartly. "She's been poorly all year."

You hardly ever saw Mrs. Wills. She was a wraith of a woman, pale as a butter bean. Sometimes she would sit for an hour or two on their porch in the cool of the day. They didn't visit back and forth with anybody though.

"There's Willadean," my father would say mildly.

My mother would make a funny kind of sound that meant disgust. "He cares more about that seed melon that he does his wife," she'd say. "I wish somebody *would* steal it. Maybe then . . ."

"Helen," my father would say, chiding, "you shouldn't even think of such a thing."

About the time the great watermelon was due to come ripe, there was a night of a full moon. J.D. and Freddy Gray and I had decided we'd go swimming in the creek, so I left the house when the moon rose and went to meet them. The moon floated up into the sky, making everything almost as bright as day, but at the same time softer and gentler than ever daylight could be. It was the kind of night when you feel as though you can do

anything in the world, even boldly asking Willadean Wills for a date. On a night like that, you couldn't help but feel that she'd gladly accept.

"Boy, what a moon!" J.D. said when I met them.

"Wouldn't you like to take old Willadean out on a night like this?" Freddy Gray said.

We scoffed at him, but secretly in our hearts we knew how he felt. We were getting old enough to think that that sort of thing might be a lot more fun than going swimming in the moonlight.

As I said before, I was a part of the bunch. J.D. and Freddy Gray were my good friends. But because I was still new, there were certain things and certain feelings where I was left out. This was one of them; they were afraid, because I was more of a stranger to Willadean, that she might like the idea of dating me better than she did either of them. This was all way down under the surface, because none of us had admitted to ourselves that we wanted to be Willadean's boy friend. But far down though it was, I could feel it, and they could feel it.

"I wish I had a newspaper," I said then. "I'll bet you could read it in this moonlight."

We had reached the swimming hole in the creek, and we began shucking off our clothes. We were all excited by the moonlight, yelling at one another and rushing to be first into the water. Freddy Gray made it first, J.D. and I catapulting in right behind him. The water was cold, and the shock of it struck a chill into us. But we got rid of it by a brisk water fight, and then we were all right.

We climbed out finally, to rest, and sat on the bank. That big old moon sailed serenely overhead, climbing higher into the sky, and we lay on our backs to look up at it.

"Old Man Wills won't have to worry about anybody stealing his melon tonight, anyway," Freddy Gray said. "Wouldn't anybody dare try it, bright as day like it is."

"He's not taking any chances," J.D. said. "I saw him sitting up in that hayloft when I came by, his shotgun loaded with buckshot. That melon is as safe as it would be in the First National Bank."

"Shucks," I said in a scoffing voice, "he ain't got buckshot in that gun. He's just got a load of salt, like anybody else guarding a watermelon patch."

Freddy Gray sat upright, looking at me. "Don't kid yourself, son," he said loftily. "He told my daddy that he had it loaded with double-ought buckshot."

"Why," I said, "that would kill a man."

"That's what he's got in mind," Freddy Gray said, "if anybody goes after that seed melon."

It disturbed me more than it should have. After all, I'd never had it in mind to try for the melon, had I? "I don't believe it," I said flatly. "He wouldn't kill anybody over a watermelon. Even a seed melon like that one."

"Old Man Wills would," J.D. said.

Freddy Gray was still watching me. "What's got you into such a swivet?" he said. "You weren't planning on going after that melon yourself?"

"Well, yes," I said. "As a matter of fact, I was."

There was a moment of respectful silence. Even from me. I hadn't known I was going to say those words. To this day I don't know why I said them. It was all mixed up with Willadean and the rumor of Mr. Wills having his gun loaded with double-ought buckshot and the boys still thinking of me as an outsider. It surged up out of me – not the idea of making my name for years to come by such a deed, but the feeling that there was a rightness in defying the world and Mr. Wills.

Mixed up with it all there came into my mouth the taste of watermelon. I could taste the sweet red juices oozing over my tongue,

feel the delicate threaded redness of the heart as I squeezed the juices out of it.

I stood up. "As a matter of fact," I said, "I'm going after it right now."

"Wait a minute," J.D. said in alarm. "You can't do it on a moonlight night like this. It's two hundred yards from the creek bank to that melon. He'll see you for sure."

"Yeah," Freddy Gray said, "wait until a dark night. Wait until..."

"Anybody could steal it on a dark night," I said scornfully. "I'm going to take it right out from under his nose. Tonight."

I began putting on my clothes. My heart was thudding in my chest. I didn't taste watermelon any more; I tasted fear. But it was too late to stop now. Besides, I didn't want to stop.

We dressed silently, and I led the way up the creek bank. We came opposite the watermelon patch and ducked down the bank. We pushed through the willows on the other side and looked toward the barn. We could see Mr. Wills very plainly. The gun was cradled in his arms, glinting from the moonlight.

"You'll never make it," J.D. said in a quiet, fateful voice. "He'll see you before you're six steps away from the creek."

"You don't think I mean to walk, do you?" I said.

I pushed myself out away from them, on my belly in the grass that grew up around the watermelon hills. I was absolutely flat, closer to the earth than I thought it was possible to get. I looked back once, to see their white faces watching me out of the willows.

I went on, stopping once in a while to look cautiously up towards the barn. He was still there, still quiet. I met a terrapin taking a bite out of a small melon. Terrapins love watermelon, better than boys do. I touched him on the shell and whispered, "Hello, brother," but he didn't acknowledge my greeting. He just drew into his shell. I went on, wishing I was equipped like a terrapin for the job, outside as well as inside.

It seemed to take forever to reach the great melon in the middle of the field. With every move, I expected Mr. Wills to see me. Fortunately the grass was high enough to cover me. At last the melon loomed up before me, deep green in the moonlight, and I gasped at the size of it. I'd never seen it so close.

I lay still for a moment, panting. I didn't have the faintest idea how to get it out of the field. Even if I'd stood up, I couldn't have lifted it by myself. A melon is the slipperiest, most cumbersome object in the world. And this was the largest I'd ever seen. It was not a long melon, but a fat round one. Besides, I didn't dare stand up.

For five minutes I didn't move. I lay there, my nostrils breathing up the smell of the earth and the musty smell of the watermelon vines, and I wondered why I was out here in the middle of all that moonlight on such a venture. There was more to it than just bravado. I was proving something to myself – and to Mr. Wills and Willadean.

I thought of a tempting way out then. I would carve my name into the deep greenness of the melon. Mr. Wills would see it the next morning when he inspected the melon, and he would know that I could have stolen it if I'd wanted to. But no – crawling to the melon wasn't the same thing as actually taking it.

I reached one hand around the melon and found the stem. I broke the tough stem off close against the smooth roundness, and I was committed. I looked toward the barn again. All quiet. I saw Mr. Wills stretch and yawn, and his teeth glistened; the moon was that bright and I was that close.

I struggled around behind the melon and shoved at it. It rolled over sluggishly, and I pushed it again. It was hard work, pushing it down the trough my body had made through the grass. Dust rose up around me, and I wanted to sneeze. My spine was crawling with the expectation of a shot. Surely he'd see that the melon was gone out of its accustomed space.

It took about a hundred years to push that melon out of the field. I say that advisedly, because I felt that much older when I finally reached the edge. With the last of my strength I shoved it into the willows and collapsed. I was still lying in the edge of the field.

"Come on," Freddy Gray said, his voice pleading. "He's..."

I couldn't move. I turned my head. He was standing up to stretch and yawn to his content, and then he sat down again. By then I was rested enough to move again. I snaked into the willows, and they grabbed me.

"You did it!" they said. "By golly, you did it!"

There was no time to bask in their admiration and respect. "Let's get it on out of here," I said. "We're not safe yet."

We struggled the melon across the creek and up the bank. We started toward the swimming hole. It took all three of us to carry it, and it was hard to get a grip. J.D. and Freddy Gray carried the ends, while I walked behind the melon, grasping the middle. We stumbled and thrashed in our hurry, and we nearly dropped it three or four times. It was the most difficult object I'd ever tried to carry in my life.

At last we reached the swimming hole and sank down, panting. But not for long; the excitement was too strong in us. Freddy Gray reached out a hand and patted the great melon.

"By golly," he said, "there it is. All ours."

208

"Let's bust it and eat it before somebody comes," J.D. said.

"Wait a minute," I said. "This isn't just any old melon. This is Old Man Wills's seed melon, and it deserves more respect than to be busted open with a fist. I'm going to cut it."

I took out my pocketknife and looked at it dubiously. It was small, and the melon was big. We really needed a butcher knife. But when the little knife penetrated the thick green rind, the melon split of itself, perfectly down the middle. There was a ragged, silken, tearing sound, and it lay open before us.

The heart meat, glistening with sweet moisture, was grained with white sugar specks. I tugged at it with two fingers, and a great chunk of the meat came free. I put it into my mouth, closing my eyes. The melon was still warm from the day's sun. Just as in my anticipation, I felt the juice trickle into my throat, sweet and seizing. I had never tasted watermelon so delicious.

The two boys were watching me savor the first bite. I opened my eyes. "Dive in," I said graciously. "Help yourselves."

We gorged ourselves until we were heavy. Even then, we had still only eaten the heart meat, leaving untouched more than we had consumed. We gazed with sated eyes at the leftover melon, still good meat peopled with a multitude of black seeds.

"What are we going to do with it?" I said.

"There's nothing we can do," J.D. said. "I can just see us taking a piece of this melon home for the folks."

"It's eat it or leave it," Freddy Gray said.

We were depressed suddenly. It was such a waste, after all the struggle and the danger, that we could not eat every bite. I stood up, not looking at the two boys, not looking at the melon.

"Well," I said. "I guess I'd better get home."

"But what about this?" J.D. said insistently, motioning towards the melon.

I kicked half the melon, splitting it in three parts. I stamped one of the chunks under my foot. Then I set methodically to work, destroying the rest of the melon. The boys watched me silently until I picked up a chunk of rind and threw it at them. Then they swept into the destruction also, and we were laughing again. When we stopped, only the battered rinds were left, the meat muddied on the ground, the seed scattered. We stood silent, looking at one another. "There was nothing else to do," I said, and they nodded solemnly.

But the depression went with us toward home and, when we parted, we did so with sober voices and gestures. I did not feel triumph or victory, as I had expected, though I knew that tonight's action had brought me closer to my friends than I had ever been before.

"Where have you been?" my father asked as I stepped up on the porch. He was sitting in his rocker.

"Swimming," I said.

I looked toward Mr. Wills's barn. The moon was still high and bright, but I could not see him. My breath caught in my throat when I saw him in the field, walking toward the middle. I stood stiffly, watching him. He reached the place where the melon should have been. I saw him hesitate, looking around, then he bent, and I knew he was looking at the depression in the earth where the melon had lain. He straightened, a great strangled cry tearing out of his throat. It chilled me deep down and all the way through, like the cry of a wild animal.

My father jerked himself out of the chair, startled by the sound. He turned in time to see Mr. Wills lift the shotgun over his head and hurl it from him, his voice crying out again in a terrible, surging yell of pain and anger.

"Lord, what's the matter?" my father said.

Mr. Wills was tearing up and down the melon patch, and I was puzzled by his actions. Then I saw; he was destroying every melon in the patch. He was breaking them open with his feet, silent now, concentrating on his frantic destruction. I was horrified by the awful sight, and my stomach moved sickly.

My father stood for a moment, watching him, then he jumped off the porch and ran toward Mr. Wills. I followed him. I saw Mrs. Wills and Willadean huddled together in the kitchen doorway. My father ran into the melon patch and caught Mr. Wills by the arm.

"What's come over you?" he said. "What's the matter, man?"

Mr. Wills struck his grip away. "They've stolen my seed melon," he yelled. "They took it right out from under me."

My father grabbed him with both arms. He was a brave man, for he was smaller than Mr. Wills, and Mr. Wills looked insane with anger, his teeth gripped over his lower lip, his eyes gleaming furiously. Mr. Wills shoved my father away, striking at him with his fist. My father went down into the dirt. Mr. Wills didn't seem to notice. He went back to his task of destruction, raging up and down the field, stamping melons large and small.

My father got up and began to chase him. But he didn't have a chance. Every time he got close, Mr. Wills would sweep his great arm and knock him away again. At last Mr. Wills stopped of his own accord. He was standing on the place where the great melon had grown. His chest was heaving with great sobs of breath. He gazed about him at the destruction he had wrought, but I don't think that he saw it.

"They stole my seed melon," he said. His voice was quieter now than I had ever heard it. I had not believed such quietness was in him. "They got it away, and now it's gone."

I saw that tears stood on his cheeks, and I couldn't look at him any more. I'd never seen a grown man cry, crying in such strength.

"I had two plans for that melon," he told my father. "Mrs. Wills has been poorly all the spring, and she dearly loves the taste of melon. It was her melon for eating, and my melon for planting. She would eat the meat, and next spring I would plant the seeds for the greatest melon crop in the world. Every day she would ask me if the great seed melon was ready yet."

I looked toward the house. I saw the two women, the mother and the daughter, standing there. I couldn't bear any more. I fled out of the field toward the sanctuary of my house. I ran past my mother, standing on the porch, and went into my room.

I didn't sleep that night. I heard my father come in, heard the low-voiced conversation with my mother, heard them go to bed. I lay wide-eyed and watched the moon through the window as it slid slowly down the sky and at last brought a welcome darkness into the world.

I don't know all the things I thought that night. Mostly it was about the terrible thing I had committed so lightly, out of pride and out of being sixteen years old and out of wanting to challenge the older man, the man with the beautiful daughter.

That was the worst of all, that I had done it so lightly, with so little thought of its meaning. In that country and in that time, watermelon stealing was not a crime. It was tolerated, laughed about. The men told great tales of their own watermelon-stealing days, how they'd been set on by dogs and peppered

210

with salt-loaded shotgun shells. Watermelon raiding was a game, a ritual of defiance and rebellion by young males. I could remember my own father saying, "No melon tastes as sweet as a stolen one," and my mother laughing and agreeing.

But stealing this great seed melon from a man like Mr. Wills lay outside the safe magic of the tacit understanding between man and boy. And I knew that it was up to me, at whatever risk, to repair as well as I could the damage I had done.

When it was daylight I rose from my bed and went out into the fresh world. It would be hot later on; but now the air was dew-cool and fragrant. I had found a paper sack in the kitchen, and I carried it in my hand as I walked toward the swimming hole. I stopped there, looking down at the wanton waste we had made of the part of the melon we had not been able to eat. It looked as though Mr. Wills had been stamping here, too.

I kneeled down on the ground, opened the paper sack and began picking up the black seeds. They were scattered thickly, still stringy with watermelon pulp, and soon my hands were greasy with them. I kept on doggedly, searching out every seed I could find, until at the end I had to crawl over the ground, seeking for the last ones.

They nearly filled the paper sack. I went back to the house. By the time I reached it, the sun and my father had risen. He was standing on the porch.

"What happened to you last night?" he said. "Did you get so frightened you had to run home? It was frightening to watch him, I'll admit that."

"Father," I said, "I've got to talk to Mr. Wills. Right now. I wish you would come with me."

He stopped, watching me. "What's the matter?" he said. "Did you steal that seed melon of his?"

"Will you come with me?" I said.

His face was dark and thoughtful. "Why do you want me?"

"Because I'm afraid he'll shoot me," I said. My voice didn't tremble much, but I couldn't keep it all out.

"Then why are you going?" he said.

"Because I've got to," I said.

My father watched me for a moment. "Yes," he said quietly, "I guess you do." He came down the steps and stood beside me. "I'll go with you." he said.

We walked the short distance between our house and his. Though it was so near, I had never been in his yard before. I felt my legs trembling as I went up the brick walk and stood at the bottom of the steps, the paper sack in my hand. I knocked on the porch floor, and Willadean came to the screen door.

I did not look at her. "I want to talk to your father."

She stared at me for a moment, then she disappeared. In a moment Mr. Wills appeared in the doorway. His face was marked by the night, his cheeks sunken, his mouth bitten in. He stared at me absent-mindedly, as though I were only a speck in his thinking.

"What do you want, boy?" he said.

I felt my teeth grit against the words I had to say. I held out the paper bag toward him. "Mr. Wills," I said, "here's the seeds from your seed melon. That's all I could bring back."

I could feel my father standing quietly behind me. Willadean was standing in the doorway, watching. I couldn't take my eyes away from Mr. Wills's face.

"Did you steal it?" he said.

"Yes, sir," I said.

He advanced to the edge of the porch.

The shotgun was standing near the door, and I expected him to reach for it. Instead he came toward me, a great powerful man, and leaned down to me.

"Why did you steal it?" he said.

"I don't know," I said.

"Didn't you know it was my seed melon?"

"Yes, sir," I said. "I knew it."

He straightened up again and his eyes were beginning to gleam. I wanted to run, but I couldn't move.

"And my sick wife hungered for the taste of that melon," he said. "Not for herself, like I thought. But to invite the whole neighborhood in for a slice of it. She knew I wouldn't ever think of anything like that myself. She hungered for that."

I hung my head. "I'm sorry," I said.

He stopped still then, watching me. "So you brought me the seeds," he said softly. "That's not much, boy."

I lifted my head. "It was all I could think to do," I said. "The melon is gone. But the seeds are next year. That's why I brought them to you."

"But you ruined this year," he said.

"Yes, sir," I said. "I ruined this year."

I couldn't look at him any more. I looked at Willadean standing behind him. Her eyes were a puzzle, watching me, and I couldn't tell what she was thinking or feeling.

"I'm about as ashamed of myself last night as you are of yourself," Mr. Wills said. He frowned at me with his heavy brows. "You ruined the half of it, and I ruined the other. We're both to blame, boy. Both to blame."

It seemed there ought to be something more for me to say. I searched for it in my mind and discovered only the thought that I had found this morning in the grey light of dawning.

"The seeds are next year," I said. I looked at him humbly. "I'll help you plant them, Mr. Wills. I'll work very hard."

Mr. Wills looked at my father for the first time. There was a small, hard smile on his face, and his eyes didn't look as fierce as they had before.

"A man with a big farm like mine needs a son," he said. "But Willadean here was all the good Lord saw fit to give me. Sam, I do wish I had me a boy like that."

He came close to me then, put his hand on my shoulder. "We can't do anything about this year," he said. "But we'll grow next year, won't we? We'll grow it together."

"Yes, sir," I said.

I looked past him at Willadean, and her eyes were smiling, too. I felt my heart give a thump in my chest.

"And you don't have to offer the biggest melon in the world to get folks to come visiting," I blurted. "Why, I'll set on the porch with Willadean any time."

Mr. Wills and my father burst out laughing. Willadean was blushing red in the face. But somehow she didn't look mad. Flustered, I began to beat a retreat toward the gate. Then I stopped, looking back at Mr. Wills. I couldn't leave yet.

"Can I ask you one thing, Mr. Wills?" I said.

He stopped laughing, and there was no fierceness in his voice. "Anything you want to, boy," he said.

"Well, I just wanted to know," I said. "Was there double-ought buckshot in that gun?"

He reached around and picked up the gun. He unbreeched it and took out a shell. He broke the shell in his strong fingers and poured the white salt out onto his palm.

"You see?" he said.

"Yes, sir," I said, taking a deep breath. "I see."

I went on then, and the next year started that very day.

Gwen Hauser

help
i've
just
been
run
over
by
a
bus

having a relationship
       with you
is like riding
    a 3-speed bicycle
in rush-hour traffic
    up yonge st. –

too many people
       altogether
and besides
    it's dangerous –

i got hit
    by a bus 1 day
& didn't know what hit me
till i struck the pavement
& saw this great big
              bus's body
going past me
    2 inches from
             my hand on the ground

what happened
       a man asked
did your bike
       get caught
in the grating?

no i said
       grating, my foot!
a bus just hit me
       what does it look like?

(realizing i could've been killed
    & no one would've
       even noticed
    – not even the bus –)

falling in love with you
    was like
being hit
       by a bus –
i wasn't killed
    but i wouldn't do it again.

From *New: West Coast* by Gwen Hauser. Reprinted by permission of Intermedia Press.

Janis Ian

At Seventeen

I learned the truth at seventeen
That love was meant for beauty queens
and high-school girls with clear-skinned smiles
who married young, and then retired
The valentines I never knew
The Friday night charades of youth
were spent on one more beautiful
At seventeen, I learned the truth

    And those of us with ravaged faces
    lacking in the social graces
    desperately remained at home
    inventing lovers on the phone
    who called to say "Come dance with me"
    and murmured vague obscenities
    It isn't all it seems at seventeen

A brown-eyed girl in hand-me-downs
whose name I never could pronounce
said "Pity please the ones who serve
They only get what they deserve"
The rich-relationed hometown queen
marries into what she needs
a guarantee of company
and haven for the elderly

Remember those who win the game
lose the love they thought they gained
in debentures of quality
and dubious integrity
Their small-town eyes will gape at you
in dull surprise when payment due
exceeds accounts received at seventeen

To those of us who knew the pain
of valentines that never came
and those whose names were never called
when choosing sides for basketball

It was long ago, and far away
The world was younger than today
and dreams were all they gave for free
to ugly duckling girls like me

    We play the game and when we dare
    to cheat ourselves at solitaire
    Inventing lovers on the phone
    Repenting other lives unknown
    that call and say "Come dance with me"
    and murmur vague obscenities
    at ugly girls like me, at seventeen

Marc Plourde

For Monnie

I can't find her eyes
they move away
then back again

now she's imitating animals
& insects
and bends over the table
squealing in someone's ear

her friends laugh
but just out of politeness,
they don't like her stupid jokes

she's embarrassing
even dangerous
what if the cops
came into this coffee shop

we'd get busted
because of her
an eighteen-year-old

who's been taking drugs:
pot speed hash acid,
she mixes them together

too bad for us all
that she had a kid
three months ago
and it's in some orphanage

as it is I don't think
she'll last three more months,
everyone in the place is nervous
and looking around

at the other end of the table
Monnie goes on giggling
& making wild faces

Reprinted by permission of the author.

John and Ward Hawkins

Frame-up on the Highway

What he saw
filled him with nausea
and turned his bones
to rubber.

216

Jimmy Franklin didn't know how the accident happened. He was driving carefully. A seventeen-year-old with two minor accidents charged to him had to drive carefully. Too, he had just passed the scene of a crash on Lake Boulevard – police cars, an ambulance, a swirling crowd – and the memory of that held his speed down and sharpened his awareness.

The night was clear, the gentle curves of Dutch Hill Road were dry, there was little traffic. He came up on a new and expensive car going about twenty-five. "Mrs. Murphy," he said. He knew the car, knew the driver. She was married to Pop's best customer. He followed her for a time, wondering why she was just poking along. Then he pulled out and passed her, alert for any danger that might come around an approaching curve. He swung back in good time toward the right-hand lane.

Her headlights were on the high beam. They hit his rearview mirror and blinded him for a moment but not long enough to cause him any trouble. There was no car approaching, no reason to hurry the turn back. He had done everything right, everything safely, and yet he was no more than across the centre stripe when something struck his car a giant blow.

He yelled – a hoarse, wordless sound of fear. His car went out of control, tires squalling across dry pavement, the steering wheel twisting in his hands. Jimmy could not think in his panic; he could only fight instinctively and desperately, and he fought with considerable skill.

The careening car almost overturned; somehow he managed to hold it upright.

"Frame-up on the Highway" by John and Ward Hawkins. First published in *The Saturday Evening Post*. Copyright © 1958 by The Curtis Publishing Company. Reprinted by permission of Brandt & Brandt Literary Agents, Inc.

Then it began to fishtail, the rear end whipping back and forth, the front end seeking the ditch on either side of the road like a thing possessed.

He was aware that headlights had flashed crazily across the trees on the right of the road, and now he heard a second crash behind him. He was sickened, as if he'd been struck again, but he was fighting too hard to give it thought.

The fishtailing stopped at last. With the car rolling straight, he used the brake – not hard, pumping it carefully – and brought the car to a stop two hundred feet down the road from the point of collision. Shaking, weak with shock, he could not move for a moment. Then awareness came back to him suddenly.

"Mrs. Murphy," he said hoarsely.

He hammered the door of his car open, and lunged through it, stumbling, to the road. The road back of him was dark and empty. He yelled the name of the woman again and ran that way – seventeen, a lanky, gangling boy in desperate haste.

The woman's car had left the road on the right side, plunged down a small incline and into a grove of trees. It had struck two trees hard. The chrome-laden front end was crushed; the long and shining hood stood open to the sky. The headlights were out, smashed, but the dash lights glowed. Looking down from the shoulder of the road, Jimmy saw that a man had reached the car before him.

"Is she hurt?" he called fearfully.

The man was leaning into the car. He straightened and looked at Jimmy. "Yeah, she's hurt." He turned to the car again.

Jimmy went down the bank in clumsy, great strides. There was enough light from the interior of the car, the stars, and the newly risen half moon to see the man who had preceded him. He was wearing overalls, a vest, a short-sleeved shirt – a stringy wisp of a man, near fifty. He was trying to pull the inert body of the woman from the car. Jimmy caught his shoulder.

"Don't move her!" He'd had first aid in high school; he knew that much. "You can hurt her bad!"

"She's hurt bad now. She — "

Jimmy pushed past the man and leaned into the car. What he saw filled him with nausea and turned his bones to rubber. Mrs. Murphy had been a very pretty woman, twenty-five or six, long blonde hair, dark blue eyes. She'd been an actress or something, and there'd been talk about her after she'd married Mr. Murphy. Jimmy hadn't listened much to the things people said; they sure didn't matter now.

Her face had hit the steering wheel. She was half-lying on the seat, unconscious, breathing heavily. There was quite a lot of blood on the seat, in her hair, on her face, and she was still bleeding. Jimmy fumbled helplessly, mind numb with shock, almost blank. Then, suddenly, he found his senses. He backed out of the car and turned on the thin wisp of a man.

"Call a doctor!" he said. "Get an ambulance!"

"Why me? I — "

"Because I can't leave!" Jimmy yelled at him. "There's plenty of houses on the other side of the road! Get up there and get to a phone! Tell 'em Dutch Hill Road near Forty-seventh. And for gosh sakes, hurry!"

The man stared open-mouthed at Jimmy, then wheeled and scrambled up the bank. He reached the road and began to run. Jimmy turned back to the injured woman. He tried desperately to control his panic, to think clearly. Arterial bleeding — look for that first. There was none. Jimmy tore off his warm-up jacket and covered her. He ripped his white shirt apart, made pads, and applied them gently to the woman's face.

Cars passed on the road above, driven by people too preoccupied to read the story the skid marks had to tell. But others stopped. Jimmy was aware of men's voices, excited, questioning. He answered briefly, if at all. He resisted one hand that tried to pull him away from the little he was able to do for the woman. Presently, sirens moaned to a stop on the road above, doors slammed, and uniformed men came down the slope. A hand touched Jimmy's bare shoulder.

"We'll take over, son," a quiet voice said. "Stand aside."

The police and the ambulance crew took care of Mrs. Murphy, giving her emergency treatment. They lifted her gently to a stretcher and took her away – bandaged, blanket-wrapped, and still unconscious. Jimmy watched it, sitting in the police car, as he'd been told to do. He tried to ignore the curious who peered in at him, he tried not to hear their voices.

"Darn kid! Wouldn't you know?"

"A hot rodder!"

"Look at that car of his. Flames painted on the fenders! You see a wreck, you see one of those, practically every time! They oughta rule 'em off the road!"

Jimmy held his head in his hands. A hot rod – that was a laugh! Roy Wyatt had painted those fenders when he'd owned the car, trying to make it look sharp. A hot rod! A beat-up, worn-out oil hog was more like it. Fifty miles an hour, down a steep hill with a tail wind, was the best you could get. Buying the car, paying for insurance, feeding it oil – he couldn't afford to repaint the fenders. But if you were seventeen and had a car you were a hot rodder – a dirty word.

The police cleared the road. There were two of them, sober and frowning. They came back to the car where Jimmy waited. One of them had Jimmy's warm-up jacket in his hand. "You better put this on, son." Jimmy got out of the car, so shaken he could barely stand.

"How is she?" he asked. "Will she be all right?"

The officer with the jacket, Sam Riggio, was a lean-hipped, heavy-shouldered man with a fighter's dark, tough face. Mark Bradford, his partner, was tall and wore glasses. Neither man was a stranger to blood and broken bodies. Both knew the damage youngsters can do. Bradford resented teenage drivers, sometimes to the point of hate, but Bradford had no children of his own. Sam Riggio had a son, fifteen.

Riggio decided that whatever else this skinny, man-tall boy was, he was not just a punk. He was neatly dressed and his clothes were clean. He had a homely-good-looking face with brown eyes that looked pleadingly at Sam Riggio.

"She'll make it," Riggio said gruffly.

Grimly, Bradford said, "How about her face?"

"Hold your lip," Sam Riggio said.

The two officers left Jimmy in the car while they took measurements and made sketches. Then they came back to get Jimmy's statement for their reports.

"We're short the name of the guy in overalls," Riggio said. "That's a must. Get the name of anybody who might be a witness."

"How could I?" Jimmy asked. "He never came back!"

"Who needs witnesses?" Bradford asked. "The facts speak for themselves. The kid cut back too fast and jammed her wheel."

Riggio scratched his cheek. "At least he didn't make it a hit-and-run like the guy on Lake Boulevard a little while ago. That one left a woman in tough shape. It's ten to one against her."

"I didn't cut back too fast," Jimmy said.

Bradford made a soft sound of ridicule.

Riggio got out of the car suddenly.

"Come on, son," he said. When Jimmy was beside him, he shut the door and spoke through the window to his partner, "I'll ride home with the boy in his jalopy. You follow us. And wait outside, will you?"

"I'll be glad to," Bradford said.

The right rear door of Jimmy's car was smashed, the glass broken, the right rear fender was crumpled against the wheel. Officer Riggio pulled the metal away from the tire and checked the running gear.

"Looks all right," he said. "Let's go."

He got into the front seat on the right side. Jimmy had to get behind the wheel. His hands were shaking, his legs were weak. He didn't want to drive.

"I...I don't know if I can," he said.

Riggio got a cigarette from his blouse pocket and took his time lighting it.

"This isn't the end," he said. "You've got a lot of years to go, a lot of cars to drive. The time to try again is now. I think you can do it."

Jimmy's eyes watered and his throat hurt. Kindness always did that to him. Then he set his jaws. The man said drive, so he'd drive! He got the car going and felt his confidence return.

"I didn't know there were cops like you."

"Only a million of them," Riggio said.

Jimmy kept his eyes on the road. "A couple of things I didn't tell you," he said. "I went past that accident on Lake Boulevard after it happened. It scared me. Y'know, a guy thinks how easy it could happen to him. That's one reason I was being careful. The other reason, I recognized Mrs. Murphy's car before I pulled out to pass it. Her husband is a contractor. My father sells heavy equipment. He sells a lot to Mr. Murphy."

Riggio sighed. "How tough can it get?"

"That's one car I wouldn't want to scratch," Jimmy said. "I gave her plenty of room. You can see why I would."

Riggio shook his head. It was a gentle lie – a gesture that spoke of equal puzzlement, when there was no question in his mind as to the cause of the accident.

"Your father buy this car for you?"

"No," Jimmy said. "Pop told me I could have a car when I could pay for it and the insurance and the gas and oil. I've saved my money since I was fourteen. I work at Keefer's Supermarket after school. That's where I was tonight. I just came from there."

Where, Riggio wondered tiredly, was the reward for virtue he'd always been hearing about? The hit-and-run driver who had left the elderly woman broken and bleeding on Lake Boulevard would probably never pay for that piece of dirty work. The chance of finding him was slim. But this lad – he'd stayed at the scene, done all he could, seen the blood and felt the pain – this lad and his family would pay dearly.

Jimmy turned into the driveway of the house where he lived. It was a comfortable home with white siding, white brick, green lawn. Suddenly it didn't matter who was to blame. He had to tell his mother and father he'd had another accident, had to watch what hearing it would do to them. This was a prospect that brought him sickness almost beyond bearing. Officer Riggio knew what was in his mind.

"I'll be with you, son," he said.

They went up the walk together. Jimmy opened the front door. There were voices in the living room. The television was going. Pop was in there, resting after a day at the plant and three hours in the garden. Pop grew the best flowers in the neighborhood.

"Jimmy," his mother said, as they walked into the hall, "you're late."

She came into the hall. She saw Officer Riggio and stopped. She was small and slim; she had brown hair and brown eyes. Her name was Ann, but Pop called her Cricket because she was never still. She took care of her house and her people at a dead run. Pop had a joke about that. "If she thinks she's going to get double time," he'd say, "she's got a busted sprocket." Pop didn't like his Cricket very much; he was pure crazy about her.

"Jimmy," Cricket whispered, "where's your shirt?"

"I had an accident," Jimmy said.

Cricket closed her eyes. Her mouth got the pinched look it had when she was scared or hurt. Pop came out of the living room then. He was a big man, heavily muscled, deeply tanned. He had thick, dark hair, dark brows, grey eyes. A laborer at fourteen, a construction superintendent at twenty-five. At forty, he was close to being a partner in Western Machinery, selling heavy equipment to highway contractors. Jimmy had always thought he'd be satisfied if he turned out to be half the man Pop was.

"This is Officer Riggio," Jimmy said.

"Come in," Pop said.

He led them into the living room and switched the television off. Officer Riggio sat on the davenport. Cricket would not let Jimmy beyond the reach of her hands. She made him sit in a chair, then sat on the arm of it beside him.

"Was anyone hurt?" Pop asked.

"A woman," Riggio said. "The driver of the other car."

Jimmy tried to swallow the lump in his throat – tried and failed. "It was Mrs. Murphy, Pop."

Twenty years of construction work had given Roger Franklin a tough face. His thick brows came down in a scowl. The scowl didn't scare Jimmy, though it made him feel immeasurably worse. Pop looked like that only when he'd been hit cruelly.

"Hurt bad?" Pop asked.

Riggio glanced briefly at Jimmy, then

gave the boy's father a look of warning. "Too early to say," he said. "Facial cuts…cheeks, lips, forehead. Concussion, but I don't think a skull fracture. An ambulance took her to Mercy Hospital."

"I'll be right back," Pop said quietly.

He used the telephone in the hall, listening more than he talked. His face had lost color when he returned.

"Still in emergency surgery," he said. He looked at Jimmy. "Maybe you'd better fill us in."

Jimmy told them what had happened, trying to straighten it out in his head. He did it badly because each part of the memory frightened and sickened him again – the crash, fighting to keep his car under control, the second crash, the woman's ruined car, her bleeding face. He was shaking and sweating when he finished.

"I see," Pop said. He looked at Cricket. "Clean him up, will you? Get him a shirt, try to get some food in him…not that he'll eat. Some milk maybe."

Cricket touched Jimmy's arm. "Come on, son."

"Pop," Jimmy said, "you'll call the hospital again?"

"In a little while," Pop said.

He waited until Cricket and Jimmy were beyond hearing behind the swinging door, then turned to Officer Riggio, his tough face softened with concern.

"Is it as bad as it sounds?"

Officer Riggio took a deep breath. "I like to call on parents after accidents, y'know? When the youngster's committed a crime – speeding, drinking, reckless driving – I warn the parents so they can take a hand. A lot of kids need a whipping." His eyes came up to meet Pop's. "Your son's not like that. He's a good boy."

"I know that well," Pop said. "But both his mother and I thank you for saying it."

"The hospital told you about the woman's face? That it could be disfigured?"

Riggio waited for Pop's nod, then went on, "I didn't think it was time to hit the boy with that. He'll have to know, but why not a little at a time?"

"Thanks again," Pop said.

"The accident…" Riggio said. He got his notebook from his pocket. "Weather clear, road dry. The woman was driving at a moderate speed. The boy passed her, going about forty-five. No visibility problem, no oncoming traffic. The cars collided in the right-hand lane. The tire marks, glass, mud on the pavement show that, beyond doubt. The woman was taken to the hospital, unconscious. I couldn't get a statement from her. The boy honestly believes he did everything according to the book, safely. The facts say something else."

Pop said, "He cut back too fast."

"He's seventeen," Riggio said. "He's got a right to drive, a right to learn. But how long does it take to learn? And who pays for the mistakes kids make while they're learning?"

"A tough question," Pop said. "I don't want to answer it now…not for the record."

"I know…they don't give kids much insurance."

"And I'm not a rich man," Pop said.

He walked to the front door with Officer Riggio, thanked him again, and let him out. Then he called the hospital. Mrs. Murphy was off the critical list, sleeping under sedation. No, there had been no skull fracture. Yes, her face had been damaged. Broken nose, broken cheekbone, severe lacerations. Pop put the telephone down, a very sober man. He went into the kitchen to face two worried people.

"Off the critical list," he said, "but her face took a real beating."

"I knew it!" Jimmy said. "I saw her." He

slammed a fist into a cupped palm. "She was so pretty."

Cricket whispered. "The poor woman."

"One of us has to call Charlie Stern," Pop said. "The insurance company is going to get hit hard on this one; they'd better know."

"It's my insurance," Jimmy said. "I'll call him."

Pop and Cricket waited in the kitchen. They listened to the one-sided conversation, anguish in their faces. They expected him to be heartbroken and utterly defeated when he came back, but his round face was tight and there was anger in his eyes.

"He didn't believe me either!" he said.

"Believe what?" Pop said.

"That I didn't cut back too fast. I told him how the accident happened. He didn't say it right out. He said, 'Don't admit the blame to anybody,' but he might as well have said it."

"Jimmy—"

"I had two other accidents," Jimmy said. "An old lady with thick glasses and a dog jumping around in her car; a fat guy who smelled like a brewery. His fender, the one that got nicked, had dents so old they had rust in them. I'm a teenager; I'm wrong all the way. He gets a new fender and I get the blame. The old lady—"

"The facts say this one's your fault."

"The cop's facts." Jimmy was pacing the kitchen. "While you were in there talking to Riggio, telling each other what lousy drivers kids are, I was out here, thinking about my facts. I'd like to have somebody listen while I tell 'em."

Pop's voice was firm. "Whoa, Jimmy."

Jimmy paused in mid-stride, dropped his hands. "I was yelling. I'm sorry," he said. "But I was driving with extra care because I'd passed where there'd been a hit-and-run accident...cops all over, ambulance, crowds."

Pop said, "On Lake Boulevard. We heard about it on television."

"Yeah," Jimmy said. "Accidents scare me, so I was driving carefully. And I recognized Mrs. Murphy's car. Mr. Murphy's one of your best customers. I'd run in the ditch before I scratched that car. Wouldn't I?"

"If you had a choice," Pop said.

"I tell you I gave her plenty of room."

"The collision was in the right-hand lane."

"Does that mean it was my fault?"

Pop said, "I'm afraid it does."

"What if she ran into me?" Jimmy said. "What if she hit the gas? With all the horses she'd got in that car, she'd be up my back before I knew it."

Pop stared at the boy. "Jimmy, for the love of Mike!"

"It could happen," Jimmy said.

"How fantastic can you get?"

Cricket said, "Please, Pop. He's upset. Let's not talk about it now."

Jimmy looked at her. "You don't believe me either."

"I didn't say that, son, I—"

"You don't have to say it." He looked at his father. "Or you, Pop. You both think I'm trying to alibi, trying to chicken out of my responsibility. You both think I'm a liar."

"I do not!" Cricket said.

"Honestly mistaken," Pop said. "I don't doubt for a moment you believe you were driving safely. You may have been thinking too much about the accident you'd seen and not enough about your driving. You may have misjudged speed and distance. Face it, Jimmy. No one would overtake a passing car deliberately or by accident. You can't sell it to me or anyone. Don't try to sell it to yourself."

Jimmy's face was tight. "That's the last word?"

"That's it." Pop stood up. "I've got to go

222

and talk to Ben Murphy and tell him how I feel about his wife being hurt." He looked at his son. "You don't have to go."

Cricket said, "Not tonight!"

"I'm all right," Jimmy said. "I'll go."

Pop and Jimmy reached Ben Murphy's gate at ten o'clock. The yard lights were on, a dozen or more scattered over an acre of tableland bulldozed out of the hillside. A brick wall paralleled the road. "High enough to discourage outsiders," Pop had once said, "and low enough to let them see what they're missing." The house, ablaze with lights, was long and low, white brick and glass and red tile roof. Pop parked the family station wagon beside a bullet-nosed sports car in the drive.

"Pop," Jimmy said, his face still tight, "no matter what you think or I think, I can't take the blame. Charlie Stern told me not to."

"We're not here to take the blame," Pop said. "We're here to show we're responsible people, and that we're as sorry as people can be that Mrs. Murphy was hurt."

They got out of the car and followed a white walk around the house to the front door. Ben Murphy answered their ring. He was wearing a light topcoat and a hat and held a drink in one hand. He was a stocky bull of a man. His face was round and flushed, his mouth full-lipped. His eyes were hard, flat chips of glass that caught and held the light.

"Franklin," he said, "what do you want?"

Pop said, "This is my son, Jimmy. He was—"

"Sure!" Murphy's voice was harsh. "James Franklin! That was the name they gave me, but I didn't tie it to you." He looked at Jimmy, sudden fury clouding his face. "You lousy little punk! Do you know what you did to my wife? You damned near killed her, that's what you did. You tore her face all to hell!"

Jimmy said, "I'm sorry, Mr. Murphy. I—"

"Sorry! You should see her! I just came from the hospital, and I tell you it tore me apart. A beautiful face...in shambles. Nose smashed, eyes closed, deep cuts." He lifted his glass and swore. "You're sorry! You're gonna be worse than sorry!"

Pop eased his big bulk in front of Jimmy. "Slow down, Ben." His voice was soft, but it held an edge. "We came to tell you we couldn't feel worse about it and that we're standing by. Don't rough the lad; he's feeling bad enough."

"Let him talk," Jimmy said.

"What's that?" Murphy's voice was sharp. He tried to see past Pop. "You smart-talking me, kid?"

"No, sir, I'm not," Jimmy said. "I know how you feel about Mrs. Murphy. Take it out on me if you want to. I saw her after the accident; I took care of her. And I wish I had somebody to take it out on."

Murphy stared at Jimmy a moment. Then, to Pop, he said, "Get this kid outta here!" His voice was hoarse, shaking. "I don't trust myself. That murdering brat of yours...I'd like to use my hands on him. Run my wife off the road...." His mouth jerked. "You'll hear from me, Franklin. You'll hear from me!"

Pop turned and took Jimmy's arm. "Come on, lad."

Pop and Cricket sat in the kitchen, facing each other across the kitchen table, after Jimmy had gone to bed. They didn't joke as they usually did, hunting light words to make a serious moment less painful. Cricket's hands were locked together. Pop rubbed his face.

"Ben Murphy is not what you'd call a kind man," he said. "He's rough and at times he can be as ugly as sin. I think he'll be ugly about this. A second wife, twenty-five years younger than he is, a beautiful woman; to a man like Ben, a woman like that is more than a wife. She's a prize possession, proof he's a success as a man and as a businessman."

Cricket said, "She's no better than she —"

"Hey, now!"

Cricket caught a lip in her teeth. She was silent a long moment struggling with herself. Then her eyes came to meet Pop's. "Can I take that back?"

"Sure, hon," Pop said gently. "I thought the same thing; I had to take it back too. No matter what she is, she's suffering now. Calling her names won't help us or Jimmy."

Cricket nodded miserably. "I know."

"Ben would sue his grandmother for a scratched fender," Pop said. "For a personal injury, he'll be downright savage."

"Jimmy has public liability insurance."

"Ten thousand." Pop got up from the table to pace the kitchen slowly. "How much is a woman's face worth, Cricket? Any woman, and a beautiful woman in particular?"

Wearily, Cricket said, "Whatever you can get."

"Right," Pop said. "And anything over the insurance will come out of us. Fifty thousand, a hundred thousand. What's the difference? We've done all right, but it wouldn't take a big judgment to clean us out. Jimmy's insurance company will fight the suit and we'll fight it. But we might as well take the truth by the nose: Jimmy was to blame. We haven't got a chance."

"Don't tell Jimmy, please!"

Pop went to her, put his hands on her shoulders. "He'll have to know," he said, "but later will be soon enough."

"I wish they hadn't invented automobiles."

"Or damage suits," Pop said. "I've wor-

ried about this every time I heard the boy start his car."

Jimmy was up early the next morning and gone early. He did his homework in the study hall before school took up. That was part of the deal he'd made with Pop. He could work at the supermarket earning money to pay for the car, but if his grades went down – blooie! – no job. The car went into the garage and stayed there. And he was campused – no movies, no dates, until his report card was good again.

He had a little trouble concentrating. The accident and the memory of Mrs. Murphy's bleeding face kept getting in the way. But he got through the school hours somehow. And he went from school to the police station. The law said he had to file a report within twenty-four hours of the accident. A uniformed man gave him a blank and pointed to a desk. Jimmy filled in the spaces of the blank. He drew a diagram – Car A, Car B – showing how the accident had happened, then took the form back to the man at the counter.

"Car A hit Car B." The policeman looked at Jimmy. "Car B is your car. Are you trying to say she ran into you after you passed her?"

Jimmy's face flushed. "Yes, sir."

"Of all the flimsy alibis I ever heard," the officer said, "that takes the cake!" He threw the form in a box. "Now I've heard everything!"

Jimmy left the counter and the police station, cheeks flaming. He got into his car and fumbled with the keys. Every time, every gosh-darned time! If you were seventeen, you were a slob, a lying slob! The cops, Charlie Stern, Pop, Cricket, Mr. Murphy – not one of them would even say "maybe."

"I'll show 'em," he said, "or bust something!"

He stopped at the supermarket and talked to the manager. "You've got time off

224

coming," the manager said. "Take as much as you need."

Jimmy went back to his car. He drove out Dutch Hill Road to Forty-seventh, parked there and looked around. Houses on one side of the road, brush and trees on the other. Most of the houses close by were big and new with fine lawns and lots of shrubs. But there were old places, weathered and shabby, on the side streets that wandered away toward the hill.

"One of those," Jimmy said.

He left the car. He climbed sun- and rain-warped steps and rang an old-fashioned doorbell. He talked to a woman with grey hair and watery eyes.

"I'm looking for a man who saw an accident last night," he said. "He wears bib overalls and a vest and a shirt with chopped-off sleeves."

"Nobody here like that," the woman said.

"Thanks anyway," Jimmy said.

He knocked on other doors. He talked to an old man, to a girl who wouldn't smile because she had braces on her teeth, to a woman whose hair was redder than any fire engine he had ever seen. He walked up one street and down another. Before he ran out of daylight, he had been to every old house within a quarter of a mile of the scene of the accident.

After dinner he spread a map of the city on the kitchen table and began to pencil out the streets he'd covered. Pop and Cricket came to look over his shoulder and ask what he was doing.

"Keeping track of where I've been," Jimmy said. "That way I don't have to go over the same ground twice."

"You're looking for the witness?" Pop said.

"Yes," Jimmy said. "He was on foot. I figure he lives within maybe a mile of where the accident happened."

"That could be." Pop's frown said he was thinking hard. "One thing you'd better face, son. When you find him, he may break your heart. He may not have seen it or he may say you're to blame."

"Then I'll know," Jimmy said.

The next afternoon Jimmy took up the search as soon as school was out. He knocked on fifty or sixty doors, asking the same questions every time. Most of those he talked to were interested; most of them tried to help. Two people were sure they knew the man he was hunting, but both were wrong. One of the men they sent Jimmy to see was confined to a wheel chair; the other had been in Alaska for more than a month.

He used up the afternoon. He was walking back to his car when the bullet-nosed sports job came down the street, Ben Murphy at the wheel. The stocky man parked at the curb, close by.

"Over here," he said. "I want to talk to you."

"Yes, sir," Jimmy said.

"I was rough with you the other night," Murphy said. He wasn't smiling, but there was no anger in his face. "My wife goes downtown to buy a hat; next thing she's in the hospital. I was worried sick about her. Naturally. Since then, I've had time to think. I've known and liked your father for a long time, done a lot of business with him. I don't want him hurt or you hurt."

Jimmy said, "Well, thanks, Mr. Murphy."

"The bills have to be paid...hospital, the doctors, the garage. Your insurance will take care of them." Murphy's eyes had no part in his brief smile. "This is between friends, boy. Let's keep it that way."

"I don't know what you mean."

"You're a worried guy," Murphy said. "You'd be less than human if you weren't. It could be unpleasant...complaints, litigation, your driver's licence gone." He smiled again. "I see your car out here every time I go by. You're scrambling around trying to find something or somebody to get you off the hook. Right?"

"The witness," Jimmy said.

"A waste," Murphy said. "Forget it. Nothing's going to happen to you. Go home and rest your feet. The insurance company will pay the bills and everything will be fine." He put the car in gear. "And be careful, kid. The next guy might not be a friend of your father's."

Jimmy said, "Mr. Murphy, I..."

But the sports car was moving, gravel spurting under the wheels. The tail lights flared red, and it was gone around a corner. Jimmy stared after it.

"Fine!" he said. "As long as my insurance company has to pay, it's fine! And what does it do to me?" Jimmy set his jaws. No matter what Mr. Murphy said, he wasn't quitting yet. The man in the bib overalls had to live somewhere. He'd been afoot. He—"

"Wait a darned minute!" Jimmy said. He went back to his car, a new idea in his mind. The house nearest the scene of the accident was new and very big. The woman who answered the door was a young, a pretty woman. She listened gravely to Jimmy's description of the witness.

"No," she said. "He doesn't live here."

"What I thought, he might work for you," Jimmy said. "Mowing the lawn, trimming the shrubs. One of the odd-job men that come around. Sometimes they leave a card."

"Sorry," the woman said.

Jimmy tried the house next door, the one next door to that. He found a blond and chunky man who had seen the witness. "Asked me to call an ambulance," he told Jimmy. "A stranger, though. I'd never seen him before. I've never seen him since."

Jimmy found people who'd heard the crash, who'd gone to see what had happened, but none of these remembered a thin grey man who wore overalls and a vest.

"Somebody must know the guy," Jimmy said.

He went on with it, until dusk thickened into dark. He went home to find Pop and Cricket talking quietly in the kitchen. They stopped talking when he walked in, looked at him, waiting. He didn't have to tell them he'd had no luck; they saw it in his face. Cricket was suddenly very busy at the range.

"Charlie Stern called," Pop said quietly.

Jimmy said, "I'm fresh out of insurance?"

"That's the size of it," Pop said. "Charlie'll try to get you in the assigned-risk pool, but that'll take time."

"And cost more," Jimmy said.

"I can drive you around evenings," Pop said.

"No," Jimmy said. "But you gave me an idea."

Two people could cover twice as much ground as one. Ten or twelve could hit every house within a mile in just one afternoon. A lot of kids he knew had cars; not all of them had jobs. Jimmy made a list and got on the telephone. Beans Hall had an appointment with a dentist. Jack Davis had a tennis date.

"I'll skip that," he said. "Ringing doorbells might be fun."

"I'll buy your gas...two gallons," Jimmy said.

He had it organized before he went to bed. Nine cars and twenty kids showed up on Dutch Hill Road at Forty-seventh, the next afternoon. Jimmy spread his map on the hood of Jack Davis's car.

"Each car gets a street," Jimmy said. "Up one side and down the other. Every house. Don't miss even one. Then come back and report and get a new assignment."

"What if we find the guy?" Jack Davis said.

Jimmy said, "You get two extra gallons of gas."

He stayed behind as the cars fanned out through the neighborhood. He found a stump beside the road and used it for a desk. Just keeping track of where the kids had been turned out to be a job. Sometimes there were two or three cars lined up, waiting to report. And twenty searchers could have as little luck as one. The kids turned up several people who had seen the man but none who knew his name or where he lived.

"We'll keep her goin'," Jimmy said.

He was talking to Fats Porter and Bob Hently when he heard the blaring horn. Busy with the map and pencil, he did not look up. The horn yelled again and again. Fats Porter grunted his disgust, turned away, and then turned back.

"Jim," he said, "the guy wants you."

Jimmy looked up. The bullet-nosed sports job was back again, parked on the shoulder of the road. Ben Murphy was peering over his shoulder. He hit the horn again, beckoned impatiently.

"I'll be right back," Jimmy said.

There was no smile on Ben Murphy's face. "You!" He thrust the word at Jimmy with a lifted chin. "I told you to go home and rest your feet!" he said. "Didn't you hear me, kid?"

"Yes," Jimmy said, "I heard you."

"So now you brought your gang!" Murphy's voice was harsh. His big hands gripped the wheel so tightly the cords of his wrists stood out like iron wire. "I was nice to you. Let it alone, let the insurance company pay the bills. That's all I asked. But no! You want to mess it up, shove it into court, make it tough for me to collect!"

"It wasn't my fault," Jimmy said.

"I'm giving you one more chance!" Mur-

phy said. "Keep on and you'll get it...in the neck! You and your old man. I'll take care of you first. My wife will sign a complaint, criminal negligence, reckless driving. You'll be looking at a judge before you know it. You'll lose your licence, get slapped with a fine and maybe a jail sentence. And that's only the beginning! We'll sue your father for a hundred thousand dollars for what you did to my wife's face!"

Jimmy said, "You can't—"

"The hell I can't!" Murphy said. "You're a minor; he's responsible for what you do. I'll sue and I'll win and I'll clean him out... every last dime, house, car, everything. He'll be the rest of his life paying off the judgment, and that's a promise, kid!" His lips flattened. "Go home and stay there, or you and your father will be in more trouble than you ever dreamed about!"

"Yes, sir," Jimmy said.

He watched the sports car roar away and then went back to the stump he'd used for a desk. He picked up the map and folded it carefully. He looked at his friends, eyes dull.

"You can take off," he said. "We're all through."

He found Pop working in the garden, stripped to the waist. Pop wouldn't use a power cultivator. "These mitts of mine like the feel of an idiot stick," he'd said. The truth was that Pop liked hard work. One look at Jimmy's face was enough to bring him out of the garden.

"You found your witness," he said.

"No. And I guess I'm not going to. Mr. Murphy said he was going to sue you if I kept trying to cause him trouble." Jimmy swallowed. "Can he do that, Pop? I mean, for a lot of money. A hundred thousand...everything you've got?"

"I've been expecting him to," Pop said quietly.

Jimmy's voice broke. "Why didn't you

tell me? I thought my insurance would be enough. I could have gone on looking and ruined you."

Pop's face was tight with thought, his eyes searching. "When did Murphy make this pitch about cleaning me out?"

"Just a while ago," Jimmy said. "The first time I saw him, he said he wasn't going to sign a complaint. All he wanted was for my insurance company to pay for everything. Great for him, but not for me. I kept on looking. This time he got real mean. Said if I didn't quit trying to get out of paying he'd clean you out."

"He did, did he?" Pop took Jimmy to a set of lawn chairs and made him repeat every word of both conversations he'd had with Murphy. There was anger in Pop's face, mixed with deep concern. "Still think you were in the clear on the accident?" he asked.

"I know I was."

"But now you're willing to throw in the sponge?"

"For gosh sakes, Pop! If it was just me, I wouldn't care. But it's you and Mom now. I can't do anything that would make Mr. Murphy ruin you!"

Pop laid a big hand on Jimmy's shoulder. "That's a tough thing to say to your old man, lad. You'd give up fighting for something you feel is right to protect me. Am I so helpless?"

"Pop, I didn't mean..."

The big hand tightened on Jimmy's arm. "Don't ever quit," Pop said slowly. "Don't ever quit anything you think is right as long as you've got a breath left in your body. Every man's got a light that guides him. Turn it off for me, for anybody, and you'll get lost in the dark."

"You want me to go on?"

Pop nodded. "Come hell or high water. And if you want help, I'll bear a hand."

Jimmy got up from the chair, excitement growing in him. "I could use some help, Pop.

There are places we couldn't look because we're minors. I thought a man like him might spend a lot of time in taverns and bars. They won't let me in alone, but if you were with me they might."

"What do you mean, might?" Pop stood up, six feet tall, one hundred ninety pounds of hard bone and muscle. He swelled his chest for Jimmy. "Who's going to argue?"

Jimmy grinned, delighted. "Nobody!"

"So, O.K.," Pop said. "Get the wagon out."

Jimmy watched him cross the yard toward the house, so proud he could hardly stand it. "What a guy to have for a Pop!" he said. "A one-man army!" He ran for the garage and backed the station wagon into the drive. Pop came out of the house presently, wearing slacks and a sports shirt, and got behind the wheel.

"You're the skipper," he said. "Where to?"

"He was walking," Jimmy said. "He could have been on his way to a place or on his way home from one. We could start where I had the accident and hunt in one direction. If we don't have any luck, we can come back and hunt the other way."

"Will do!" Pop put the car on the road.

They began their search at a crossroads a half mile from the scene of the accident. There were two stores here – a service station and a tavern. The men in the tavern swung around to stare at Jimmy; the bartender came down the bar to wave him away. Then Pop came through the door.

"Hold fast," Pop said. "This is my son."

The bartender looked at the spread of Pop's shoulders, at the size of his arms, at the thick brows that were down in a scowl.

"Yes, sir," he said. "What can we do for you?"

Pop said, "Take it, Jimmy."

"I'm looking for a man who saw an accident," Jimmy said.

He got to look in the face of every man

228

there, and no one protested. They listened to his description, they tried very hard to place the man, and all of them were genuinely sorry when they could not be of help.

"I'll ask around," the bartender said. "Come back in a day or two if you don't have any luck."

"Thank you all," Jimmy said.

The next place was another tavern, and the scene was repeated. It was followed by four more taverns, three cheap bars, and a package store where wine was sold. They didn't find their man, but it was not because of resistance. The round-faced, man-tall boy and the quiet, big-shouldered man were a team no one cared to deny. When they had covered every place within a reasonable walking distance in one direction, Pop turned the car and they began to hunt in the other.

"Still with me?" Pop asked.

"We'll find him," Jimmy said. "We can't miss."

They found him in a dingy, hole-in-the-wall joint. He was drinking wine with a beer chaser in a booth toward the back. Jimmy almost missed him because he was wearing a suit instead of overalls and a vest. A thin wisp of a man, older than his fifty years, unshaven. He had a weak mouth and blurred eyes.

"Do you remember me?" Jimmy asked.

"Maybe I do," the man said. "And maybe I don't."

Pop came up behind Jimmy. He put a big hand on the table. "Make up your mind," he said quietly.

The blurred eyes looked at the hand for a long moment. "Yeah," the man said then. "I remember you, kid."

Jimmy's knees almost folded under him. After all the hours of searching – finally! He tried to swallow and found his throat too dry. "Did you see the accident happen?"

"I was there, wasn't I? I saw it."

"Whose fault was it?" Jimmy asked. "Mine or hers?"

The man rubbed his stubbled chin. He took a drink of wine and a swallow of beer. Then he grinned at Jimmy. "Yours, kid," he said. "You cut in on her and ran her off the road."

The color drained from Jimmy's face; the strength drained from his legs. Pop put a hand on his shoulder and turned him. Jimmy started a protest, but the hurt and deep sympathy in his father's face told him the case was closed.

He pulled free of his father's hand and went out and got into the car. In a few moments, Pop came out and got in beside him.

"Tough," Pop said gently. "I'm sorry, lad."

Jimmy didn't answer.

Pop fumbled with the car keys. "It was a chance we both knew you were taking. So you lost. But I'm still proud of you. You gave it a good fight."

Jimmy turned a quivering face toward his father. "I wasn't taking a chance," he said. "I knew if I found the guy, if he'd seen the accident, he'd clear me. Why? Because I know I didn't cut back too fast!"

"He saw the accident. He said—"

"Pop! He lied!"

Pop stared at Jimmy. "What in blazes is the matter with me?" he asked. "I can believe a booze-brain or I can believe my son. Who do I believe? The booze-brain. I ought to have my rump kicked!" He slapped the door of the station wagon open. "Be right back!" he said.

He was gone five minutes – an eternity for Jimmy. And when he came back, he was grinning. "You're the champ," he said.

Jimmy's face began to light. "Pop, did he really—"

"He sure did," Pop said. "I offered him twenty-five bucks to see the accident our way. He said 'No.' I said fifty bucks and he said 'No.' I said a hundred, and he said 'Yes.' "

"No, Pop!" Jimmy's voice was agonized.

Pop grinned. "Easy does it, boy. All I wanted was to find out if he was for sale. He was. So I put my fist under his nose and asked if maybe he hadn't sold out to Murphy first. Turns out he had. For fifty bucks."

"Murphy paid him?"

"This is a wino," Pop said. "His brains are pulp. He'd sell his soul for the price of a few bottles, and he can't think farther ahead than a few. He saw Mrs. Murphy run into you after you'd passed her; the accident was her fault. You're a kid, driving a heap. You couldn't pay anything to testify. But a man who owned the car Mrs. Murphy was driving could afford to pay him not to testify. He got Murphy's name and address from the newspaper account of the accident, went around to Murphy and made his pitch: pay or he'd look you up. Murphy paid."

"But that makes Mr. Murphy a crook!"

"So it does," Pop agreed.

"Why...why would he do it?"

"It's a chance to clip your insurance company for your public liability, ten thousand bucks, and for a bandit like Murphy that's important. Sure, he's got insurance of his own. One-hundred-dollar deductible and maybe seven-fifty medical; about a tenth of what's going to be needed. And without that witness, he's got grounds for a lawsuit against you and your insurance company because his wife's beautiful face has been smashed. What's the value on that? Ten thousand? Fifty thousand? All this he gets for just fifty bucks."

"No wonder he was afraid I'd find the witness."

"Yeah," Pop said. "No wonder." He put the car in gear.

"Wait a minute, Pop," Jimmy said. He was staring through the windshield. "Now we've got to think about something else... something that's been driving me nuts. She ran into me. We can prove that now. But how? And why? Stop and think about it. The only way...she'd have to do it deliberately."

"Her foot could slip off the brake —"

"And jam the gas down? And hold it down that long?"

"For the love of Mike!" Pop said. "She wasn't mad at you. She couldn't gain anything by running into you. She could get herself in a bad smash-up, and she did! Jimmy, lad, it just doesn't make sense!"

"Maybe it does." Jimmy turned his head slowly to look at his father. "Remember the tangle I had with the guy who smelled like a brewery? He had a beat-up fender; he got a brand-new fender out of the accident. Maybe Mrs. Murphy wanted to hit me just a little, to cover up a bent fender or something like that. But she hit me a lot and went out of control."

"The Murphys can afford to fix their own fenders."

"You've got to run into something to bend a fender," Jimmy said. "Can they afford to fix what Mrs. Murphy hit before she ran into me?" He looked at his father. "I may be wrong, but I've got to talk to the cops. Right now. Will you take me downtown?"

"When you tell me what's in your head," Pop said.

They walked into the police station together, faces grave with concern. There was doubt in their minds, but their responsibility was clear to them, and responsibility can sometimes be an enormous burden. Jimmy talked to the lieutenant in charge of traffic.

"I went by that hit-and-run accident on

230

Lake Boulevard, just after it happened," he said. "It scared me pretty bad. I've been thinking about it a lot, watching the papers. But I've never read that you found the driver."

"We haven't found him." The lieutenant was a thin, sharp-nosed, dour man. Light glinted on his rimless glasses. "But I'd give my right arm to find him. The old woman he left in the gutter will live, but she'll never walk again."

Jimmy swallowed. "Could the driver have been a woman?"

The lieutenant looked at Jimmy's pale face, wondered if the boy was going to be sick. "It could have been a woman," he said slowly. "All we've got is a description of the car...a big, late-model sedan."

Jimmy turned his stricken eyes to Pop, asking for help, for guidance. But what help could there be? And what guidance, except to point the way straight forward? Pop put a big hand on Jimmy's shoulder.

"I don't know for sure," Jimmy said. "I'm not accusing anybody, see? But I've got to tell you what happened. After I passed the accident on Lake Boulevard, I went out Dutch Hill Road. That's they way I go home. There was a woman driving real slow out there. I passed her. And then she speeded up and ran into me."

The lieutenant tipped his head. "She ran into you? After you passed her?"

"We've got a witness," Pop said.

"All right. Go on, son."

"The woman, Mrs. Murphy, had been downtown buying a hat; her husband told me that. She'd go home by way of Lake Boulevard. Everybody does who lives out our way. It's quickest by fifteen minutes. So she had to go past the place where the woman was hit. If she'd stopped to think what she could do or drove real slow, I'd have caught up with her where I did." Jim-

my's eyes were miserable. "Why would anybody run into a guy on purpose?"

"You tell me," the lieutenant said.

"To cover up something like a bent fender?"

"Or a cracked headlight," the lieutenant said softly, "or a dented hood. Because every car that's gone into any garage with that kind of damage has been reported to us and we've checked it out. Mrs. Murphy's car was checked out and the damage charged to you. You'd better tell me the name of your witness, son."

Patrolman Sam Riggio came to the Franklin home early the next evening. There was no need for him to do it. But he, too, was a man with a sense of responsibility. He made his partner Mark Bradford go to the door with him. Bradford was the man who resented teenage drivers, sometimes to the point of hate. Riggio was smiling when Pop opened the door.

"We'd like to talk to Jimmy."

Pop led them into the living room. Jimmy was playing cribbage with Cricket. He stumbled to his feet awkwardly at the sight of the police officers, his round face twisting in a worried frown.

Cricket said, "Oh, my goodness!" and flew around the room, picking up papers and straightening cushions.

"We've come with an apology," Riggio told Jimmy. "We didn't call you a liar, but we refused to believe you, and that adds up to the same thing."

Bradford stepped forward. "You've got a right to chew us out," he said, "but I've got to tell you there's not much left to chew. The lieutenant got to us first. We jumped to a wrong conclusion; we let a hit-and-run driver get away. The lieutenant takes a dim view of that kind of work. We're lucky to be alive."

Jimmy said, "Did...did Mrs. Murphy do it?"

Riggio nodded. "Once we'd talked to your witness, it was easy going. We went from him to Murphy to ask Murphy why he'd paid the fifty dollars, and from there to Mrs. Murphy to ask why she'd run into you on purpose, since it had to be that way. She's not a tough criminal with a thought-out plan. She's a frightened woman with an enormous burden of guilt. She wanted to be rid of it. She gave us a confession."

Pop was frowning. "Did Murphy know about the hit-and-run when he paid the wino the fifty bucks?"

"No," Riggio said. "And neither did the wino. When the wino showed up at Murphy's front door with an offer to get lost and keep his mouth shut for fifty dollars, Murphy grabbed it like a shot. It was small money, money he could throw away or deny he'd ever spent. And it cleared his wife of the blame of hitting Jimmy."

"It also paved the way to a damage suit," Pop said, "against Jimmy, his insurance company, and me. A damage suit that could go fifty or a hundred thousand. A bargain for fifty bucks."

"Not such a bargain." Riggio smiled. "When he'd thought about it awhile, Murphy saw that his wife must have run into Jimmy on purpose. He asked her why, she told him, and then he had a can of beans he was afraid to open. What could he do about the wino? He couldn't go to him with more money and a ticket out of the state. The wino would want to know why. All he'd asked for, all he'd wanted, was fifty bucks. And if the wino found out why, he could blackmail Murphy for the rest of his life."

"But leave it alone," Pop said, "and it was a million to one the wino would never put the two accidents together. The police didn't and their brains aren't pulp."

"That was his choice," Riggio agreed. "A Hobson's choice, and Murphy made the wrong pick. He calls it bad luck. I call it the kind of thing that happens to a man with larceny in his heart."

Cricket said, "He should have gone to the police and admitted his wife was the hit-and-run driver."

"And face criminal action and a lawsuit that could bankrupt him?" Pop said. "Not Murphy!"

When the police had gone, Pop put his arm around Jimmy's shoulders and grinned proudly at Cricket. "This is my boy," he said. "His guts and good sense saved me a lousy fortune."

Cricket knew her son well, knew why there was no light in the boy's eyes, why he tried to pull away from his father.

"Mrs. Murphy will be all right, sonny," she said. "I've talked to her doctor. It isn't so bad as they first thought. There may not even be noticeable scars. She'll be pretty again."

Jimmy turned to her, doubting. "Mom, honest?"

"I promise."

"That's...that's wonderful." Now Jimmy's face began to glow. "If you could have seen her the way I did. I thought...well, I was afraid to think!" He caught his mother's face suddenly between his hands and kissed her. "You're the most!" he said to her, and went quickly away.

Pop stared after him. "After what she did to the old lady, after what she tried to do to him, he's worried about her face! How do you like a dope like that?"

Softly, Cricket said, "Only very, very much."

231

Joan Rattner Heilman

How to Survive Your Adolescent

An interview with Martin Symonds, M.D.

A child,
especially an adolescent,
needs consistency and
harmony.

Q. Dr. Symonds, are all adolescents problems?

A. Yes, in one way or another, at one time or another. They have what I call a psychological sunburn – they're fantastically touchy. You say, "Hello," and they say, "Don't bother me!" You ask them to wash their hands, and they accuse you of parental brutality. They question, defy, resist, insist. They complain, gripe, suffer. They live in extremes – happy one minute, miserable the next. They have great plans and little follow-through. They're so preoccupied with their own suffering that they have little time for others. On the other hand, they have the lowest self-esteem and self-confidence of any age group.

Q. Why do adolescents behave this way?

A. Because they're troubled. They're growing up and, at the same time, growing away. They are leaving childhood, which is essentially a period of dependency, and trying to "find themselves." They say no to just about everything, feeling that they can show that they are different only by differing. Any agreement is seen as submission to the enemy.

When an adult sees a "Wet Paint" sign on a park bench, he doesn't touch the bench. An adolescent, however, must touch the bench, look at his fingers and say, "Yes, it's wet paint." This looks like defiance of authority, or even stupidity. Actually, it's his way of discovering for himself the real world. He does this in all areas of his life, to the despair of his parents – who would like to spare him the grief of trial and error. Parents must remember, however, that trial and error is the function of adolescence. Parents cannot *make* their adolescents happy.

Q. What causes the most difficulty in the parent-adolescent relationship?

A. It is parents abdicating their role as parents. In all the children in trouble that I've seen, one thing stands out: their parents are not providing the anchorage, the support, the guidance they need. Adolescents grow very rapidly and erratically, and need a solid point of view to push against. As parents, you must let them know what your values are – without belligerence. To take a simple example, if you don't like long hair, say so, with something like, "I happen to like short hair." Not, "You look disgusting with that long, stringy hair."

Q. But in this changing world can parents rightly be so authoritarian?

A. To declare one's position doesn't mean being rigid and authoritarian. It means that you are not an unknown quantity to your children. It doesn't make your adolescent do as you do, or do as you want; it tells him who you are and what you believe in. Too often parents give up, let their children lead them. It's not true, though, that youth today has all the answers. We must be the leaders. The sickest children are the ones who have never experienced frustration.

Q. What about parents who think that they've done everything wrong?

A. There's always something to feel guilty about, because no one is perfect. But guilt erodes judgment and causes more problems than the original error. My advice to parents is to stop torturing themselves about the past, to stand up and be responsible *now*, which means doing the best they can, day by day.

Q. If parents feel confused, what should they do?

A. I believe they should read, listen, talk with other adults, verbalize their thoughts, expose themselves to probing, then sift things through. It's amazing what can happen when adults talk together. First, it's a relief to "get it out," to learn that your situation and your reactions are not unique, that other parents battle with their kids, come to an impasse, are often filled with despair. Talking out thoughts and feelings helps to unearth the feelings behind the feelings.

For example, a mother feels great anger toward her fourteen-year-old daughter whom she feels she cannot trust, who may be lying to her, whose friends she dislikes. She discovers, in talking, that her anger covers over her *fear*, her fear of being out of control, of "losing" her child, of disquieting competition. She also discovers that her anger has been masking her love and concern for her daughter – both to herself and her child.

Q. If the worst thing you can do is not to make clear where you stand, what's the next worst thing?

A. It is for you and your spouse to disagree about how to deal with your child. Behind every troubled adolescent I've come across in my work, I've found parents with conflicting attitudes. The minute the parents join forces, even though their attitudes may be eccentric, the child does better. A child, especially an adolescent, needs consistency and harmony.

Q. But it's unrealistic to think that both parents will always feel the same way about behavior.

A. Of course. But they should iron out their differences between themselves and come to an agreement. Suppose one parent doesn't want his fifteen-year-old daughter out after 10 P.M., and the other feels it doesn't matter. The two of them must choose. I don't think it matters which decision is made, so long as there is one. What does matter is that there be no undermining, no playing off one parent against the other, no father saying, "If it were up to me, I'd say okay, but your mother doesn't want you to do it."

234

Q. When you say that parents must have a position, declare themselves, aren't you advocating old-fashioned discipline?

A. No. I'm advocating being firm, telling your children what you expect and would like from them, but not being uncompromising. If you are too constricting, you run the risk of the adolescent becoming even more rebellious in his fight for self-expression. Avoid phony ultimatums like, "If you see that boy again, don't come home." Instead, consider "I'd like you to do so and so," or "I wish you would..." That way you give the youngster some choice, and you have a much better chance of obtaining co-operation.

Q. But if you can't issue orders to an adolescent, how do you get him to do as you want?

A. He'll do it only out of respect for you. Parental approval and disapproval carry a lot of weight with an adolescent, even though it may not appear that way. He wants to know your opinion. And he wants your approval of him as a human being, though not necessarily of each of his decisions.

I'd suggest telling your adolescent what you want and expect but always in terms of yourself. For example, "I think that dress you're wearing is too short," rather than "You look awful in that dress."

Don't make an issue of everything that your adolescent says or does. Don't react to everything. Don't listen too intensely, ready to challenge. Try to respond to the spirit of the message rather than the words alone. Accept some things, don't accept others. Feel what you can go along with.

Q. How would you resolve a difference in opinion, say, on what time a boy of fourteen should be home from a party?

A. I'd discuss the party first, where it is, how the boy will get there and back. Then I'd say, "I'd like you home by 11 o'clock." If he says, "But everybody else is staying

till 12:30," I'd talk it over with him and decide whether it seems reasonable for him to stay out that late. If it doesn't, I'd say, "I still don't think 12:30 is a good idea. I'd like you home by 11:30." If your adolescent has respect for you, I can almost guarantee he'll be home by the appointed time. Another approach might be, "If there's going to be a problem, maybe it would be best to skip the party."

Q. Aren't adolescents more difficult to bring up now than they were years ago?

A. I believe so. The present-day adolescent, in addition to all the usual problems, is experiencing the effects of adult hopelessness. If parents believe that the world is going to hell, or feel defeated and trapped in a job, why should their adolescent feel that learning self-discipline is worth the struggle?

Parents have to be optimists. They have to have faith in the world and its future, or they can't expect their children to have it. Without faith, it's like an army captain muttering, "We'll never take that hill," before the battle begins. If you really feel that the world is in a hopeless mess, hide it. Whatever you say should be honest, but don't confuse honesty with total confession; not everything must be said. Don't share your uncertainties about the future with your adolescent. Allow him to explore the future on his own, with your support.

A parent must be optimistic, as well, about his children. Criticism destroys a child's self-image, which is the most essential part of him. Parents must look for his assets, not his failings. They must have hope for him, a confidence that he will do well — and communicate that to him. I have found that when I project the conviction that my patients are going to do well, they *do* progress. Hope is the most helpful thing we can provide.

Anonymous

What's Wrong with Grown-ups?

1. Grown-ups don't do the things they're always telling children to do – like pick up their things, or be neat, or always tell the truth.

2. Grown-ups won't let their children dress the way they want to – but they never ask a child's opinion about how they should dress. If they're going out to a party, grown-ups wear just exactly what they want to wear – even if it looks terrible, even if it isn't warm enough.

3. Grown-ups interrupt children all the time and think nothing of it. If a child interrupts a grown-up, he gets a scolding or something worse.

4. Sometimes grown-ups punish children unfairly. It isn't right if you've done just some little thing wrong and grown-ups take away something that means an awful lot to you. Other times you can do something really bad and they say they're going to punish you, but they don't. You never know, and you ought to know.

5. Grown-ups talk about money too much, and bills, and things like that, so that it scares you. They say money isn't very important, but the way they talk about it, it sounds like the most important thing in the world.

6. Grown-ups make promises, then they forget all about them, or else they say it wasn't really a promise, just a maybe.

7. Grown-ups make mistakes but they won't admit them. They always pretend that they weren't mistakes at all – or that somebody else made them.

8. Grown-ups never really listen to what children have to say. They always decide ahead of time what they're going to answer.

9. Grown-ups never understand how much children want a certain thing – a certain color or shape or size. If it's something they don't admire – even if the children have spent their own money for it – they always say, "I can't imagine what you would ever want with that old thing!"

10. Grown-ups gossip – but if children do the very same thing and say the same words about the same people, the grown-ups say they're being disrespectful.

11. Grown-ups pry into children's secrets. They always think it's going to be something bad. They never think it might be a nice surprise.

12. Grown-ups are always talking about what they did and what they knew when they were ten years old – and it usually sounds as if it couldn't have happened the way they say. But grown-ups *never* try to think what it's like to be ten years old *right now*.

Ben Wicks

"Look on the bright side, Herbie.
If you weren't at school
you'd be unemployed!"

David French

Leaving Home

Characters

MARY MERCER,
the mother

BEN MERCER,
her eighteen-year-old son

BILL MERCER,
her seventeen-year-old son

From *Leaving Home* by David French. Reprinted by permission of General Publishing Co., Limited.

The lights come up on a working-class house in Toronto. The stage is divided into three playing areas: kitchen, dining room, and living room. In addition, there is a hallway leading into the living room. Two bedroom doors lead off the hallway, as well as the front door which is off-stage.

The kitchen contains a fridge, a stove, cupboards over the sink for everyday dishes, and a small drop-leaf table with two wooden chairs, one at either end. A plastic garbage receptacle stands beside the stove. A hockey calendar hangs on a wall, and a kitchen prayer.

The dining room is furnished simply with an oak table and chairs. There is an oak cabinet containing the good dishes and silverware. Perhaps a family portrait hangs on the wall – a photo taken when the sons were much younger.

The living room contains a chesterfield and an armchair, a TV, a record player, and a fireplace. On the mantel rests a photo album and a silver-framed photo of the two sons – then small boys – astride a pinto pony. On one wall hangs a mirror. On another, a seascape. There is also a small table with a telephone on it.

It is around five-thirty on a Friday afternoon, and Mary Mercer, aged fifty, stands before the mirror in the living room, admiring her brand new dress and fixed hair. As she preens, the front door opens and in walk her two sons, Ben, eighteen, and Bill, seventeen. Each carries a box from a formal rental shop and schoolbooks.

MARY: Did you bump into your father?

BEN: No, we just missed him, Mom. He's already picked up his tux. He's probably at the Oakwood. (*He opens the fridge and helps himself to a beer.*)

MARY: Get your big nose out of the fridge. And put down that beer. You'll spoil your appetite.

238

BEN: No, I won't. (*He searches for a bottle opener in a drawer*.)

MARY: And don't contradict me. What other bad habits you learned lately?

BEN: (*teasing*) Don't be such a grouch. You sound like Dad. (*He sits at the table and opens his beer*.)

MARY: Yes, well just because you're in university now, don't t'ink you can raid the fridge any time you likes.

Bill crosses the kitchen and throws his black binder and books in the garbage receptacle.

MARY: What's that for? (*Bill exits into his bedroom and she calls after him*.) It's not the end of the world, my son. (*pause*) Tell you the truth, Ben. We always figured you'd be the one to land in trouble, if anyone did. I don't mean that as an insult. You're more...I don't know...like your father.

BEN: I am?

Music from Bill's room.

MARY: (*calling, exasperated*) Billy, do you have to have that so loud? (*Bill turns down his record player. To Ben*) I'm glad your graduation went O.K. last night. How was Billy? Was he glad he went?

BEN: Well, he wasn't upset, if that's what you mean.

MARY: (*slight pause*) Ben, how come you not to ask your father?

BEN: What do you mean?

BILL: (*off*) Mom, will you pack my suitcase? I can't get everything in.

MARY: (*calling*) I can't now, Billy. Later.

BEN: I want to talk to you, Mom. It's important.

MARY: I want to talk to you, too.

BILL: (*comes out of bedroom, crosses to kitchen*) Mom, here's the deposit on my locker. I cleaned it out and threw away all my old gym clothes. (*He helps himself to an apple from the fridge*.)

MARY: Didn't you just hear me tell your brother to stay out of there? I might as well talk to the sink. Well, you can t'row away your old school clothes – that's your affair – but take those books out of the garbage. Go on. You never knows. They might come in handy sometime.

BILL: How? (*He takes the books out, then sits at the table with Ben*.)

MARY: Well, you can always go to night school and get your senior matric, once the baby arrives and Kathy's back to work.... Poor child. I talked to her on the phone this morning. She's still upset, and I don't blame her. I'd be hurt myself if my own mother was too drunk to show up for my shower.

BILL: (*a slight ray of hope*) Maybe she won't show up tonight.

MARY: (*glances anxiously at the kitchen clock and turns to check the fish and potatoes*) Look at the time, I just wish to goodness he had more t'ought, your father. The supper'll dry up if he don't hurry. He might pick up a phone and mention when he'll be home. Not a grain of t'ought in his head. And I wouldn't put it past him to forget his tux in the beer parlor. (*Finally she turns and looks at her two sons, disappointed*.) And look at the two of you. Too busy with your mouths to give your mother a second glance. I could stand here till my legs dropped off before either of you would notice my dress.

BEN: It's beautiful, Mom.

MARY: That the truth?

BILL: Would we lie to you, Mom?

MARY: Just so long as I don't look foolish next to Minnie. She can afford to dress up – Willard left her well off when he died.

BEN: Don't worry about the money. Dad won't mind.

MARY: Well, it's not every day your own son gets married, is it? (*to Bill as she puts on large apron*) It's just that I don't want Minnie Jackson looking all decked out like the *Queen Mary* and me the tug that dragged her in. You understands, don't you, Ben?

BEN: Sure.

BILL: I understand too, Mom.

MARY: I know you do, Billy. I know you do. (*She opens a tin of peaches and fills five dessert dishes*.) Minnie used to go with your father. Did you know that, Billy? Years and years ago.

BILL: No kidding?

BEN: (*at the same time*) Really?

MARY: True as God is in Heaven. Minnie was awful sweet on Dad, too. She t'ought the world of him.

BILL: (*incredulously*) Dad?

MARY: Don't act so surprised. Your father was quite a one with the girls.

BEN: No kidding?

MARY: He could have had his pick of any number of girls. (*to Bill*) You ask Minnie sometime. Of course, in those days I was going with Jerome McKenzie, who later became a Queen's Counsel in St. John's. I must have mentioned him.

The boys exchange smiles.

BEN: I think you have, Mom.

BILL: A hundred times.

MARY: (*gently indignant – to Bill*) And that I haven't!

BILL: She has too. Hasn't she, Ben?

MARY: Never you mind, Ben. (*to Bill*) And instead of sitting around gabbing so much you'd better go change your clothes. Kathy'll soon be here. (*as Bill crosses to his bedroom*) Is the rehearsal still at eight?

BILL: We're supposed to meet Father Douglas at the church at five to. I just hope Dad's not too drunk. (*He exits*.)

MARY: (*studies Ben a moment*) Look at yourself. A cigarette in one hand, a bottle of beer in the other, at your age! You didn't learn any of your bad habits from me, I can tell you. (*pause*) Ben, don't be in such a hurry to grow up. (*She sits across from him*.) Whatever you do, don't be in such a hurry. Look at your poor young brother. His whole life ruined. Oh, I could weep a bellyful when I t'inks of it. Just seventeen, not old enough to sprout whiskers on his chin, and already the burdens of a man on his t'in little shoulders. Your poor father hasn't slept a full night since this happened. Did you know that? He had such high hopes for Billy. He wanted you both to go to college and not to have to work as hard as he's had to all his life. And now look. You have more sense than that, Ben. Don't let life trap you.

Bill enters. He has changed his pants and is buttoning a clean white shirt. Mary goes into the dining room and begins to remove the tablecloth from the dining room table.

BILL: Mom, what about Dad? He won't start picking on the priest, will he? You know how he likes to argue.

MARY: He won't say a word, my son. You needn't worry. Worry more about Minnie showing up.

BILL: What if he's drunk?

MARY: He won't be. Your father knows better than to sound off in church. Oh, and another t'ing – he wants to you polish his shoes for tonight. They're in the bedroom. The polish is on your dresser. You needn't be too fussy.

BEN: I'll do his shoes, Mom. Billy's all dressed.

MARY: No, no, Ben, that's all right. He asked Billy to.

BILL: What did Ben do this time?

MARY: He didn't do anyt'ing.

BILL: He must have.

MARY: Is it too much trouble to polish your father's shoes, after all he does for you? If you won't do it, I'll do it myself.

BILL: (*indignantly*) How come when Dad's mad at Ben, I get all the dirty jobs? Jeez! Will I be glad to get out of here! (*Rolling up his shirt sleeves he exits into his bedroom.*)

Mary takes a clean linen tablecloth from a drawer in the cabinet and covers the table. During the following scene she sets five places with her good glasses, silverware, and plates.

BEN: (*slight pause*) Billy's right, isn't he? What'd I do, Mom?

MARY: Take it up with your father. I'm tired of being the middleman.

BEN: Is it because of last night? (*slight pause*) It is, isn't it?

MARY: He t'inks you didn't want him there, Ben. He t'inks you're ashamed of him.

BEN: He wouldn't have gone, Mom. That's the only reason I never invited him.

MARY: He would have went, last night.

BEN: (*angrily*) He's never even been to one lousy Parents' Night in thirteen years. Not one! And he calls *me* contrary!

MARY: You listen to me. Your father never got past Grade T'ree. He was yanked out of school and made to work. In those days, back home, he was lucky to get that much and don't kid yourself.

BEN: Yeah? So?

MARY: So? So he's afraid to. He's afraid of sticking out. Is that so hard to understand? Is it?

BEN: What're you getting angry about? All I said was...

MARY: You say he don't take an interest, but he was proud enough to show off your report cards all those years. I suppose with you that don't count for much.

BEN: All right. But he never goes anywhere without you, Mom, and last night you were here at the shower.

MARY: Last night was different, Ben, and you ought to know that. It was your high school graduation. He would have went with me or without me. If you'd only asked him.

A truck horn blasts twice.

There he is now in the driveway. Whatever happens, don't fall for his old tricks. He'll be looking for a fight, and doing his best to find any excuse. (*calling*) Billy, you hear that? Don't complain about the shoes, once your father comes!

BEN: (*urgently*) Mom, there's something I want to tell you before Dad comes in.

MARY: Sure, my son. Go ahead. I'm listening. What's on your mind?

BEN: Well...

MARY: (*smiling*) Come on. It can't be that bad.

BEN: (*slight pause*) I want to move out, Mom.

MARY: (*almost inaudibly*) What?

BEN: I said I want to move out.

MARY: (*softly, as she sets the cutlery*) I heard you. (*pause*) What for?

BEN: I just think it's time. I'll be nineteen soon. (*pause*) I'm moving in with Billy and Kathy and help pay the rent. (*pause*) I won't be far away. I'll see you on weekends. (*Mary nods.*) Mom?

MARY: (*absently*) What?

BEN: Will you tell Dad? (*slight pause*) Mom? Did you hear me?

MARY: I heard you. He'll be upset, I can tell you. By rights you ought to tell him yourself.

BEN: If I do, we'll just get in a big fight and you know it. He'll take it better, coming from you.

Charlene Keel

The Threshold

Heather let her mind drift backward
to the people who had shared and shaped her life
for as long as she could remember....

Heather blinked in the southern autumn sunshine like a fat, lazy toad. The ground was warm, and the curves of her young body felt comfortable and secure against it. She smiled sleepily to think what they would say if they caught her lying in the grass like this.

"Get up, Heather," from her father, sternly and without emotion.

"Lying there on the front lawn – just inviting men to look at her," from her mother.

Her younger sister: "Mother! Heather's lying in the grass out in the front yard where *everybody* can see her!" Dorothy was thirteen, and everything had to be proper in homage to her new maturity.

Her brother would be sarcastic: "Heather, why don't you get up off your butt and go help Mother?"

As if Mother needed help. Mother didn't need help from anyone, least of all Heather.

Heather stretched, turned over on her

242

stomach, and pressed her cheek to the cool ground. A sun-drugged insect protested weakly, so she turned over on her side, propped her head in her hand, and unconsciously reached for her book. When she heard footsteps on the walk that passed between her house and the street, she almost got up, but it was too much of an effort. Besides, she was amused at the prospect of the surprised looks on the faces of the passers-by. Everyone gave Heather looks of surprise – especially when she stretched out on the front lawn or when she walked barefoot to the park and sat among the children in one of the swings.

She lifted her gaze slightly. As they passed, June and Sarah smiled a greeting. Sarah even waved. Best friends in high school, they were now college freshmen and still best friends. Heather was nothing. No best friend, no money for college, a whole summer gone by since graduation, and no job.

Not that she hadn't tried. Interview after stupid interview. There was not much available during a recession summer. She could have filled in for a couple of weeks as a salesclerk in the dime store. But when Mr. Johnson had asked her in all seriousness why she had chosen a career in sales, she had laughed out loud. *Right in the man's face*, her mother had said.

So, no job. Jimmy, who had graduated only two years before, was working and terribly independent – and quite happy to remind everyone in the house of that fact.

She turned over again, and the blinding reflection of the sun on the white stucco apartment building across the street blurred her vision for a moment. Or was it tears again? They always started so unexpectedly. She wondered if *he* was home.

When her vision cleared, *he* was standing over her, an amused expression on his

face. Heather felt she had dreamed him across the street. Almost reluctantly, she sat up and pulled her dress down over her knees.

"Hello," she said, to break the silence.

"Hello. Is Dorothy home?"

"No, she's over at Laura's. Laura is her best friend," Heather said in a low voice.

"I know that, too. I can hardly keep them separated in class. After all, I'm Dorothy's teacher."

As if she didn't know. As if she had not been listening for his car and watching the lights go on and off in his apartment for the past two weeks.

"Is Dorothy in trouble?" she finally blurted out, more sharply than she intended.

"Oh, no. I was just coming in from the library, and I thought I'd check on how her term project was going. She seemed worried about it."

"She hasn't said anything."

"That's what I suspected," he grinned. "Well, she certainly needs a good grade, and she has been doing research on North American Indians."

"Well, we're part Indian. On my mother's side. Only it doesn't show in me like it does in Dorothy. We're not much alike."

"She's a little chatterbox," he chuckled. "Somehow you don't strike me as that type. What's that you're reading?"

"Oh, poetry. A collection of poems with the stories of how they came to be written."

"Do you write?"

"Some."

Then they talked about poetry, sitting there in the sun. About Keats and Poe and Byron. He asked to see her poems sometime. Not now, but sometime. He wanted to know what she planned to do now that she had graduated from high school. She shrugged her shoulders and mumbled the standard thing about finding a job and saving up for college.

A half an hour of more wonderful talk passed before Dorothy came home with Laura in tow. They said hello in unison to their teacher and they both blushed. Heather felt uncomfortable for them.

"Hello, girls," he laughed. "I brought you a book on North American Indian tribes, Dorothy." He produced a book from the bottom of the pile next to him and gave it to her.

"Oh, *thank* you. I thought maybe I was in *trouble* or something. Am I ever relieved. Heather, did you ask Mr. Rogers if he'd like some lemonade?"

"No, I didn't think of it," Heather murmured, hoping against hope that Dorothy wouldn't make her feel stupid again.

"Oh, for heaven's sake." Dorothy shot Heather one of her famous scathing looks and then drawled sweetly, "Won't you have some, Mr. Rogers? I made it myself. It ought to be real cold by now."

"No, I don't believe so, Dorothy. I really should be going. Thanks just the same."

"Oh – well – thanks for the book."

Heather could see that her sister was hurt at the teacher's obvious lack of feeling and that Laura felt hurt as well. It would certainly be no trouble for him to stay five more minutes. He seemed to read her mind.

"On second thought, a glass of lemonade would hit the spot. Could we have it out here?" When the two girls had scurried off to get the lemonade, he said, "That was stupid of me. Thirteen-year-olds are so damned sensitive."

"Yes. Yes, they are," she replied. His use of "damn" made her feel a camaraderie. Dorothy and Laura came back with the icy drink. They all sipped in an uncomfortable silence. When his glass was drained, he smiled graciously and handed it back to Dorothy.

"You read the book I brought," he said in mock authority, "and pull that grade up."

"Yes, sir," Dorothy whispered adoringly.

"Think of a new approach for your project. Your sister could probably help you."

Dorothy looked at Heather in surprise. She continued to stare until Heather wanted to writhe under her gaze.

"Maybe," Heather said to make Dorothy look some place else. She picked up her book and went toward the house. As she stepped up onto the porch, she could feel the chipped paint of the floorboards with her bare feet. She thought with some sadness that it would soon be winter and she would have to wear shoes. But she knew if she concentrated hard enough, she would be able to feel the concrete of the sidewalk through the soles of her shoes. She smiled. Like the princess and the pea, she thought, because of how special I am.

Just in time, she realized her mother was in the living room. She performed an abrupt about-face, and slipped quietly around to the backyard. She laughed softly to herself as the cool grass tickled her feet. Noiselessly she let herself in the back way. Before she put her book on her bedside table, she gripped it hard between her palms and pressed it with all her strength, as if to draw the words on its pages out into her body.

"Heather, is that you?" called her mother.

"Yes, ma'am."

"I want you to do the dishes. I'm exhausted."

"Yes, ma'am. Just a minute."

"If I ever asked you do anything for me and you didn't say 'just a minute,' I think I'd fall over in a dead faint. I want them done before I start supper."

She didn't answer. Smoothing the front of her dress, she sighed almost inaudibly, and then started the phonograph. She sat down on the edge of her bed, but she didn't mean to put her head down. She just did, and soon she was lost in the Scottish moors. The

244

violins tripped and raced over the notes until the needle dug cruelly into her precious record as a heavy hand swung it across the turntable.

"Those fiddles make me sick," said her brother. He took the record off and tossed it on her bed.

"They're violins," she said, forcing her voice out in an even tone. "When I finished listening to this side, I was going to do the dishes for Mother." He just didn't realize how badly she needed to hear it right at this moment.

"You do the dishes now. What else have you done all day? Anything? I've worked like a dog. How about some iced tea?" He put on an old Elvis Presley record that was so scratched that her needle would be ruined.

"I'll get you some of the lemonade Dorothy made. There isn't any tea."

"Make some. It won't kill you."

She plodded into the kitchen and put water on to boil. She thought her head would burst with the silent fury.

"Heather!" her mother called.

"Yes, ma'am."

"Have you started the dishes yet?"

"I'm making Jimmy some iced tea."

"Let him make his own. Those dishes should be done before your father gets home from work."

Heather returned to her bedroom to find Jimmy sprawled across her bed in his dirty work clothes. "Mother says to make your own iced tea." A note of triumph crept into her voice. "I have to do the dishes."

"You're too dumb to live," he told her as he pushed her out of his way and went into the kitchen. "I went out and got a job as soon as I graduated. You're just no good to anybody."

He banged about in the kitchen, leaving twice as big a mess as there was before. She sat quietly until he was done. Then she

spurted liquid detergent into the sink and watched the hot water make a thick foam of it. She plunged her hands into the basin and squiggled the suds through her fingers, wondering as she did if there was really any such word as "squiggle."

Dorothy came in and made herself a sandwich. Heather, her arms submerged up to her elbows, watched quietly. Her sister left the sandwich things on the counter and said sweetly as she went into the living room, "Why don't you stop playing and get on with it?"

"Heather!" Her mother's voice rang out seconds later. "You hurry with those dishes. I don't want to tell you again!"

She dumped the glasses and silverware in first. She didn't mind it so much once she got started. The soapy water felt nice, and threads of a singsong rhyme began to tug at her brain. "In a dishtub," she chanted softly, "my castles are built, around the pots and plates and pans. I pour in soap and water, and I'm in another land. An Eskimo with white igloo, and awhaling I will go in my kayak through a land of soapy snow. I'm a fairy queen with elves so fine to wait for my command, drinking dew from flower cups, while stars shine on soap-bubble sand. Titanic! A ship sailing the sea, a bubble-captain at the wheel, nothing can take me off the course! Now a snow maiden dressed in white, riding my tureen sleigh. Through milk-white hills and valleys it carries me away."

Her mother's voice brings her back from excursions through the foam: "Your pa's home." Heather rinsed her hands and dried them. The words she had hummed at the sink were taking form now and she must write them down on paper before they left her head.

She rummaged around in the old desk before she finally resorted to Dorothy's notebook. She hate using anything that was Dorothy's, but with a sigh she ripped two blank pages out and hastily scribbled the poem. When she returned to the kitchen, her mother was finishing the dishes, her mouth set in a hard line.

"Heather, you are going to be my death."

"Mother, I had a poem..."

"Couldn't it have waited?"

Dishes could wait. Poems couldn't. The dishes would be there, the words could well leave her head completely, never to return. Sometimes she wished they would.

"What were you doing all this time?" her mother asked.

Writing a beautiful poem, Heather replied silently, an ode to dishes, dishes, dishes. She felt weak and stupid.

"You better set the table," her mother ordered, as her father manoeuvred the car into the garage.

Heather took the dishes from the drainer and hurriedly put them on the table, leaving her own place empty. Then she darted through the kitchen, grabbed an apple, and ran as fast as she could out the back door and down the steps, gaining momentum as she went. She ran through the neighbors' yard, and their fat, bald grandfather yelled at her, as he did every time she ran through their yard. She didn't stop running until she reached her secret place.

At the beginning of the summer she had stumbled upon a lovely, quiet grove of trees in the middle of a residential area not far from her house. The city had purchased it as a site for a youth centre, then had abandoned the project. It was completely deserted and, except for a rusty set of swings, the grove was unchanged. A small brook curved through the trees. When Heather sat by the water, she was completely hidden from the outside world. That was the real joy.

She had to catch her breath before she could eat the apple. She put her feet into the cool water and settled back so she could look through the tops of the trees. She thought of the dishes. Of course they could have waited. She couldn't understand the importance of doing them at that particular moment in time and space. There were so many moments in time and space, any of which would be appropriate for washing dishes. Not so many appropriate for writing poetry.

A movement in the grass caught her attention, and she pressed her face close to the earth. As she watched, a ladybug retreated into the grass. She was abruptly, suddenly aware of her own smallness in the universe. Heather had once seen a movie about a man who shrank away to nothing. Now, she felt smaller than that, and it terrified her. She wanted to call someone to keep her company so she would not be alone with the enormity of it. But she couldn't think of anyone she wanted to be with. Heather let her mind drift backward to the people who had shared and shaped her life for as long as she could remember, and there was no one she wanted badly enough to reach out to.

She realized then that she had not even seen anyone outside her own family for two whole days except for the teacher.

She could have dated. She'd been asked. The fellow who had sat next to her for three years of journalism has asked her. He'd had polio as a child, and he used his cane and braces as weapons to blackmail people into accepting him. He was overweight, obnoxious, and overbearing in spite of or perhaps because of his infirmity. For three years he had asked her out. For three years she had firmly declined.

One or two of her brother's friends liked her, and had hinted at the possibility of taking her to a movie. But she was a little afraid of them. She was certain they would be exactly like her brother. It was getting dark, and she got up. She liked walking home in the twilight but not in the dark.

He said he wanted to read her poetry sometime. Well, *now* was sometime. He liked her, and he would like her poetry – she was sure of it. She would go home and get it and take it right over to him. Maybe they could have coffee and just talk. It would be so nice to talk to someone who would really listen.

She got the poems from her room. The dining room was still alive with voices as her mother and father discussed local politics. She knew it would lead eventually to an argument. Her brother and sister were contentedly pointing out each other's faults over their dessert. She ducked her head and managed to pass the dining room unnoticed, but she saw that her feet were dirty. That would not do at all.

As she stood in the bathtub, holding her skirt back and letting the cold water wash the dust away, she supposed she ought to shave her legs. But there wasn't time. They'd soon be finished at the table, and she did not want any of them, especially Dorothy, to know where she was going. It would be dark anyway, and she would sit on his carpet – or his floor – and try to keep her legs tucked under her dress.

He might not be home. While she was waiting to cross the street, she convinced herself that surely he would be. Even though it was Friday night, he was a teacher, and he probably had papers to grade. Well, she wouldn't keep him long unless he wanted her to.

She found his apartment number easily on the row of mailboxes on the ground floor and then ascended the stairs, smoothing the front of her skirt as she went. She rang the bell with one hand and clutched the pages to her bosom with the other. She licked her lips.

There was a horrible silence and she waited, distressed. She rang again.

"Coming!"

She breathed a sigh of relief and was smiling when he opened the door.

"Why – Heather!" He had to grope for her name, but she didn't mind.

"I – I – you said you'd like to read my poetry sometime so I brought it over," she stammered before she noticed he was wearing a suit and tie. "You're going out," she said.

"Well, yes, I am. Look, why don't you come in for a minute while I finish packing." He took her arm and led her in. His rooms were bare but neat. "My fiancée's parents have invited me up to Savannah for the weekend."

She didn't say anything, but she was painfully aware of her bare feet and the fact that her legs needed shaving.

"Say, why don't you let me take the poems with me? I'll read them up there, and then we can have a good talk when I get back."

"Oh, no thanks. I'd rather keep them. Only have one copy." *No thank you. Having you laugh at them in private is one thing. Having you and some woman laugh at them together is another.* He was closing his suitcase as she walked toward the door. "See you later," Heather said. Before he could say anything else, she ran down the stairs, across the street and back to the shelter of her own front porch. She didn't know why she minded so much. What had she expected, anyway? But *he* would never read her poems. Never, until they were published for the world to read.

She sat for a while in the shadows, watching the night activities about her. She saw him leave. She saw couples pass in cars on their way to the drive-in movie down the road. Jimmy backed the car out of the drive and stopped when he saw her on the porch.

"Wayne and me are going to the dance at

the armory. I'm taking Ruthie. You want to go with Wayne?"

She shook her head. *What's wrong*, she thought? *Couldn't Wayne get anybody else?*

He let out his breath in exasperation. "You going to sit there for the rest of your life?" Then he pulled out of the drive and roared off down the street. Dorothy came out with her books under her arm.

"I'm going to Laura's for the night. She's helping me with my Indian project." Heather just kept rocking, her feet tucked under her, until Dorothy left.

She listened to her mother and father talking in front of the television set. She rocked and rocked, the poems resting in her lap, and she thought about what her brother had said. *The rest of her life*. How long she sat there, she didn't know. Finally her parents turned off the television and went into their bedroom. They knew she was out there, but they also knew when to leave her alone. When she heard them close the door, she went into the house.

She was hungry. She was not surprised to find that the dishes were in the kitchen sink, awaiting her special attention, and that took away her appetite.

If she could go to Atlanta and stay with Aunt Gwen for a couple of weeks, she knew she could find a job. Atlanta had real theatres – not just movie houses – and museums and huge stores and important office buildings. After she found a job and learned her way around the city, she could get an apartment with some other girls or maybe take a studio all by herself. And she could get herself a typewriter and some clothes.

How she was going to convince them to let her go was beyond her. She turned on the tap and spurted soap into the dishpan. But she would convince them. Why she'd just pack and go. She had enough babysitting money saved to buy a one-way ticket on the bus. She would ask her father to loan her enough for her transportation to and from work and her lunches until she had her first paycheque. Or maybe she'd ask Jimmy. Or maybe she'd go on a diet and find a job close enough to Aunt Gwen's house to walk. As she put the last dish away, she knew the time had come.

One house was not big enough for two families, and she was, after all, a separate family. That was the only explanation she could find for her growing discontent in their constant company.

There was no longer any excuse for her depending on them or for them holding her back. She loved them and they loved her, and they would have to let her go.

She picked up the phone and asked the operator for time and charges on a long-distance call. She would pay for it as soon as she got her first cheque. A contented calm spread slowly through her chest as she waited for Aunt Gwen to answer.

It was Friday. If she left the next day, she would get there in plenty of time to unpack, rest, and be ready to look for work on Monday morning.

Glen Kirkland

Departure

leaving home
I stand with my dead
grandmother's suitcases in hand
coat slung carelessly over my shoulder
the car loaded down with
all my possessions
packed in boxes tied doubly
with string
(like a refugee from some
old movie)

my father coughs
shakes my hand
and offers me a last-minute
yellow screwdriver with
interchangeable heads

my mother kisses me
and says
as long as I have a sense of
humor
I will
survive

in the doorway now
I smile awkwardly and mutter
goodbye

my mother asks
again
have you
got
everything

yes
I say
I've got it
all

and
frightened suddenly
I want to paint my name
in huge red letters
on the ceilings and walls
of every room
carve my initials in
the coffee table
and leave a life-sized reproduction of myself
asleep upstairs

Reprinted by permission of the author.